QUABBIN

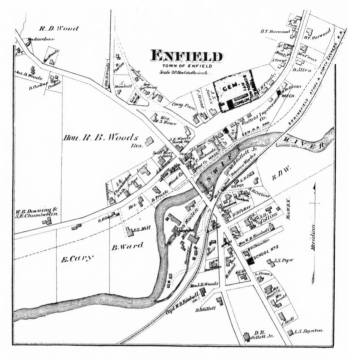

Map of Enfield, 1873, in County Atlas of Hampshire, Massachusetts. From surveys by F. W. Beers, courtesy of Massachusetts State Library.

QUABBIN

THE STORY OF A SMALL TOWN
WITH OUTLOOKS UPON PURITAN LIFE

by

Francis H. Underwood

With a Foreword by
Robert A. Gross

NORTHEASTERN UNIVERSITY PRESS
Boston

Northeastern University Press edition 1986
Foreword © 1986 by Robert A. Gross
First printed in 1893 by Bliss, Sands & Foster, London

Library of Congress Cataloging in Publication Data

Underwood, Francis Henry, 1825–1894.
Quabbin : the story of a small town with outlooks
upon Puritan life.

Reprint. Originally published: Bliss, Sands &
Foster, 1893.
Includes bibliographical references.
1. Enfield (Mass.)—Social life and customs.
I. Title.
F74.E5U5   1986   974.4'6   86-842
ISBN 0-930350-88-X (pbk. : alk. paper)

Printed and bound by Murray Printing Company, Westford,
Massachusetts. The paper is Glatfelter Offset, an acid-free sheet.

MANUFACTURED IN THE UNITED STATES OF AMERICA
91   90   89   88   5   4   3   2

To those, wherever they are, who have inherited the blood and shared the progress of the descendants of Pilgrims and Puritans, this book is respectfully dedicated.

Of those, comparatively few are now to be found in Massachusetts or in New England : most of them are settled along the belt of migration through Western New York, Ohio, and Michigan, the Mississippi Valley, and across the continent.

It is by men and women of Puritan lineage, developed by religious tolerance and universal education, that the institutions and the glory of New England are to be preserved, after the homes of their ancestors have been occupied by people of other races and other ideas.

CONTENTS

————

ILLUSTRATIONS

QUABBIN REVISITED
THE LOST WORLD OF FRANCIS UNDERWOOD

Foreword to the 1986 Edition

SIXTY-SIX miles west of Boston and one thousand feet above Massachusetts Bay, Great Quabbin Mountain keeps watch over the last great wilderness in the state. To the north, the view extends over a vast freshwater lake, surrounded by thickly wooded hills. No houses, no highways, no utility lines: no signposts of settlement intrude. On a lucky day, a visitor may spot an American bald eagle soaring overhead. It is tempting to imagine oneself in a land untamed by man. But that is all illusion. This refuge from urban life is, in fact, an enormous public reservoir, built in 1938–39 to supply water, billions and billions of gallons, for the thirsty inhabitants of metropolitan Boston. And beneath Quabbin Lake and along its shores lie the traces of civilization: cellar holes, stone walls, dirt roads, even a village green. Ghost towns in the wilderness, they form the only remains of the four communities of the Swift River Valley—Dana, Enfield, Greenwich, and Prescott—that were deliberately flooded, by order of the state, to create the Quabbin. By then, they were dying towns, brought by decades of decline and emigration to their end. But in the middle years of the nineteenth century, the towns of the

Swift River Valley flourished with farms, factories, and mills. Victims of twentieth-century progress, they once belonged in the front ranks of change, advance-agents of an expanding New England civilization.[1]

Francis Underwood's *Quabbin* tells the story of one of those lost towns, his birthplace and boyhood home of Enfield, at that brief, historical moment when a little community in the hill country of western Massachusetts could embody the large social forces of its times. Located along the Swift River, hemmed in by mountains on three sides, Enfield was always a tiny place, containing little more than a thousand people at its peak. It was settled in the late eighteenth century, as part of the town of Greenwich; by 1825, when Underwood was born, it had been independent for only ten years. Even so, the pioneer era was over; the great forests of Quabbin had given way to the ax, and Enfield's future lay with the Industrial Revolution. Like many other towns in the well-watered region of New England, Enfield put its location to use, harnessing the power of the Swift River for the production of cotton and woolen goods. It soon encompassed two mill villages, surrounded by outlying farms. Though overshadowed by the giants of Lowell and Lawrence, such small textile towns once dotted the landscape and fully engaged in the great transformation of New England life.

With economic revolution came social and cultural change. From the 1820s to the 1840s, the years of Underwood's boyhood, Enfield shed its mountain seclusion and opened up to the wider world. New turnpikes and highways ran through the town, carrying the regular stage and the news from Boston and quickening the pace of life. The central village became a small outpost of urban society, with its own hotel, stores, post-office, even a printing office, which turned out a popular almanac that sold widely in New York City and beyond. From the encounter between country and city arose a lively impulse for reform, and advocates of temperance and education fought to impose a new middle-class morality on the town. In short, it was "an age of Revolution," as Ralph Waldo Emerson, one of Underwood's culture heroes, put it, a time "when the old and the new stand side by side, and admit of being compared; when the energies of all men are searched by fear and by hope; when the historic glories of the old, can be compensated by the rich possibilities of the new era." Enfield and Underwood shared in this spirit, and in *Quabbin*, Underwood gives us an extraordinary evocation of that time.[2]

Long known only to a few specialists, *Quabbin* is a classic portrait of New England in transition, rendered with an artist's eye for the distinctive details of everyday life, yet always sensitive to the grand panorama of historical change. Told from the retrospective view of a perceptive participant in the great events of the day, it is, at once, an important document of its times—a powerful, ideologically charged statement of the meaning of nineteenth-century progress— and a pioneering work of social and cultural history that is still innovative today. With this reissue, the first since its original publication in 1893, Underwood should emerge from his long obscurity and win recognition as a major interpreter of New England life.[3]

Francis Underwood's own life (1825–1894) epitomizes the outward movement of his generation of rural New Englanders into the cosmopolitan currents of the modern world. Author, lawyer, and diplomat, Underwood "had his share of the varied experiences commonly attending the career of a typical self-made American," according to one

associate. Descended from first settlers of Puritan Massachusetts, the son of an ordinary farming family, Underwood
came of age during Enfield's era of expansion, but quickly
outgrew its limits. After getting what he could out of the
town's district schools—whose benighted condition he bitterly recalled in *Quabbin*—he joined the exodus of bright,
ambitious boys from the hills of western Massachusetts to
the rising college in nearby Amherst. It was a natural
choice: Enfield's minister, Joshua Crosby (depicted as
Joshua I in *Quabbin*), was a founder of Amherst College,
longtime trustee, and, briefly, acting president of the
school, which had been established in 1821 to educate
"indigent young men of piety and talents, for the Christian
Ministry." Amherst stood for the evangelical Calvinism that
had dominated the religious atmosphere of western Massachusetts ever since the days of Jonathan Edwards. It
represented the church militant, embarked upon a popular
crusade to defend Congregational orthodoxy against the
liberal heresies of Unitarian Harvard to the east. No doubt,
Underwood, the child of pious church members, went
there, at Rev. Crosby's encouragement, with vague hopes
of entering the ministry, but that was not to be. After one
year, he ran out of money, and, worse, out of faith. When
an uncle offered to pay for his education, on the condition
he join the orthodox clergy, Underwood turned him down;
placing conscience over career, he refused to pledge loyalty
to doctrines in which he no longer believed. With that
decision, the young man was to move ever farther from the
evangelical world of the fathers, until he found his calling
in the enemy camp. His ambitions were realized in the
literary circles of Unitarian Boston and Cambridge.[4]

Law and letters formed the basis of Underwood's career.
After leaving Amherst, he headed for Kentucky, where he

studied law, entered the bar, and met his wife. But he quickly returned to Massachusetts, driven by hatred of what he had seen of slavery in the South. Enlisting in the Free Soil movement, he impressed its leaders and was elected clerk of the State Senate in Boston when the anti-slavery coalition triumphed in 1852. But politics were not for Underwood; like many others in his generation, he pursued law as a means to literature. In antebellum America, the characteristic man of letters was the gentleman of the law who cultivated learning and literature as a leisurely avocation; a taste for letters proved a mark of gentility and an avenue to fame. Lawyers, boasted Joseph Dennie, himself a member of the club, were "unquestionably the best patrons which literature can hope to find in this country. . . . Quick to invent ingenious and useful papers and powerful to disseminate them; eager to encourage and generous to reward merit, they frequently unite in one the author, the publisher, and the patron." Indeed, nearly all the major male writers of the early republic had been trained as lawyers: Charles Brockden Brown, Washington Irving, William Cullen Bryant, James Fenimore Cooper, William Gilmore Simms, James Russell Lowell, to name only the best known. But circumstances had changed by the time Francis Underwood arrived in Boston. The literary marketplace, once restricted to an Eastern, upper-class elite, was expanding to serve a vast, democratic nation, and upon that broad base were built the great publishing houses of Boston, Philadelphia, and New York. With books and periodicals reaching thousands upon thousands of readers, it was no longer necessary for the writer to be a literary amateur, gaining his living from the law or some other source; the market could now sustain the professional author. Some old-fashioned gentlemen disdained the idea of writing for pay, but not Francis Underwood. He took up a post as "the literary man" for the prominent Boston publisher, Phillips, Sampson & Company, where he read manuscripts and cultivated authors. From that position he set out to make his reputation.[5]

Underwood's great object was to establish a New England literary magazine, combining antislavery principles with the best writing in the region—and with himself as editor. He would achieve only half his ambition. Thanks to his constant efforts, the publisher Phillips agreed in 1857 to sponsor a new periodical, christened *The Atlantic Monthly*, but Underwood got none of the credit. He was overshadowed by the literary eminences of Boston—Emerson, Oliver Wendell Holmes, Henry Wadsworth Longfellow, James Russell Lowell—whom the publisher enlisted in the project, and his hopes of editing the periodical were dashed when the poet Lowell was placed in charge. The story is told that Underwood voluntarily pulled himself out of the running, when Lowell's prestige was judged indispensable to the magazine's success, but other factors may have been involved. Lowell thought his friend Underwood unsuited to the task, too "cast-ironish" intellectually for the top post. The publisher Phillips saw him merely as a hired hand— "our literary man," he called him—charged with doing his employer's bidding. That included writing "puffs" for the firm's books and planting them in the newspapers. Indeed, only a year and a half earlier, Underwood's integrity had been impugned in a nasty public debate over the ethics of the publishing industry. He had brought that attack upon himself by accusing George Ripley, the literary editor of Horace Greeley's *New York Tribune*, with being in the pay of a prominent New York publisher. Greeley turned the tables on his critic. Underwood, he claimed, was himself a publisher's bribe-master, a "small and unclean insect" who had turned on the *Tribune* only after it had panned one of his company's "stupid" books. Underwood protested his virtue, but his name had been tarred; no doubt the incident helped to sink his hopes of running *The Atlantic*. Whatever, Underwood loyally took up the job of being assistant editor. He submerged his disappointment in the excitement of putting out the periodical, meeting with famous authors, turning down contributions, making up each issue for Lowell's approval, and working closely with the editor, who was the great hero of his life—"the best friend, the most charming companion, and one of the ablest and wisest of his generation," he later said. The experience lasted for little more than three years; in 1861, the magazine was sold to the great publishing house of Ticknor & Fields, and Underwood was out of a job. But the *Atlantic* post was clearly the great moment of his life, the engagement with ideas, books, and literary men for which he had been striving ever since leaving the Connecticut Valley, and it would mark him and his masterpiece *Quabbin* for good.[6]

For a quarter-century after the *Atlantic* experience, Underwood was a minor figure in Boston literary circles, turning out novels, biographies of famous writers, and manuals of American and English literature, none of which gained him fame. It was political patronage that provided his living and, eventually, made his name. After leaving *The Atlantic*, he obtained a profitable sinecure as clerk of the Massachusetts Superior Court, where he earned enough after a decade to be able to retire and write. Then, in 1886, political connections brought him wider recognition. Having joined the Republican "Mugwumps" to support the Democrat Grover Cleveland for president, Underwood was rewarded with the post of United States consul to Glasgow. Such appointments were viewed as literary laurels, and Underwood enthusiastically took his up. In Britain, he carried himself "as a representative American and man of letters," lecturing frequently on the subject of American literature, so successfully that the University of Glasgow awarded him an honorary LL.D. for his contribution to Anglo-American culture. His consulship ceased after Cleveland was defeated in the election of 1888, but when the Democrats regained the White House in 1893, Underwood was named to the comparable post at Edinburgh. During the interval, Underwood stayed on briefly in Scotland, where, from the distance of three thousand miles and a half-century, and at a long-sought moment of triumph as a spokesman for American letters, he returned in memory to Enfield and recreated the world and the young boy of *Quabbin*.[7]

Underwood took up his historical project at a time when a good many New Englanders were anxious to define and to consolidate the cultural achievements of their region. The impulse was narrow and nativist; in reaction against the mass immigration of southern and eastern Europeans to the United States since the mid-1880s, many writers and readers wished to escape into an idealized Yankee past, from which they would peer out suspiciously at the alien newcomers. New England's legacy, as they interpreted it, was to prescribe the American way. Underwood's *Quabbin*, fortunately, partakes little of this mean spirit. True, he did dedicate the work "to those, wherever they are, who have inherited the blood and shared the progress of the descendants of Pilgrims and Puritans," and he did pointedly remind his readers that "It is by men and women of Puritan lineage, developed by religious tolerance and universal education, that the institutions and the glory of New England are to be preserved, after the homes of their ancestors have

been occupied by people of other races and other ideas."
Still, it was not the new circumstances of the turn of the
century, but the old battles of the era before the Civil War
that were on his mind. The dominant themes of his work
reflect the formative experiences of his life: the rejection
of Calvinism, the celebration of books and reading, the
opening up of New Englanders to the intellectual influences of the wider world. *Quabbin* serves as a reprise of
Underwood's life and a justification of his career.

Underwood derived his very approach to the past from
the literary aesthetic of the early *Atlantic Monthly*. During
his years as editor, James Russell Lowell had articulated a
creed of literary realism that was to inspire the local color
movement in New England writing in the 1870s and
1880s. Lowell insisted that literature "copy Nature faithfully and heartily," without any emendation to satisfy sen-
timental tastes. What mattered was closeness to the small
details of real life. Under Lowell and his successors, *The
Atlantic* published "the first genuinely local color stories,"
which were distinguished by concern for "authentic dialect,
authentic local characters, real geographical settings, authentic local customs and dress." Eventually, this aesthetic
would constitute a distinctive genre, closely associated with
such female writers as Harriet Beecher Stowe and Sarah
Orne Jewett. Underwood, too, was a master of the method,
and in *Quabbin*, he gives us a major work of this literary
tradition. Indeed, it is his steeping in the local color aesthetic that accounts for his strength and distinctiveness as
a historian today.[8]

Long before scholars began to ponder the meanings of
material culture and to speculate on the significance of body
language, Underwood made the small things of everyday
life into the stuff of history. "The life of any community,"

he declared, "is made up of infinite details. One can hardly say that the smallest point in town management, church polity, or domestic economy is absolutely unimportant. Solid growth is never visible in the present tense" (p. 29). In this spirit, he evokes the look of the landscape—the scars on the denuded hills; the worn-out lands overrun with weeds and brush; the gray, unpainted, weather-beaten houses of the "poorer sort," whose picturesque qualities, in the eye of the artist, were no compensation for the dirt and the misery inside. He captures the physical appearance of the people as well: their dress, their gestures, their facial expressions, their gaits, the twang in their voices, the movements of their eyes, even the several ways they fell asleep in church. And then there is their speech in all its varieties, from the vernacular slang of hill-town farmers to the ornately polished sermons of the third minister. Underwood was equally attentive to social customs—quiltings and teas, road parties and militia trainings—and to the nuances of social geography, encompassing everyone from the worldly China trader who had retired to the town and the wealthy farmers whose daughters went off to distant academies, through the disorderly dirt-farmers in the hills, down to garrulous Aunt Keziah, the impoverished old crone who was grudgingly shunted among the neighbors after her own family refused her support. It was this authenticity of detail that captivated Underwood's reviewers. "The little town of Quabbin as it was sixty years ago," said *The Critic*, "is reproduced with what seems absolute fidelity." The reviewer for *The Dial* agreed, praising the work as "unsurpassed and unsurpassable for fidelity to fact." As an exercise in social portraiture of backcountry New England, *Quabbin* is a stunning achievement; it is rivaled only by Harriet Beecher Stowe's *Oldtown Folks* (1869) and Sarah Orne Jewett's *Country of the Pointed Firs* (1896).[9]

From the painstaking presentation of these absorbing details, there emerges a larger, intellectual purpose. Underwood aimed to identify the hidden movements in thought and action that explained the transformation of the New England Puritan into the modern Yankee of the nineteenth century.

> The question constantly recurs, how was it that the sombre Puritan became a poet, romancer, inventor, engineer, or scientist? and how has a people of limited knowledge and narrow views, without worldly ambition, who renounced all things for the sake of the life to come, and were content to toil without hope of enfranchisement on earth, grown into the marvellously active and versatile society of to-day? (p. 32)

The pursuit of this problem shaped the structure of *Quabbin*. Convinced that the key to the changes could be found in the religious ideas and sentiments of the community, Underwood organized the history of Quabbin according to "the reigns of its successive ministers" (p. 31), from Joshua I to Robert IV, covering roughly the years from 1787, when parson Crosby was ordained, to the mid-1840s, when he himself left home. Within this framework, he carefully etched the old regime of late Puritanism over which Joshua had presided, then laid out the gradual adaptations it made to the modern world, particularly to the moral reforms launched by the second minister, set back by the third, and consolidated by Robert IV. In the process, Underwood took the measure of the theological tradition in which he was reared and which he eventually repudiated. This encounter with the Calvinist past is remarkably akin to that of Harriet Beecher Stowe in *Oldtown Folks,* and like Stowe's, it is, perhaps inevitably, an apology for Underwood's own apostasy. But it was far more than that. Given the deep roots of that tradition in an entire way of life, his book became an effort to weigh the costs and gains of nineteenth-century progress.

Central to his judgment of the old order is Underwood's depiction of Quabbin as a town divided into two, mutually antagonistic parts. On one side stood the respectable, pious villagers, whose lives were centered about the schools and the church, the primary instruments, in Underwood's view, of civilization. Arrayed against them were the ignorant, disorderly people of the hard-scrabble farms in the hills, cut off "from the village and its modernizing influences." "The difference between these people and those in the social centre," Underwood observed, "was like a gulf between centuries; and the rooted antipathy on the part of the hill people toward the better-dressed villagers was almost past belief" (p. 128). Underwood identified closely with the villagers "of the better sort," through whose eyes he viewed, unsympathetically and uncomprehendingly, the "half-civilized" strangers in the hills. But his is no easy acceptance of the one, nor unthinking dismissal of the other. Both cultures—the piety of the village and the disorder of the hills—were, he thought, fatally flawed; despite their differences, both stunted and distorted the personalities and the possibilities of Quabbin people. Both belonged to a world that was rightly cast aside in the march of progress. Together, they formed preindustrial New England's *ancien régime*, whose passing away, in the face of modern, middle-class capitalist society, is the central drama of *Quabbin*.

The ruling ethos of Quabbin's village culture is vividly captured in Underwood's brilliant metaphor of the age. This was a "heavy" world, whose every expression was ponderous. People had no ease, no grace of movement: they dragged themselves heavily, awkwardly, lumberingly through life, with heads bowed to the ground. "They walked like ploughmen, with a slow inclination from side to side. There was no flexibility in the arms, no erectness in the spinal column, no easy carriage of the head" (p. 189). Nor was there any vigor to their speech; instead, people measured their words with care, drawling them out in "subdued" tones (p. 72) and in a grating nasal twang. Seldom did they display strong emotions. They presented formal, frozen faces to the world, and kept their feelings tightly "shut-up" within. "Few have the power, like the rustic Yankee, to batten under hatches any revolt of feeling, and to walk the deck with an air of unconcern" (p. 49). Theirs were lives of self-suppression, buried in the constant discipline of duty and work. To the youthful Underwood, life seemed endless chores all week and "gloom" on the Sabbath, with its tedious Bible study and joyless worship; Quabbin lacked any real day of rest. True, many children enjoyed occasional pastimes, but in the "melancholy" (p. 188) homes of the most pious, there was no sense of play, no appreciation of nature, no intellectual curiosity about the wider world. The "meagre supply of reading" consisted chiefly of heavy religious books—the Bible, Alleine's *Alarm to the Unconverted,* Baxter's *Saints' Rest,* "a few lives of celebrated preachers"—interspersed with a few, such as *Pilgrim's Progress,* that might appeal to a boy's imagination (p. 131). No Shakespeare, no Pope, no Burns, no Byron, no Wordsworth, no Keats: nothing "profane" was sought out. How could it be? "In the tone and temper of theology," Underwood explained, "was the key of the situation" (p. 47). The reverent villagers yielded to the grim decree of late Puritanism: this life was to be endured, not indulged, in somber expectation of the judgment day to come. In the "scarcely veiled fatalism" (p. 46) of old-regime Calvinism, as Underwood perceived it, a passive resignation to "this dying world" pervaded popular habits of body and mind.

Against the self-suppressive piety of the villagers stood out, as if in deliberate mockery, the violent, disorderly culture of the hill people. Unfortunately, Underwood views this world entirely from the outside, without the slightest effort to comprehend the organizing terms of its inhabitants' lives; the hill people are simply something "other," deviant folk in need of reform. Yet we can glimpse from his portrayal the existence of a distinctive culture that was common throughout preindustrial, rural America, but has seldom been located in early New England. This was a masculine culture of competitive display, where aggressiveness and strength proved the measure of a man. In the histories of the real Enfield, of the Scotch-Irish Presbyterian settlement that Underwood constructed as Quabbin, the legendary figures of that world still live on. There are the Patterson boys, famous as "mighty hunters and expert wrestlers," whose father once was called out of bed at midnight to meet an unbeaten challenger in nearby New Salem: "he responded to the call, laid the champion on his back, and returned the same day." There is Moses Woods, a pious deacon, who gave up wrestling in his youth after he, too, was "dragged out of bed, transported ten miles to meet a new rival, and broke his adversary's leg in the first trial." Even the minister, Joshua Crosby, enjoyed a youthful reputation as a superior fighter and athlete, and "few men," Underwood remarks, "were better judges of a foot-race, a tug-of-war, or a jumping-match" (p. 42). Hard living and hard fighting, strong language and strong drink: in an inversion of village values, the men of the hill country asserted their capacity to act to *excess*. Through boisterous rivalry and constant tests of physical skills, we may imagine, they simultaneously forged bonds of community among themselves and honed their talents for surviving in a rough, natural world. Not surprisingly, they treated with total disdain the well-ordered institutions of the prosperous villagers, particularly, the church and the schools, which were so central to Underwood's civilizing project. But Underwood could see only "irregularity" and "disorder" in the "dark corners of the land." He was repelled by the poverty, the crudity, the ignorance, and the violence; what sympathy he felt was for the innocent victims, real and imagined, of the hill people—especially, the women and children.

> Brave women were striving to cover the family nakedness, and to put a good face upon despair. Modest girls had reason to shrink from young men whose education was acquired at the bar of the tavern. The schools barely lifted the children above illiteracy. Uncleanliness in manners and speech, if not universal, caused little remark. As for literature and science, they were not only unknown, but inconceivable. (p. 46)

If he had to choose, Underwood preferred the diluted world of the self-denying village to the brawling disorder of the hill culture of excess.[10]

Despite the formal opposition between them, the two cultures of Quabbin, in Underwood's analysis, belonged together, for they were the product of a common condition: the failure of late Puritanism to address the vital necessities of human life. So rigorously, so insistently did Joshua I preach the Calvinist doctrines of arbitrary predestination, natural corruption, and resignation to Providence that human misery and sin were accepted as the inevitable order of things. To Underwood, such religion was all talk and no action, a dead dogma that served only to darken the minds of the pious, without altering in the slightest people's outward lives. The hill people were simply left to their fates, presumably to burn in hell.

> There were just so many who would refuse the offers of grace; and so many who would become slaves to appetite, and be content with ignorance, poverty, and degradation, as long as the supplies of rum and tobacco held out. (p. 46)

Against this theological formalism, Underwood, in common with many reformers of his generation, held out a new standard: that of "moral tendency." The test of true religion lay in its potential to transform people's moral lives. No longer a matter only of belief, religion was now also to be judged by its effects.

Seen in this light, the late Puritanism of Quabbin was as demoralizing to the respectable people of the village as it proved indifferent to the disorderly folk in the hills. To be sure, Underwood balanced his judgment with an appreciation of the positive virtues of rural New England Calvinism. It built character, toughened the mind, and strengthened the will. Like Harriet Beecher Stowe in *Oldtown Folks*, he paid tribute to the power of the old religion to train independent, hardy men of principle.

> Chief among the elements of character and training, must be reckoned the influence of a stern theology, which, in silence and loneliness, sobered thought, stiffened the mental fibre, and set up Duty above every personal advantage. If the sons of New England have any one great heritage, it is this. (p. 102)

But that heritage had run itself out. It was too narrow intellectually, too closed to modern literature and science, too insistent upon suppressing dissent. More than this: Calvinism proved false to the feelings of the most sensitive, demanding that they deny their observations of life and their inner selves in order to conform to a creed. The old regime stifled emotions, crippled joy, and blinded people to the beauties of nature. The young Underwood had given up his college education, rather than pin his conscience to a creed. Now, as an old man, he took his intellectual revenge. Invoking the same principles that lay behind the realist aesthetics of his book, Underwood upheld the standard of nature. Leave metaphysical systems behind, he told readers: follow "natural sentiments of justice" and "return to nature" (p. 306).

Nowhere does Underwood set out his indictment of the old regime as systematically as the foregoing summary suggests. He builds his case over the course of the book, through reminiscence, character sketches, dialogue, and occasional formal arguments. All together, the presentation carries formidable intellectual power, but as a piece of literature, it must be said, *Quabbin* fails to sustain the drama of its contending ideas. There are a few fascinating pieces of local color: the long courtship of "Patient Emily," who waits for years for her diffident suitor George to win his widowed mother's consent to the match; the poignant story of the Widow Carter, a proud, once-wealthy widow fallen on hard times, and of the poor, generous blacksmith, who secretly brings her firewood in the dark of night, only to be the object of the lady's condescension when she remarries and recovers her proper station; the comic performance of an irreverent bass-player at Sunday meeting, whose musical flourishes shatter the solemnity of the day, to name a few. But such vignettes, for all their charm, come at the expense of the larger plot. So carefully does Underwood develop his portrait of the old regime that a reader looks forward to its inevitable confrontation with the new middle-class morality. We get part of that story, including the dramatic opening of the crusade for temperance, when the second minister throws down the gauntlet to his parishio-

ners at a funeral for a notorious drunk. And we learn of the
exposure of Quabbin's own Gunpowder Plot, the conspir-
acy by the enemies of reform to blow up the meetinghouse.
But Underwood cuts his account short; he announces, but
never shows, the triumph of reform. Too sure of the righ-
teousness of his cause, too conscious that his late Victorian
readers share his values, he never explores the motives of
the reformers, and he simply dismisses the opponents of
temperance as "the weak or dissolute" (p. 150).

As for his larger argument with the old Calvinism, Underwood sets that forth through the thinly veiled autobiographical narrative in the closing sections of the book. In
the persona of the collegian David Wentworth, who is
temporarily keeping a "select school" at Quabbin, Underwood rehearses his grievances in lengthy debates with the
minister, affirms his own religion of nature, and all the
while loses the woman he loves because of his heterodox
opinions. Despite the passing of nearly a half-century, it is
evident that Underwood remained unreconciled to the
world he left behind. He had no choice but to go, he seems
to be saying; the intolerance of Quabbin drove him away.
"There is a provincial, or rather a parochial narrowness"
here, Wentworth says; "things move slowly, the old shadow
overhangs" (p. 338). But the narrative fails to carry conviction. Underwood gives his alter ego the best lines, and
the victory of enlightenment over bigotry is assured. In
Quabbin, the prodigal son returns home, only to prove that
he had been right to leave in the first place.

If Underwood liberates himself in *Quabbin* from the re-
pressive theology of late Puritanism, he nonetheless im-
poses a new ideology of his own: the ideology of high
Victorian culture. In this genteel vision of late nineteenth-
century New Englanders, social progress was measured

through the steady advance of morality and truth, dispelling
ignorance and prejudice through the benevolent agency of
mass communications. By this standard, Underwood deems
Quabbin to have improved over the years; under the influence of Robet McEwen, "the equal in intellectual force of
the foremost orthodox preachers of his time" (p. 256), the
town gradually polished its manners and entered the modern era.

> This was an epoch. Quabbin became a part of the great
> world, and felt the universal pulsations of humanity. It could
> never be solitary again. Many influences contributed to its
> enlightenment, but the railroad and the daily newspaper
> were the chief. Home and foreign news, politics, inventions,
> and discoveries in arts and science, were brought home to
> people who had never had anything to occupy their minds
> except neighborhod gossip and sermons. The educational
> power and stimulus effected an entire transformation. . . .
> (p. 271)

Thanks to the power of the press, the entire tone of society
had lightened; "the old fixedness and torpor were gone,
and society was full of motion" (pp. 270–71). Open to
new ideas, people readily adopted the latest innovations.
"Heavy, rumbling" wagons gave way to "light buggies moving without noise" (p. 271), "heavy and awkward" farming
tools to light instruments "perfectly adapted to use" (p.
272). People, too, moved more quickly, dressed more
neatly, spoke more smoothly and correctly. Best of all, the
inhabitants of Quabbin had finally put their dusty, theological tracts behind them and were keeping up with the
literature and the news of their day. Quabbin had even
established a public library! "With morning newspapers,
the telegraph, and three daily mails, Quabbin belongs to
the great world" (p. 341). "As good English is heard in the

pulpit and in the schools, and as a well-chosen and growing library is to furnish the coming generation with knowledge and broad ideas, the future of Quabbin is assured" (p. 342).

Underwood was fooling nobody but himself—and the generation of high-thinking exponents of the positive power of print to change people's lives. The fact is that Enfield had established its library only ten years before Underwood wrote, long after many other towns had done so. And there is no evidence in *Quabbin* that the rowdy culture of the hill people had gone away. In the late nineteenth century, Enfield remained a largely Scotch-Irish, working-class town, dominated by two textile mills. In such places, middle-class morality—the respectable, orderly, work-disciplined ethics of the employing class—met sullen and open resistance. But Underwood was less interested in social reality than in making an ideological statement. His faith in communications was shared by many other local historians and local color writers. In *The Country of the Pointed Firs*, Sarah Orne Jewett expressed this perspective through the character of Captain Littlepage, who laments the barren provincialism that has grown up on the Maine coast in the wake of its long economic decline.

> I view it . . . that a community narrows down and grows dreadful ignorant when it is shut up to its own affairs, and gets no knowledge of the outside world except from a cheap, unprincipled newspaper. In the old days, a good part o' the best men here knew a hundred ports and something of the way folks lived in them. They saw the world for themselves, and like's not their wives and children saw it with them. . . . they got some sense of proportion.[11]

Still, in Underwood's view, there was always the armchair travel of the book. To Underwood, the act of reading was the highest value of all, the culmination of man's striving for betterment. No matter the commercial realities and corruptions that facilitated the production and distribution of print—circumstances that the editor and publisher's man Underwood had experienced at first hand. In the reification of literature as the supreme achievement of civilization, all aesthetic realism drifted away. Expressing the credo of his life, Underwood exposed the central faith of the nineteenth-century man of letters.

> When men come to see that literature and art are the only enduring titles to renown, and that merely commercial nations have no place in history, then the great poets, thinkers, and artists loom up like mountains. People who have taken up reading systematically, or who read much, even cursorily, soon recognize the fact that there is no pleasure like it, and that it is almost the only distinction between the wise and fools. (p. 351)

Yet, even as he wrote, the high Victorian faith in books and culture was passing, and lesser writers like Underwood were being forgotten. To the next generation of reformers, the numerous volumes of refined literature to which Underwood had devoted his life had become a way to avoid the real world, not to learn about it. As the settlement-house pioneer Jane Addams complained, "This is what we were all doing, lumbering our minds with literature that only served to cloud the really vital situation spread before our eyes." Nor could Underwood comfort himself with recognition in his own day. *Quabbin* won praise from critics, but sold few copies; the author spent his last years complaining that his publishers had let the book "go to the dogs," despite the fact that the work "cost him two years of labor; part of the story was written four or five times, and no part less than three times." Perhaps worst of all, when he returned to Enfield, nobody knew him; he could not even bask in acclaim for a successful returning son.[12]

Then again, the approval of Enfield was, perhaps, not

worth having. On his final return to the town, Underwood
noticed all the signs of its impending decline: the farms
were miserable, the houses had "a plaintive look," most of
the young had gone. Even the old virtues of honesty and
frugality had slipped away, replaced by a pretended cyni-
cism about the world. The remaining youth now imitated
the worst of city ways—rudeness to parents, flippant dis-
regard for sacred subjects, admiration for "successful
sharpsters"—even as their own fashions and slang were,
invariably, a few years behind the times. Such signs of the
times belied Underwood's earlier confidence that the future
of Quabbin was assured. Indeed, it would be the very
opening of the town to the wider world that ultimately
brought about its demise. Two years after the publication
of *Quabbin*, the Massachusetts Board of Health made its
first suggestion that the waters of the Swift River be
dammed up, and the surrounding towns destroyed, in order
to provide water for Boston. It would take another forty
years before that happened, but the end could be foreseen
even as Underwood wrote. For if modern communications
had liberated Quabbin from the intellectual and religious
parochialism of old New England, they also introduced
competing interests and values that defeated local busi-
nesses, drained off the young, and ultimately overwhelmed
the town. Just as Francis Underwood was lost in the expanding multitude of modern authors and books, so the
town of Enfield disappeared before the remorseless demands of urban Boston. Despite Underwood's intentions,
then, *Quabbin* stands as an unintended elegy to a place and
to an author time passed by.[13]

Amherst, Massachusetts   ROBERT A. GROSS

NOTES

1. Thomas Conuel, *Quabbin: The Accidental Wilderness* (Brattleboro, Vt.: The Stephen Greene Press, 1981); J. R. Greene, *The Creation of Quabbin Reservoir: The Death of the Swift River Valley* (Athol, Mass.: The Transcript Press, 1981); Donald W. Howe, comp., *Quabbin: The Lost Valley* (Ware, Mass.: The Quabbin Book House, 1951); Evelina Gustafson, *Ghost Towns 'Neath Quabbin Reservoir* (Boston: Amity Press, 1940).

2. Howe, *Quabbin*, pp. 56–59, 104, 107–8, 175–90; John Warner Barber, *Historical Collections, Being a General Collection of Interesting Facts, Traditions, Biographical Sketches, Anecdotes, &c., Relating to the History and Antiquities of Every Town in Massachusetts, with Geographical Descriptions* (Worcester: Dorr, Howland, & Co., 1839), p. 320; Richard D. Brown, "The Emergence of Urban Society in Rural Massachusetts, 1760–1820," *The Journal of American History* LIX (1974): 29–51; J. S. Wood, "Elaboration of a settlement system: the New England village in the federal period," *Journal of Historical Geography* 10 (1984): 331–56; Ralph Waldo Emerson, "The American Scholar," in Robert E. Spiller and Alfred R. Ferguson, eds., *Nature, Addresses, and Lectures* (Cambridge, Mass.: Harvard University Press, 1971), p. 67.

3. Jack Larkin, Chief Historian of Old Sturbridge Village, has recently called attention to Underwood's significance as an ethnographer of everyday life. Let me acknowledge here my debt to his essay and to our many conversations about Underwood, rural New England, and social history. See Larkin, "The View from New England: Notes on Everyday Life in Rural America to 1850," *American Quarterly* 34 (1982): 248–49.

4. George F. Whicher, "Francis Henry Underwood," in Allen Johnson et al., comps., *Dictionary of American Biography* (20 vols.; New York: Charles Scribner's Sons, 1928–36), XIX: 112–13; J. F. Trowbridge, "The Author of Quabbin," *Atlantic Monthly* LXXV (Jan. 1895): 108–16 (quote, p. 109); Bliss Perry, "The Editor who was never the Editor," in Perry, *Park-Street Papers* (Boston and New York: Houghton Mifflin Com-

pany, 1908), pp. 205–77; Thomas Le Duc, *Piety and Intellect at Amherst College 1865–1912* (New York: Columbia University Press, 1946), pp. 1–10; Claude Moore Fuess, *Amherst: The Story of a New England College* (Boston: Little, Brown, and Company, 1935), pp. 27–59; David F. Allmendinger, Jr., *Paupers and Scholars: The Transformation of Student Life in Nineteenth-Century New England* (New York: St. Martin's Press, 1975).

5. Frank Luther Mott, *A History of American Magazines 1741–1850* (New York and London: D. Appleton and Company, 1930), pp. 154–56, 339–74; William Charvat, *Literary Publishing in America 1790–1850* (Philadelphia: University of Pennsylvania Press, 1959); Robert A. Ferguson, *Law and Letters in American Culture* (Cambridge, Mass.: Harvard University Press, 1984); Trowbridge, "Author of Quabbin," p. 109.

6. Trowbridge, "Author of Quabbin," pp. 113–14; Perry, *Park-Street Papers*, pp. 233–36; Martin Duberman, *James Russell Lowell* (Boston: Houghton Mifflin Company, 1966), pp. 162–63; William Charvat, *The Profession of Authorship in America, 1800–1870*, ed. Matthew Bruccoli (Columbus: Ohio State University Press, 1968), pp. 174, 183–86; Francis H. Underwood, *The Builders of American Literature: Biographical Sketches of American Authors Born Previous to 1826* (Boston: Lee and Shepard, 1893), p. 224.

7. Trowbridge, "Author of Quabbin," p. 114.

8. Josephine Donovan, *New England Local Color Literature: A Women's Tradition* (New York: Frederick Ungar Publishing Co., 1983), pp. 5–7.

9. Harriet Beecher Stowe, *Oldtown Folks* (Boston: Fields, Osgood & Company, 1869); Sarah Orne Jewett, *The Country of the Pointed Firs* (Boston and New York: Houghton, Mifflin and Company, 1896); *The Critic*, new series, XIX (Jan. 21, 1893): 30; *The Dial* XIV (Feb. 1, 1893): 87.

10. William Burton Gay, comp., *Gazetteer of Hampshire County, Mass., 1654–1887* (Syracuse, N.Y.: W. B. Gay & Co., 1886?), pp. 240, 243.

11. David Bonnell Green, ed., *The World of Dunnet Landing: A Sarah Orne Jewett Collection* (Gloucester, Mass.: Peter Smith, 1972), pp. 27–28.

12. Jane Addams, *Twenty Years at Hull-House: With Autobiographical Notes* (New York: New American Library, 1960); "Boston Letter," *The Critic*, n.s., XXII (Sept. 1, 1894): 144.

13. Greene, *The Creation of Quabbin Reservoir*, p. 14.

QUABBIN

CHAPTER I

QUABBIN

AMONG the memories of childhood, — next after the impressions of a mother's brooding love, and of the home wherein the new unit of humanity first becomes conscious of being the centre of a universe, — the most indelible is the visual line that encircles his birthplace, with the perspectives that stretch out to it. To the Quabbin boy the boldly marked sky-line on the ridges of hills that shut in the valley under its blue roof was the boundary of the known world. Strangers must have looked upon the little village with compassion; but for the natives it was cheerful ; they knew no other. In the small houses there was no luxury surely, but no lack of wholesome food or seasonable raiment. There were schools for six months in the year, and sermons twice every Sunday, — Sahbaday it was in the vernacular.

News brought by the county paper was seldom more than two weeks old; and authoritative expositions of public affairs were given at the tavern and the post-office by persons who had actually seen New York, and who spoke of Boston with an air of familiarity.

The valley and neighborhood have not essentially changed in the hundred and sixty years since their first settlement; for the natural features are too marked to be affected by the superficial touches of man. Ploughs and axes do not disturb the eternal basis of landscape; and a few houses more, or a few trees less, do not matter.

The hill that rises south of the village was once covered with great oaks and chestnuts which had sheltered Indian hunters. The red men called the hill Great Quabbin, and the name belonged to the district as well. Year after year the white settlers waged war upon the venerable trees: instead of being a patriarchal forest to be cherished, it was a piece of stubborn "woods" to be cleared away. By and by lines of fence, like geometric diagrams, were traced on the hill's broad shoulders, enclosing sage-green pastures, sparsely tufted with wood-fern and huckleberry bushes, and known by all boys of the village to be rosy with strawberries every summer.

It was a Delectable Mountain for children, even after the majestic trees were felled. The ascent was easy; for a primitive road, partly grass-grown, led to the table-land at the summit, where were two small, decaying farmhouses, since destroyed. To one looking back when half-way up, the village below, nestling under shade-trees on both sides of the river, had a soft and almost unreal beauty; but as one climbed, it sank out of sight under the swelling buttress of the hill. The upper region was alpine in its cool serenity, its airy pastures, sparkling brook, and broad horizon. Sixty miles away rose a grand mountain, pyramidal and blue, — a melting vapory blue that one expected to see blown away; while in the opposite direction was grouped a confused and retreating mass of hills, seen beyond the golden mist of the Connecticut valley.

It was a delight to take deep draughts of the exhilarating air, to watch the thin, spectral wreaths of smoke rising from distant houses, to count afar the many steeples, mere glimmering white lances, and to seek out the purply-gray forms of well-known mountains around. No voices, nor hum of machinery, nor ring of hammer were heard from the valley. The only sounds that broke the stillness were the occasional lowing of cattle, the murmur of brooks, and the light, silvery strokes of the meeting-house clock. The bell had a tender, harmonious tone, full of solemn suggestion, associated with an austere worship and with funerals, but never with weddings or public rejoicings. Earth was beautiful in remoteness, and heaven near. The mountain lifted an imaginative child toward infinity, and he clung to it as if conscious of the desperate whirl of the globe through space.

Opposite, behind the village, rose the lesser northern hill (Ram Mountain), a somewhat irregular but beautiful cone of granite, jagged here and there with projecting edges of rock, and at that time thinly covered with soil. Once there were thick bushes and dwarfish trees on its sides, and plumes of tall pines were set jauntily on its crest; but it was ravaged and stripped by choppers, and left with scarred forehead, and dreary, naked flanks. When clad in green, the hill had been stately and joyous, but in its bereavement was shame-faced and dispirited. Still, it had a placid look for the meeting-house at its foot, and its rugged mass made an effective background for the white steeple.

The hill on the east side of the village, known as Little Quabbin, was rather too far away to have much part in the landscape. However, it did its best in delaying the morning sun, in upholding the north end of summer rainbows, and in sending back reflections from its massy ledges at sunset.

Quabbin is at its best in summer, in its rich vesture of green. The numerous springs and the dewy air keep the pastures and meadows fresh, while the shade-trees in streets and gardens, the adjacent forests, and the scattered wild growths (from hazel or alder bushes to vigorous oaks and chestnuts), are so luxuriant and widespread that it is difficult to find a clear vista in any direction. The main roads, it must be confessed, would be dull, if it were not for the outlooks upon hills and farms ; but there are many by-ways, exquisite as the dreamy idyls of Corot. One road by the western side of Ram Mountain, after passing a beautiful slope of farming-land, leads into a young forest where there is a flecked shade even at midday, and a sense of cool-ness, with a fresh, cheery smell, that is partly earthy, and partly leafy. The road meanders under the living arch among countless (and nameless) bushes and wild flowers, and appears to consist of a faintly worn path for a horse, two dim wheel-tracks, and intervening lines of tufted grass, which is often tall enough to brush the axle-trees. After reaching the open "front yard" of a small house two or three miles beyond, it comes to an end.

Another road, around the northern end of Little Quabbin, passes along the fringe of woods that hangs upon the mountain side ; and the visitor finds himself in a long, winding, arched way, dim as a cathedral aisle, but with glimpses of warm sunlight reflected from the fertile lands that lie just outside of the screen of white birches on his left. What artist or photographer could give an idea of the strong yet grateful contrast between the green gloom on the one hand, and the flickering splendors that come to him through tender birch leaves and vellum-cased branches on the other?

The three hills, standing at different angles, shut in the village, which partly rests on the rounded bases of two of them, while the river, which is the life of the valley, glides in swift curves at their feet.

The banks of Swift River have been sadly maltreated. Once, near the cove, above the dam, a belt of young pine-trees, uniform, softly rounded, and velvety green, followed the stream and the cove in many a coil; and, below the dam, there were at intervals thickets of alders, water-maples, shad-bushes, willow clumps, with myriads of lithe red shoots, wild-grape vines, tangled clematis, and the " swamp pink," parent of the garden azalea. But the meandering belt of pines fell under the axe long ago; and in its place sprang up white birches, as if to make a fringe on the naked border; while, little by little, the banks down stream were cleared of the " brush " that yielded no income except to children and poets. Many of the shrubs that crowded the wet margins, such as the blushing, sweet-scented azaleas, and the shad-bushes that wore fresh bridal veils every May, became only memories. Utility had its way, and this part of the river's edge was for years like an eyelid without lashes.

There is a pretty reach of still water near the cove, full, black, and lustrous. On one side is a meadow with a few hickory-trees; on the other, the high bank covered with young birches. On a windless afternoon might be seen a boat, with children rowing, its stem silently cutting through reflections of leafy sprays, of slender white trunks, leaning at all angles, and of sunny clouds in distant blue below.

In early times the whole region was dripping with springs, and shaggy with vegetation ; and even to-day, such is the struggle for existence, there are few trim lawns or meadows of grass free from the intrusion of coarser species. The leafy robes of the hills trailed on the lowlands ; while bushes, briers, ferns, or brakes filled the fence-corners and road-sides, and bordered the water-courses.

A mile above the centre was the north village, grouped around another dam, and at some distance beyond was a lake, framed in sombre hills. Its margin was surrounded by such trees as burn with richest colors in autumn; so that from the uplands, after the first light frost, the distant sheen of water appeared in a setting of crimson, yellow, gold-brown, and dark red ; and, coming nearer, one would say that the trees were standing in the water's edge and admiring themselves in the mirror.

There was a good view from a farmhouse on the side of the eastern hill (Little Quabbin), or, better, from the hill-top, looking westward. This view embraced the cove, the river winding through meadows, the village, tufted with maples and elms, the white spire standing out from the northern hill, and the broad expanse of the southern hill, which dominates the region. The traveller who has seen something of the Old World finds that the tranquil beauty of this scene lingers in memory, and will not be displaced. Something must be allowed for early associations, but the image of this landscape remains clear. It needs only to have been celebrated in song or famous in story. Quabbin is not famous.

The meeting-house of the village formerly stood sidewise to the road in a green space, flanked by rows of horse-sheds, some of them decrepit, and all unpainted. In its first estate it was of a dingy sulphur color, and without a steeple ; but its oaken frame and trussed roof were made to endure. Later, a steeple was set astride the roof ; the building was painted white, furnished with green (outside) blinds, and turned with its end to the street. The vane, of sheet metal, gilded, was cut in form of a man, the head cleaving the wind, and the legs extended for rudder. As it turned with a sharp cry on the rod which pierced its body, it needed but little aid from the imagination of a boy to become the image of some sinner transfixed in air, and held aloft to swing in lingering pain.

In later days the boys found, in the cob-webbed and dusty space below the belfry, a long-forgotten cask of ball cartridges, which had been kept, according to law, to be ready for an emergency that never happened. The paper covers were rotten, and the powder decomposed ; and it was great fun to drop the leaden ounce-balls from the belfry railing, and then find them flattened and hot upon the stone steps below.

The pulpit within was high, approached by flights of stairs, and above it was hung a sounding-board, in shape like an extinguisher. It was often a matter of wonder as to what would happen to the minister if the chain should break ; but the boys were assured by the thought that "The Lord is mindful of his own."

The pews were square, each family being enclosed as in a pen, all facing inwards. The uncushioned wooden seats were hinged, and were raised as people stood up during prayer, to fall with a multitudinous clatter when the prayer ended. There was a gallery on three sides, the part facing the pulpit being occupied by the choir.

A century earlier it was the custom in New England to "seat the meeting;" that is, to assign seats to the town's people according to their rank, as magistrates, elders, deacons, college-bred men, land-owners, mechanics, and laborers. In Quabbin each head of a family owned the pew he occupied, paying an annual tax thereon to the parish. The best places in the meeting-house belonged to those who had the money to pay for them.

The sheds adjoining the meeting-house were for the shelter of the "teams" of the country people; and in summer, when the windows were open, the services were frequently enlivened (for restless boys) by the stamping, whinnying, and squealing of lonesome or fly-pestered horses. The village schoolhouse was next beyond the eastern sheds, and behind them was the hillside burying-ground.

The boy of Quabbin who returns to his native town a man of sixty does not walk alone through the street. People of the old time meet and accost him, or nod to him from their wonted places. He knows every figure and face, and the color and cut of their clothes. His youth comes back, and he sees his playfellows become bridegrooms, then fathers of families, then patriarchs, — the same beings passing through the successive changes of a lifetime while he looks, — and he, meanwhile, able to recall any phase of their career at will.

He sees, with the eye of memory, sunburnt and grizzled men in blue frocks leaning at the posts of the blacksmith's open door, while within, by the lurid light, sinewy arms turn the glowing horseshoe, and showers of golden fire fly at each strenuous blow. The names of those grizzled men have long been chiselled on tombstones, but there they are by the smithy, and the man of sixty, once more a boy, knows them well. Others he sees driving ox-teams with logs for the saw-mill, men and oxen alike calmly chewing the cud, while long whips are waved encouragingly, and "Haw, Buck!" or "Gee, Bright!" enlivens the slow procession.

Another, from a former generation, comes in a heavy wagon, thorough-braced and well spattered with ancient mud. His wife sits by him, in camlet cloak and scoop bonnet, and they are bound for the store. In the box behind the seat they have a basket of eggs, a "four-meal" cheese, and a firkin of butter, to be exchanged for tea, molasses, and other "boughten" goods. Another, younger and livelier, is whirling by in a buggy, showing off his trotting-horse. The animal is not groomed to a satin gloss, and, in fact, is rough in coat, and perhaps tangled in mane and tail ; but his great haunches work powerfully, and his feet appear to be all the time in the air, reaching ahead. He "gets over the ground," and often sends a dash of gravel back at his keen and tricky driver.

If it is Sunday, our friend of sixty years sees groups of men and youths whom he knew long ago, loitering upon the meeting-house steps, all visibly uncomfortable in holiday clothes, discussing the affairs of town and church ; the bachelors, with eyes in ambush, demurely watching the in-coming maids. Some of the ungodly and disreputable are haunting the dilapidated and windy old tavern across the green. He knows these pariahs, though they have long lain in nameless graves.

As the Quabbin boy of sixty continues his rounds, other faces, long forgotten, are projected in memory's camera. All of them belong to people who were once his townsmen. One brilliant man, after many vicissitudes, was a banker, and heaped up wealth, which his prodigal son in after years was to waste. His brother, the man with studious, meditative countenance, was a physician. That beautiful youth, the banker's nephew, after a successful beginning, and with the haven of love in sight, returned to Quabbin to die; while his betrothed, white as a lily, drooped under the weeds of eternal widowhood. This gentleman with gold spectacles went from the principal "store" of Quabbin, and set up in Boston an establishment whose name is a household word and a synonyme of honor. That boon companion, whose talk was illustrated with oaths, dissipated an ample fortune, and laughed away with merry curses his friends and reputation. Another, with dazed and vacant look, lost the savings of a lifetime by trusting them to a stock operator, who posed as a Christian philanthropist.

The plainly dressed man, he with devout expression and "looks commercing with the skies," was a mill-worker, whose soul was so full of the love of God that men felt holier and stronger for the touch of his hand, or the sound of his voice. Neither wealthy nor learned nor eloquent, he had inexhaustible riches, celestial knowledge, and the pentecostal gift of tongues. At least one spot in the bleak hillside is holy ground.

CHAPTER II

THROUGH THE VILLAGE

TIME is busy in levelling hills, abrading garden terraces, flattening grave-mounds, and abasing old families.
The gulf between the rich and poor may continue as
absolute as that between Dives and Lazarus; but the
traditional prominence of old families, if not already a
thing of the past, is departing, along with gracious
memories, and with much that used to inspire admiration and deference. In a village like Quabbin there is
little at this day to render one old house more venerable than another, but sixty years ago there were differences not to be explained by value or picturesqueness.
More was thought of intangible qualities and associations, such as cluster about the homes of beloved men
and scenes of historic interest. A few houses in the
village had an indefinable charm for those who remembered their former occupants. There is one in a
commanding position near the cross-roads which is
venerable in slow decay, and out of relations with
modern neighbors. Two ancient elms tower over the
grounds, and are seen afar. One of the patriots who
fought at Bunker's Hill built the house, then considered a mansion. His wife, the descendant of a
Huguenot family, had three sons by a former marriage; and these, in their maturity, were the only per-

sons in Quabbin that could, in the strict sense, be called gentlemen. The bright old lady long survived her husband, and made a striking picture as she moved about in her wheeled-chair, accompanied by one of her sons, a grave and stately man, who lived with her. Another son built a dwelling nearer the meeting-house. It appeared to be the dream of some inspired carpenter, a dream of wooden pilasters, wreaths, and scrolls, with a fretwork balustrade of wheel patterns upon the eaves, and an arched and decorated gateway, all in glittering white. Hillside terraces at the rear, with flower-beds and fruit-trees, were to youthful eyes like the hanging gardens of Babylon. The owner, with his tropical complexion of pale orange, his gold-rimmed spectacles, and his distinguished manners, in which dignity, courtesy, and kindness had equal share, was a wonderful person in Quabbin sixty years ago. For he had actually sailed around the world ; his cheeks had acquired their rich color in China, where he had been a tea-merchant ; the bronze idols and the great vases that adorned his rooms had come from farthest East. Besides, he knew European capitals, and, along with his well-earned wealth, he had brought to the village an aroma from spice-lands, a knowledge of the world, and the grand air that so becomes a travelled man.

The third of the brothers, a manufacturer, built a fine house, but with less ornament, on a knoll not far distant. All three could have been presented with credit at any court. They spoke the language of the educated world ; but, along with their somewhat ceremonious manners, they had a sense of what was due to others, especially to humble neighbors ; and as they were public-spirited, just, and generous, they were respected and loved. No one envied them their good fortune—a rare experience, whether in Quabbin or elsewhere.

The sombre old house with its two elms connected the village with the by-gone days of the colony; and the little old lady, while she lived, was a link with the great world, as her family was justly distinguished. But there may not be a living descendant of her three sons, and few of the present inhabitants know even the names of the men who first gave distinction to Quabbin.

What views the three original proprietors had in regard to religion, letters, schools, or art, it would be difficult now to say. They "went to meeting," apparently as a duty, and they took a modest part in town affairs; but between them and the town's people there must have been little intimacy. The general dulness in their time must have been impenetrable. They owned the water-power, which was the source of the town's prosperity and their own, but they sold it to two brothers who were born in one of the old farmhouses which once stood on the top of the southern hill. These latter were shrewd, able, and honorable men, but were less courtly, and reputed to be less generous, than their predecessors.

They were for a long time the great men of the town, until a third family, which had long ruled the north village, acquired a paramount interest in the property.

The principal store of the town is remembered chiefly by its permanent odor, in which there were suggestions of dried codfish, pickled mackerel, spices, snuff, plug tobacco, molasses, and new rum, re-enforced in wet weather by the steam of soaked garments and oily boots

by the hot stove, and the occasional whiff of a pipe.
The storekeeper was quiet and shrewd, and knew the
cumulative power of compound interest. A farmer
who had fallen behind-hand could get a continuance of
supplies, including the indispensable jug, by giving a
mortgage upon his land, — a backward step which was
seldom retrieved, — so that in the course of years the
storekeeper's roofs might have been measured by acres.
He was not in the least dishonest, but he worked frankly
for his own interest ; and it must not be forgotten
that, in transactions with customers who are habitually
fuddled and confused, a clear-headed man has all the
advantage.   Farms were exchanged for rum or cider-
brandy, with shabbiness, degradation, and family misery
thrown in.   As the use of spirits was universal, a dealer
incurred no obloquy, nor injury to his social standing.

There were other storekeepers, although they sold no
spirits.   One of them did a snug business, though
noted for a scrimping nicety in weights and measures,
and for a keen lookout after fractions.   People were
not overjoyed to see a fig torn in halves in case of over
weight,—that a fig was *bitten* in such an emergency
was a slander,— nor to pay invariably thirteen cents
for twelve and a half ; yet the proprietor once, in a
glow of virtuous pride, referred to the substantial sum
realized in a year from this salutary rule of retaining
the half-cents in making change.

The perplexities of the currency in olden times were
manifold.   Though the present decimal coinage had
been long established by law, the custom of reckoning
by shillings, six to the dollar, was well nigh universal
in Massachusetts.   At the same time, a large part of
the silver coins in use consisted of Mexican dollars,

halves, quarters, eighths, and sixteenths, all bearing the pillared arms of Spain; and between these coins and the traditional but imaginary "shillings" there was a rare confusion, demanding a mastery of vulgar fractions which only "Colburn's Mental Arithmetic" could give. A Mexican eighth was worth 12½ cents, but it was always called a "ninepence," that being its value in the traditional "shilling" of 16⅔ cents. A Mexican sixteenth, 6¼ cents, was called a "four-pence ha'penny." Prices of goods were marked in shillings; e. g., "two-and-three-pence" in place of 37½ cents, four shillings in place of 66⅔ cents, five shillings for 83⅓ cents, etc. The constant multiplication of the fractional tags insensibly drew from the public, and sensibly added to the dealer's till. It was in comparatively recent times that the Mexican coins were driven out, and that the custom of reckoning by shillings fell into disuse.

In this store, conducted on such sound financial principles, an Exalted Personage in the government of the United States received his first mercantile training, and began his successful career. In the sketches of his life, published during the campaign prior to his election, it is a matter of regret that the lonely place of his apprenticeship was overlooked. It was a misfortune for Quabbin.

Some sixty years ago the old tavern opposite the meeting-house having "run down," a new one of three stories was built in the centre, at the cross-roads. There was a daily stage-route from the county town to Boston, and a four-horse coach, announced by a far-echoing horn, came thundering down the hill road in the early morning, and discharged its passengers at the tavern for breakfast. There were few travellers who put up there, except the stage passengers. The chief revenue was from the bar. The sound of the toddy-stick was often heard, even in the street. It was a rhythmical roll, and each bar-keeper prided himself upon his special tattoo. Farmers coming to mill or shop, especially in winter, stopped there with their teams, the shivering animals being often forgotten while they drank hot toddy by the bar-room fire. The stable was haunted by day, and the bar-room by night, by shady and mysterious creatures, willing drudges for food and drams. To one coming from the fresh air without, the breath of that fiery bar-room was overpowering. The odors of the hostlers' boots, redolent of fish-oil and tallow, and of buffalo-robes and horse-blankets, the latter reminiscent of equine ammonia, almost got the better of the all-pervading fumes of spirits and tobacco. Clay pipes for "cut plug" were much in favor, though some reckless spendthrifts, at times, smoked principe cigars at three cents each.

This was the exchange for rustic wit, the focus of hate for parsons and deacons, and of ridicule for the new-fangled temperance society. The walls were adorned with placards of stage-routes, woodcuts of enormous stallions in prancing attitudes, and notices of sheriffs' sales, — the land or the stock of some deceased or ruined farmer to be offered at "public vendue." The country people gave the word nearly the French sound, *vandue*. No one then used the term auction.

The Masonic Hall at the cross-roads was deserted. The lodge never met, and the room was used at times for a private school. Boys used to set up the Semitic pillars, and to speculate upon the mysteries of the craft. The affair of Morgan, believed to have been murdered " out in York State " for exposing the secret rites, was then recent and blood-curdling. Public opinion was overwhelmingly against the order.

CHAPTER III

FARMS AND FARM—LIFE

THE territory of Quabbin comprises little more than
the winding valley and the various slopes and tributaries that lead to it, with the hills already described ;
and it will be seen that there could have been but few
large spaces for cultivation. Some half-dozen of the
farms became long ago rich in grass and grain ; but in
spite of the labors of generations in reclaiming bogs
and clearing fields of stones, the area of productive land
does not appear to have greatly extended.

Generally a couple of towering elms stood near each
farmhouse of the better class, and not far away were
apple-trees in squares. Clumps of lilacs grew by the
front door and by the edge of the garden ; while along
the neighboring road were rows of balloon-topped
maples. Each homestead became conspicuous in the
landscape, since the American elm has a stately grace
that belongs to no other tree in northern latitudes.

The farms lying without the valley were and still are
poor ; their plain lands sometimes bore thin crops of
rye, and then, lying fallow, were overrun with mullein ;[1]
their undrained meadows were cold and wet, and in-

---

[1] At the gate of what had been Chateaubriand's house in Paris, many years
ago, there was a large mullein in blossom, evidently regarded with admiration as a
rare plant.

fested with "poison ivy" and skunk cabbage ; their hillsides rough and stony ; their pastures gray and brown, or "run to bushes." The neighborhood roads were crooked, hilly, and stony or sandy.

The houses of prosperous farmers were neat and comfortable, though invariably plain ; but those of the poorer sort were miserable. They were generally of one story, always of wood, clapboarded, rarely painted, and dusky with weather-stain. Nature's gray is pictur- esque ; so are dirt and rags, in the eyes of artists ; but a dwelling that is gray or dingy with neglect, and rifted or "chinky" with dilapidation, is no more comfortable for being in harmony with a low-toned landscape.

In those times the chief feature of every farmhouse was the central chimney, which was large and square, having a fireplace on three of its sides in as many rooms, the largest being in the kitchen, as the common living-room was called. On that face of the chimney also was the opening into the cavernous brick oven, a "notion" which the Pilgrims may have brought over from Holland. Few such chimneys are now in exist- ence ; and the universal use of stoves, both for warmth and for cooking, has made the brick ovens and the vast fireplaces, with crane, pot-hooks, and trammels, things of the past.

At bed-time the andirons in the kitchen fireplace were drawn aside, and the brands and coals, having been piled upon the hearth, were covered thickly with ashes. When this was carefully done, enough embers were found in the morning to kindle a new fire ; but if the embers had become extinct, it was necessary to strike a spark with flint and steel into a box of tinder, and then use a splinter of wood tipped with sulphur to start a blaze. When the tinder was used up or damp, as sometimes happened, a boy was sent to a neighbor's, perhaps a quarter of a mile, to bring a live coal with a pair of tongs. It was a generation which had not made the enervating discovery of the friction match.

Besides the table, the chest of drawers, and chairs, the most noticeable objects in the long kitchen were the spinning-wheels, — a small one for flax, getting out of use more than sixty years ago, and a large one for wool, which was often seen down (perhaps) to 1850.

It is a pity that no artist undertook to represent the attitudes and movements of a well-formed and active damsel in the management of the great spinning-wheel. Such a picture may have been painted, but the writer never chanced to see one. Nothing in spinning demands great strength; but there is requisite a free movement of the arms, an elastic pose, and a long gliding step, advancing and retreating. The country people said there was a "knack" in it. Diana took no such fascinating poses in archery. The arms of a harp-player, however graceful, have a limited movement. In lawn-tennis the action is often too violent or constrained to be beautiful. Such attitudes and actions have been often enough attempted in art, but they are one and all tame beside the damsel at the great wheel.

Look at her. She is leaning forward, lightly poised upon the toe of the left foot. With her left hand she picks up by the end a long slender roll of soft wool, and deftly winds the fibres upon the point of the steel spindle before her. Now holding it an instant with thumb and finger, she gives a gentle motion to the wheel with the wooden *finger* which she holds in her right hand. Meanwhile, with her left hand she seizes the roll of wool at a little distance from the spindle, measuring with practised eye the length that will be required for one drawing. Then, while the hum of the wheel rises to a sound like the echo of wind in a storm, backward she steps, one, two, three, holding high the long yarn as it twists and quivers. Then, suddenly reversing the wheel, she glides forward with a long, even stride, and lets the yarn wind upon the swift spindle. Then another movement, a new pinch of the roll, a new turn of the wheel, and *da capo*.

The backward and forward movement, the left hand controlling the yarn while the right governed the wheel, were as picturesque as any ever made " by nymph, by naiad, or by grace." The muscles of the chest and arms were in free and beautiful play, and the varied movements of the limbs, alert, emphatic, and gliding by turns, suggested enough to have fully employed the genius of Praxiteles.

There were also here and there among old people (sixty years ago), hand-looms with treadles for weaving the cloth for ordinary wear. But most of these had been banished to the lumber-rooms.

The kitchen was adorned in autumn with festoons of dried apples and of red peppers, bunches of ears of seed-corn, dried bouquets of sage, savory, mint, and other herbs ; and about the fireplace, in racks set against the walls, hung crookneck squashes. A pot of blue dye (fortunately covered) stood in the corner of the fireplace. This departed with the spinning-wheels. Adjoining the kitchen, and generally in an addition, or lean-to, were the cheese press and tubs, diffusing in mild weather the faintly sour odor of whey. There, too, were shelves, on which lay ripening cheeses, turned daily, and polished with butter and red annatto by diligent hands.

In ancient times few farmers had regular supplies of fresh meat. Except at the autumnal pig-killing, or at the slaughter of a lamb in the spring, or very rarely in winter of a steer, their tables were furnished with salted beef and pork from their own cellars, and with dried salt fish. To allay the irritation caused by such viands, many vegetables were used; but the main dependence was pickled peppers and "cowcumbers," — a dangerous indulgence, one would think, — and apple-sauce. This latter preserve was wholesome and appetizing, but is now seldom seen; perhaps on account of the scarcity of cleanly made and unfermented cider. The cider was boiled down almost to sirup, and pared and cored apples, with a few quinces for flavor, were slightly cooked in it; after which the mass was poured into a clean barrel, and kept in a cool place.

It will be seen that the cellar was one of the most important parts of a farmer's house, as it contained much of the winter's store. In early times a house rarely had stone underpinning,[1] and the cellar was protected from frost by banking the lower part of the house with forest leaves, sawdust, or tan-bark. Therein were deposited the salt beef and pork, cabbages, potatoes, and other roots, in bins, a part of the supply of apples, and several barrels of cider in different stages of development. A mug fresh from the spigot was a provocative for palate, eyes, and nose; its fumes attacked the air-passages, and the stomach soon glowed like a chafing-dish. But this genial stimulus was not enough for some hardened throats, and it was a frequent custom to set a mug of the oldest before the fire, with

[1] The upper tier of foundation stones which sustained the house above the level of the ground.

red peppers floating in it, so as to give the cider a sharper prickle, and the jaded stomach a fresh thrill.

Instead of carpets, the rooms were furnished with party-colored mats, braided of woollen rags. The bed-chambers were often partly or wholly unfinished, being mere divisions of a bare attic. In time of a winter's storm, it was not uncommon for boys to feel the snow falling on their faces as they lay in their scantily draped beds; for it found easy entrance, being sifted through the loosely shingled roof, or blown under the gaping eaves.

In such chambers on a wintry morning the breath was visibly congealed, and the thickly studded points of shingle-nails were bristling with crystals that gleamed like stars overhead.

The barn was a sure indication of a farmer's thrift. His house might be unpainted and out of repair without greatly injuring his reputation, but the neglect of his barn was decisive. For the barn and appendages were the storehouse of his crops, the stable and fold for his animals, and the shelter of his wagon, cart, ploughs, and tools. It needed but a glance to know how affairs were going.

In some cases the barn was a desolation. If, further, the wagon was unwashed and rickety, the horse rough and lean, the harness clumsily patched, or tied with cords, the ploughs left to rust, the yard untidy and undrained, and fowls allowed to roost on whatever was handiest, it would be a natural inference that the farmer's shiftlessness was abetted by hot-peppered cider or new rum.

In some farms the wretched management frustrated any kindly intentions of nature; for the application of science to agriculture was all to come. The aim was to get what could be got out of the land with the least outlay; to live upon the produce as far as possible; and to provide money for taxes and the few absolute necessities by the sale of whatever could be spared. A fat hog, one or two calves, a few fowls or turkeys, a little butter and cheese,— these would bring the cash required. On a larger farm there could be sold grain, a fat ox, a colt, or firewood. With good health and sobriety, the conditions were not too hard, but in many households life was pinched and sordid. Economy is honorable, and may be gracious, but an enforced niggardliness is degrading. For those who must struggle with an insoluble equation between outgo and income, books have no charm, genial society is unknown, nature has nothing but frowns, and the future no hope except in final rest from toil.

On the more prosperous farms, life was fairer, and better worth living. Still, few farmers were educated beyond the three R's, or were in the habit of reading in hours of leisure, excepting the Bible and weekly newspaper.

During the winter months the ordinary work was necessarily laid by; there was nothing to be done, except taking care of animals and cutting wood. The needs of the house were readily supplied from last winter's cutting, thoroughly seasoned; but periodically there was an onslaught upon some part of the "wood-lot" for timber. The cutting of trees, when resolved upon, was as thorough as the sweep of postmasters after the coming in of a new president. The scar on the hillside could no more be hidden than a slash on the farmer's cheek in shaving. Wise, conservative forestry was unknown.

When snow lay on the roads and woodland paths, it

was easy to draw out the great logs and send them to mill on ox-sleds. Under the mighty loads the tracks soon got a crystalline polish, and sleighing-parties and small boys rejoiced. The choppers, though standing all day in snow, did not suffer from cold. In the forest there was no wind, and exercise kept their blood in active circulation. Their hands were cased in buckskin or woollen mittens, their bodies in loose frocks (longish blouses), and their feet in heavy, well-greased boots. Often, with the thermometer at zero, a hearty man would drop his axe to wipe the sweat from his brow.

The winter, too, was the time for most of the recreations of country life : during the warmer seasons the pressure of work left little leisure. In the winter the stock of provisions was full, and roasted apples, genial cider, and mince-pies, — which never pall upon a Yankee's appetite, — were almost constant luxuries. Then was the time for evening spelling-schools, singing-schools, apple-paring bees, sleigh-rides, fishing through the ice, and other country frolics. Then boys trapped partridges and rabbits. Then skaters went skimming over rivers and ponds, swaying this way and that, like dancers in a minuet. Then was the time for the great slides by moonlight down long, icy hills, — a dozen big sleds, one after the other, careering down at railroad speed, and sometimes overturning, so as to pile half a dozen of both sexes in a mealy drift by the way. Do not talk to a Yankee of "toboggan"! The word belongs to Canadians, who are welcome to it. *Toboggan*, indeed! As well call a Quabbin farmer's little, scrimped parlor a "drawing-room."

Farms were known by their owners' names, at least when occupied long enough to give a notion of permanency, as "The Estes Place," "The Sherman Place," "The Deering Place." There are few names that have not been changed in sixty years ; and only one farm, it is said, remains in the possession of a descendant of the original settler. Each family has furnished emigrants to newer States, while some son or married daughter has generally kept the homestead for a time.

In the village changes have been equally frequent. The builders of its houses are dead, their children are scattered, and strangers have taken their places. In a walk of a mile and a half the man of sixty years will not pass a single house that shelters the people whom he once knew.

But a reminiscent mood has its vagaries like revery. Thoughts, events, and faces, long forgotten, start up in a hap-hazard way, and the mind is filled with flitting images that play like water-beetles in an endless maze. These pictures from memory need a frame, and the course of events should have some order. Perhaps, therefore, it is best to be done with reminiscence, and, like graver historians, begin at the beginning.

CHAPTER IV

SETTLEMENT

IT was a long time after the first westward movement from the seacoast that this unpromising region was settled. Not until the rich alluvial lands of the Connecticut valley were taken up, and the fair hillsides east of the river were covered with farms, was there any thought of occupying this narrow, wet valley, and the rugged knolls that enclosed it. The first white child was born in Quabbin in 1735, and the grant of the land was made by the General Court in 1736. The settlers were for the most part Scottish Presbyterians from Ulster. Some of these were "mighty hunters" and wrestlers. Two of them were hatters, who lived and wrought in a place well known in the village. Furs were plenty, but polls were few ; and what are hats without heads ? The trade would seem to have been preposterous. Still the long bows twanged, and downy forms were felted in hot water, then shaped and pressed ; and the surplus hats, it is to be hoped, found sale in older settlements.

But little is known of Quabbin's early progress. The increase was doubtless slow. The few Indians were wanderers, — basket-makers or beggars, or both. After the decline of the French power in Canada there were no settlements of Indians nearer than Stockbridge,

where Jonathan Edwards went to preach after leaving
Northampton.   But Quabbin had been a favorite resort
of red men ; for flint arrow-heads were ploughed up long
afterward in the valley lands, and stone bowls, pestles,
and hatchets were found on the sites of ancient wig-
wams.   The Indians who haunted the frontier a hundred years ago were vicious and degraded, but not
without shrewdness.   Said an Indian woman to a village
housewife one day, "Will ee give me little water, or
cider? — for I be so hungry I dunno where to sleep
over night."   An old Indian, who had roamed the
woods all his life, was asked what was the surest sign
of rain.   With a flicker in his beady black eyes he
answered in his deep guttural tones, " Ee sure sign o'
rain is when ee black all round, an' pourin' down in 'e
middle."

Other settlers came, some with Scottish, but more
and more with English names.   The latter were largely
from the Old Colony and from towns on Cape Cod.
Two brothers built a grist-mill at the centre of the
village, and both of them, together with a neighbor,
served in the Revolutionary army.   The first minister,
also, was a chaplain under Washington.

The meeting-house was built in 1787, when the parish
was organized ; and the minister was settled in 1789,
when the French Assembly were beginning their struggle with Louis the Unhappy.   The site for the meeting-house was given by the grandfather of General
Joseph Hooker, well known in our civil war.   At first
the worshippers sat on movable benches ; but in 1793
the pews formerly described were constructed, and the
names of the purchasers, thirty in number, have been
preserved.   Probably the population of the parish did
not exceed two hundred.

In 1814 the belfry was built, and a bell was given by an eccentric man, long remembered. Two years later the parish was incorporated as a town.

This must suffice for history. Dates are wearisome, and the happenings in a small community are in no wise interesting.

But there is another view. The evolution of the best type of a modern New Englander from the Provincial of the last century, if one could compass it, might be a theme worthy of a philosophic historian. And, even if one were not such a master as to be able to educe the philosophy of history, a faithful picture of life and manners, suggesting, it may be vaguely, the moving forces, prejudices, and whims of the old time, must have value. The life of any community is made up of infinite details. One can hardly say that the smallest point in town management, church polity, or domestic economy is absolutely unimportant. Solid growth is never visible in the present tense. Furthermore, generalizers are commonly falsifiers, sacrificing verity to epigram. Even truth lies, if she is taken too literally, and without consideration of the *milieu*. A bold sketch of the Rise of the New England Town, or of the Literary Awakening, or of the Development of the Seventeenth Century Puritan into the modern Yankee, might be brilliant writing, but would be most untrustworthy unless supported by a multitude of minute and apparently insignificant facts.

The change that has come has been both in ideas and life. With the beginning of the present century the ideas of provincial Massachusetts were giving way. Theological asperity was softening; a man might vote against the ruling majority without being mobbed; and liberty of thought was dimly recognized as something possible. The change was not simply a matter of dress, of speech, or of tone, — there was a growing refinement in these externals, — it was something deeper : no less than an overturning of old habits of thought, a general reform in conduct among the opponents of the state-church, and the establishment of society on fairer terms. The change began in the larger towns, the centres of influence, and was manifested in the decline of drinking customs, in a revived and more tolerant church, in reconstructed schools, and enlightened public spirit.

The town was the primordial cell, of which the State and nation are aggregations. While the political up-building was going on, an immense development of education was in progress ; the functions of the church and the civil power were disentangled and differentiated ; manufactures were placed on new foundations by discoveries in sciences and arts ; railways and telegraphs furnished new arteries and nerves ; the Puritan embargo on the world's literature was raised ; books multiplied, and newspapers became as necessary as breath ; the horizon of thought and the scope of human interest grew to be as broad as the world ; the bucolic dialect and costume were disappearing. In short, it came to be possible, and it would be quite possible to-day, for a resident of Quabbin to be in touch with the world of science, to exhibit a work of art at the Paris Salon, or to discuss literature and history with the leaders of the time. This claim is potential rather than actual ; but admitted possibilities are something. In recent years Parisian critics have admired the sculpture of a son of Quabbin ; in the Episcopal churches the music of a Quabbin composer is justly admired; and among ornithologists a native collector and observer is widely known.

From Quabbin well-trodden roads lead everywhere, — in which respect the proverb as to Rome is reversed, — and thither, from the modern thought of New England, electric lines carry intelligence of all that men achieve, attempt, or admire. A hundred years ago this was notoriously otherwise. Equally notorious was it that in the great centres there was little indigenous literature or philosophy worth transmitting to Quabbin or elsewhere. What, one may ask, were the influences and the successive steps by which this people has been led out of its dull, benighted, and plodding existence? Quabbin is, perhaps, an instance as fair as another, since what has gone on in its narrow bounds has been going on throughout the State on a larger scale. The history of Quabbin, then, if one could write it, would be part of a general movement upon which dogmatism would be easy and valueless, and which will be best understood in a free narrative.

The few events in Quabbin's annals are naturally grouped under the reigns of its successive ministers. Writers upon literature are in the habit of classifying it under the reigns of sovereigns, few of whom knew or cared about books, and fewer still who gave literary genius any countenance unless that genius happened to be known at court. But it is more appropriate to speak of the age of Shakespeare and Cervantes, of Molière and Milton, of Goethe, Byron, and Balzac.

In Quabbin the case is different, for the parish ministers, from Joshua I. to Robert IV., were men of marked individuality, and had each an influence, of one sort or another, upon the development of the town.

It will be remembered that about fifty years passed
from its settlement to the ordination of the first minister (1736–1789). It may be added that most of the
important changes in society have taken place during
the present century.

The question constantly recurs, how was it that the
sombre Puritan became a poet, romancer, inventor,
engineer, or scientist ? and how has a people of limited
knowledge and narrow views, without worldly ambition,
who renounced all things for the sake of the life to
come, and were content to toil without hope of enfran-
chisement on earth, grown into the marvellously active
and versatile society of to-day ? The answers must be
inferred from many observations, and, beyond doubt,
they will vary with different observers. We may find
something to think of in looking at life in country and
village homes, at town and church meetings, militia
trainings, and popular sports ; in schools, temperance
societies, psalmody, and current literature ; and all the
changes will be found to be, perhaps, reciprocally causes
and results. The movements of society are like the
processes of nature. No one ever saw a shovelful of star-
dust, yet, we are told, the whole round globe gets an
appreciable coating of it every century. Who can enter
into the spiritual evolution which began with Mistress
Anne Bradstreet, and culminated in her descendant,
Oliver Wendell Holmes ? — or that from Priscilla Mullins
to Longfellow ? There are few instances in history of
a transformation more complete than has been seen in
Massachusetts ; and perhaps a side-light can be thrown
upon it from the candlestick set in Quabbin.

CHAPTER V

ATMOSPHERE

In good old colony times,— say two centuries ago,— opinions upon religion and politics were practically unanimous. The early settlers were homogeneous ; for *idem sentire* had been the rule of association, and, as Lieut.- Governor Stoughton declared, " God had sifted three kingdoms " to gather them. Dissent from the " orthodox " form of Dissent was rigidly kept out of the infant colony ; and in later times, any incipient rebellion was repressed by an overpowering public sentiment. Religious dogma was embodied in the Westminster " Shorter Catechism."

In colonial politics, the aim was to make a show of respect to the royal authority, while the real power, under the charter, should rest with "the Great and General Court." But no, not the real power, for behind the magistrates and deputies were the clergy, who were the unquestionable rulers.

But unanimity in faith and practice cannot be eternal under any form of government, and in the course of the eighteenth century there were cleavages in society past cementing. The French war brought some changes through the increasing prominence of military men, who were more in touch with the great world than with the secluded zealots of the church ; but a far deeper disturbing force was the long war of the Revolution. In the midst of arms, it is not only law and letters that are silent ; conscience is often dumb. And when peace came, the returning soldiers brought back to their native hamlets new ideas, and often vicious habits as well. In camps and trenches, other topics were more discussed than fate and free will. Beyond doubt, soldiers were more occupied with the theories of Rousseau, a man they had never heard of, but the essence of whose doctrines was brought to their comprehension by the clear and nervous phrases of the Declaration of Independence. " Freedom is a noble thing," said John Barbour, and it ennobles while it enfranchises. With the prospect of a free republic, there was a broadening of mind, and the gradually enlightened patriot soldier, even if unconscious of any revulsion against old doctrine or custom, could never again be the obedient and contented son of the Puritan Church he had been.

Many of the soldiers had acquired the habits of dram-drinking and swearing, and in time threw off all restraint. It is obviously unjust to Jefferson to associate such vices with his political views; but it had happened that the people of Massachusetts had followed the lead of John Adams in politics, as they had followed the heads of the Church in religious dogma. A Massachusetts Federalist prior to 1810 was almost certain to be orthodox in faith ; a church member was almost certain to be a Federalist. Whenever a man, from conviction, wilfulness, or bad habits, left the church or the dominant party, no half-way course was possible ; and it was generally the case that a Democrat was a Universalist, a Freethinker, or in some way one of the "otherwise minded." The wealthy, respectable, and temperate people were

Federalists, and supporters, if not members, of the Puritan church. Outside were Democrats, hard drinkers, and deists. For more than a generation the line of demarcation was invariable. The hostile feeling between the classes deepened often to malignant hate, and was felt wherever men came in contact.

The story is told that, early in the century, at an election in Hadley, after the ballots were counted, an awful rumor spread through the town hall that a Democratic vote had been found in the box. Murmurs were heard, increasing momentarily, until the moderator confirmed the report by announcing so many votes for the Federalist candidates, and *one* for the Democratic; and then the uproar became tumultuous. Who could have been the ungodly and abominable creature to cast that ballot? No one could guess. After the proceedings were over, an old man, poorly dressed, and mounted on a lean and furry horse, having got safely into the highway, shouted back to the people, "It was I that cast that 'ere Dimmercrat vote!" and then galloped away to escape a shower of stones.

The feeling against the Democrats became more intense in consequence of the partiality of Jefferson for France. The cause of France was considered the cause of irreligion, and good men felt bound to protest against "opening the flood-gates of infidelity." Obviously, so long as the church as a body took a decided stand in politics, there could be no dispassionate consideration of public questions. These had been decided in advance. Something of the same spirit has survived. To a purely economic argument upon the tariff, no matter by whom made, it has been held to be a sufficient answer that Democrats occupied an immoral ground in regard to slavery thirty years ago. In some respects it was a misfortune to a man, in the last generation, to have been reared in a family of Democratic proclivities. A Democrat was a man to be distrusted and shunned. Even a man of genius like Hawthorne found himself " on the wrong side of the hedge." Society in Salem was almost wholly of one way of thinking, and Hawthorne was made to feel his isolation. His friends were not of the ruling party or sect. However contented he may have been with his beliefs, the reprobation of the " best people" must have given a deeper tinge of melancholy to his never too sunny nature, and added to the gloom that broods over his otherwise matchless stories.

It is needless to say there were no Hawthornes in Quabbin, nor, in fact, any Democrats with too delicate susceptibilities ; for ignorance and hard usage had, so to speak, toughened their skins. As the rule of church and society was firm and uncompromising, the opposition was rude and defiant. The existence of this recalcitrant minority was familiar enough, but the first divergence was well begun early in this century, and it is difficult to offer a suggestion as to its origin. Neither of the Revolutionary soldiers from Quabbin had any sympathy with this opposition ; and the influences that reared up Democrats in defiance of public opinion, and unbelievers among people whose life was one act of worship, must have come from some other district , one might as well expect to see a palm-tree growing on Great Quabbin, or a walrus disporting in the tepid water of the cove. In the course of years neighborhoods change by removals, and even sixty years ago some odd people had come to the town.

There was a grave and silent man who came now and then to the store and to mill, but never to meeting, and who never sought the least intimacy. One day the mystery of this taciturn being was revealed. Say not "revealed," but whispered with horror. He was a deist, had been a printer in Boston, and had even printed Bibles, but had been led astray by infidel books. The tone in which the word "deist" was uttered suggested what no epithet could have conveyed. The man was industrious, temperate, and honest; but the name of deist was a convict's brand.

Another who never went to meeting, at least never to *the* meeting, was a self-taught mathematician, who was sometimes found stretched on the floor before the fire, working out on a slate the calculations for an eclipse. It was said he voted the Democratic ticket, but he had little to say about religion or politics, and was sobriety itself. He believed in "nater," and thought that to "du as you'd be done by " was a good enough rule of life.

An old farmer, who called himself "a Dimmercrat and Univarsaller " once tried to tempt a villager into an argument upon fore-ordination. The son of the latter was near by, and heard a few sentences like these: " Eff God ain't the author of evil, an' ain't responsible for the damnation of his critters, that is, ef they air to be damned, I sh'd like to know why ! Ef things is fixed, either he fixed 'em, or he stood by an' let somebody else fix 'em. Ef they ain't fixed, then he don't know what's comin', an' ain't omnishent." When this point was reached, the father observed his boy listening, and discovered that there were " chores " for him to do in the barn.

A lawyer, who lived about three miles away, had a great reputation for wit and "sarse" in the justices' and county courts ; and though imperfectly educated, he was a man of ability, quite superior to any one in the region. He, too, was a Democrat and Universalist. He had a near relative in Quabbin, but there was not the least intercourse between them, not even a "bowing acquaintance ;" and their relationship was not known by the younger members of the Quabbin family until both had passed away. Still, there had never been any cause of quarrel, beyond the antipathy between hostile creeds.

There were, now and then, rifts in the wall that hemmed in Quabbin ; and things to set its young people thinking.

CHAPTER VI

THE FIRST MINISTER

THE ambition of the village that was growing up about the gristmill at the foot of Great Quabbin had awakened some interest in the adjacent region ; and there were coarse but not malevolent comments upon its rising pretensions.

It will be remembered that there were thirty purchasers of pews in the meeting-house, and these probably included more than half of the heads of families in the parish ; but the parish boundaries were narrow, and many came to the stores, mill, and meeting, from beyond its limits. This was the case with many excellent people, and it was also true of a set of the most depraved and drunken creatures that ever infested a village.

Quabbin did not become a "town" until 1816; it was to an outlying "parish" that the minister was called ; but the community was awake and alert, after its deliberate fashion. It had a mill to begin with, and plenty of water-power for more works projected.

The mother town was, and has always remained, one of the most sluggish of rural communities. It did not appear poverty-stricken, but limp and lifeless. One might have walked the length of its ample common, around which a dozen close-blinded houses were dozing, and not have seen a human being abroad. When a team passed along the sandy road it crawled so slowly that you thought the animals and driver asleep, and moving in a dream. Even the old tavern had scarcely an eye open. The only life of the flat landscape was in the crows searching for hidden acorns by the road-sides or pulling up replanted corn in the fields. So strong was the impression of this torpor, that to look for any gayety there seemed as impossible as to expect a blossom from a broomstick. Nevertheless, it was averred that a stanza had once been composed there, an actual stanza of four lines of verse. It might have been regarded as a lying legend had it not been for the evidence of the "local color." This is what the mockers were supposed to have said or sung : —

> " Let us go down to Puckertown,[1]
> And see them raise the steeple ;
> There we will stay, and hear Josh pray
> To save his wicked people."

This effort was exhausting and fatal ; as in the case of the aloe, which dies after its centennial blossoming, the unknown and inglorious poet drooped, and never rhymed again.

The minister of Quabbin, who had been a chaplain in the army of the Revolution, was near middle age when settled in 1789. His salary was fixed at seventy pounds, besides which the parish purchased a house and a small farm for him, and agreed to supply him with firewood. He lived to be over four-score, and, in his later years at least, was a picturesque figure, never forgotten by those who had seen him.

[1] " Puckertown," i.e. Quabbin. To *pucker* suggests a mincing facial expression, either of vanity or disdain.

His white hair, long and slightly waving, fell upon his broad, square shoulders, and the soft folds of his double chin rested upon a white necktie. His full face (clean shaved thrice a week), his shapely, but rather prominent nose, and his steady blue eyes, altogether wore a look of dignity and benevolence. In form he was short and sturdy, but not in the least unwieldy. On the street he carried a silver-topped cane, and he wore his black silk gown not only in the pulpit but (in summer time) in making pastoral calls. He was the last of Quabbin's ministers to wear it, and much of the stately grace of the olden time went out with its flowing sleeves. It was an impressive visible illustration when he raised these, as if tremblingly, while he repeated the solemn words, " And the smoke of their torment ascendeth up forever and ever." [1]   His voice was bland, resonant, and measured, and deep in power rather than in pitch.

He had a colleague ten years before his death, and as *pastor emeritus* did not preach very often in the period covered by the recollections of a man of sixty ; but, in figure, face, manners, and voice, as he appeared at more than four-score, he would have been a good specimen to show of the " degeneracy of Americans."

He had been fairly well educated for the time, although he had been unable to complete his collegiate course. Judging from his library, his reading must have been mainly professional, in biblical commentaries, church history, and polemics. Neither he nor any clergyman in Western Massachusetts could have regarded the study of general literature as other than a vain pleasure or an idle curiosity ; not absolutely harmful, but wholly

[1] The story is told of Dr Chalmers, but is true also of this minister.

unimportant compared with the "one thing needful."
His sermons were plain and vigorous expositions of
Scripture, without any pretence of rhetoric, or illustration from nature or science, or the "sentiment" to
which modern ears are accustomed. It was a time
when people were nurtured and inspired by the Bible, the
"Pilgrim's Progress," Alleine's "Alarm to the Unconverted," and Baxter's "Saints' Rest;" and when the
echoes of Jonathan Edwards' thunder had scarcely died
out of the air. The first minister's style of speech was
not Yankee, as that adjective is understood; the old
British rotund energy had survived in it. He freely used
colloquial elisions, such as *didn't, hain't, sha'n't,* etc.,
just as they are printed in the first editions of Edwards'
works, and in many English books of the seventeenth
and eighteenth centuries, but there was no offensive
drawl, nor any debasing of vowel tones.

In spite of his stern theology he was kindly and
human in his intercourse with his people. He had
been an athlete in his youth, and few men were better
judges of a foot-race, a tug-of-war, or a jumping-match.
He could fence also, and go through the manual of
arms; and in the War of 1812 he had proved to be
the only man in the region competent to drill the
company of artillery that went from an adjoining town
for the defence of Boston.

It was something to have seen and talked with a man
who had known Lafayette, and had carried musket and
Bible under the command of Washington. The imagination (even of a boy) took fire, and his heart throbbed
at the thought.

When the old man was near his end, the neighbors,
old and young, came, according to the primitive cus-

tom, to see how a Christian could die. They looked with awe upon the slow and laborious heaving of his powerful chest, the vacancy of his fast-dimming eyes, and the fitful tremor of the hands that had often rested on their heads. The scene was painfully protracted; it was nearly a whole day after he was (in country phrase) "struck with death" before his breathing ceased.

The man still living, whose hand more than once was clasped with that of the first minister of Quabbin, might well reflect what a stretch is covered by two lives, — the loss of Canada by the French; the attainment of independence by the United States; the French Revolution; the meteoric career of Bonaparte, — Marengo, Jena, Austerlitz, Borodino, Waterloo, St. Helena; the birth of literature and philosophy in Germany; in Great Britain the appearance of Johnson, Burns, Coleridge, Scott, Byron, Keats, Wordsworth, Tennyson, and Browning; a dawning literature in America; the era of gas, railways, steamships, tele-graphs, evolution, the spectroscope, bacteriology; the Civil War in the United States, with all that followed; the sudden military prominence of Germany; so much, and more, past all enumeration, in the space of two lives!

Men are prone to think their particular experiences unusual, but it would be difficult, probably, to name another period in which the events, discoveries, and movements were so momentous to mankind as that extending from the fall of Quebec to that of Richmond or of Metz. Little was heard in Quabbin sixty years ago of the far-echoing footsteps of Fate in the Old World.

It is necessary to look at the condition of the church and parish during this long pastorate.

There was no interference with healthful amusements, except in certain over-zealous families. Round-ball on the common in summer, and coasting on the hillsides, and skating on the pond in winter, were eagerly followed; but the line was drawn at dancing. The country balls took place at the old-fashioned taverns, — not always free from scandal, — and were attended only by the worldly and irreligious. A youth of sixteen in Quabbin, when he first saw people dancing to the sound of music, thought their capers silly; but it appeared otherwise later, when he threaded his way through a cotillon, led by a pretty girl.

As the minister went his rounds, everybody saluted him with respect and good-will; and children were instructed to draw to one side of the road and make bows or "kerchys" as he passed. In the minds of some of them this ceremony was associated with the approach of a floating silken robe; and once, when the minister's new colleague came upon a small party engaged in making mud-pies, it appeared to them that as he wore no gown he was not entitled to a salute. One little urchin of four got a tingling reception at home for having refused to "bow to the minister." It was feared the rebellion might be prophetic.

The minister lived prudently, reared a family, mostly of boys, and if he did not become rich, was always comfortable and self-respecting. It was not the fashion then to cosset the pastor,— to embroider slippers for him, to give him "donation parties," nor send him to Europe for a summer vacation.

Exchanges were infrequent, but sometimes there

was a sermon from a veteran in service, or from a professor of the college not far away. D.D.'s were uncommon, and it was then supposed that a man had to become a patriarch as old as Abraham before attaining such a dignity.

The minister's calls, though functional in a way, were neighborly and social. The affairs of the church and parish, personal religion, and the training and catechising of the children, were lightly touched upon in presence of the family,— all the members within reach having been summoned to meet the good man in the parlor. Generally the interview was closed with a brief prayer. Then was set out a plate of cake and a decanter of wine or of Santa Cruz rum. The latter was taken with hot water in winter, and cold in summer, and with two lumps of sugar. Then, with a parting word for each, and a gentle touch upon the heads of the children, the minister rustled out with his silk gown, and went his way.

In his pastorate of nearly half a century he was never involved in trouble or controversy. A man of keen perceptions and courage, who was given to outbursts of sympathy and to upliftings of enthusiasm, could not have maintained such serenity in view of the life around him. It is true, the regular worship was never intermitted : the Bible was expounded, and its warnings and promises rehearsed ; but upon the majority of the people these formalities made no real impression, and a large number were besotted, dull, and boorish. There were hoary heads without crowns of honor. There were horses that were accustomed to back out from the tavern shed, and trot soberly home without guidance, when late at night their stupefied masters crawled into their wagons. Brave women were striving to cover the family nakedness, and to put a good face upon despair. Modest girls had reason to shrink from young men whose education was acquired at the bar of the tavern. The schools barely lifted the children above illiteracy. Uncleanliness in manners and speech, if not universal, caused little remark. As for literature and science, they were not only unknown, but inconceivable. Did the minister see all this? Probably he did, but for all shortcomings the only remedy then known was "the stated preaching of the Word," as it had been from the beginning. There were just so many who would refuse the offers of grace ; and so many who would become slaves to appetite, and be content with ignorance, poverty, and degradation, as long as the supplies of rum and tobacco held out.

The minister was prudent, kind, and just, and did his duty according to the light of his time. The era of active and burning sympathy, and of practical philanthropy, had not dawned upon Quabbin, nor upon the State.

Is it an injustice to suggest that the scarcely veiled fatalism, which was then the indispensable doctrine of Calvinism, had something to do with this state of things? Predestination, according to hair-splitting theory, was not admittedly fatalism ; but it appears certain that the doctrine, according to which the number of the "elect" was foreknown, while the vast remainder of the unredeemed were left without hope, must have accustomed the self-contained saints to regard as inevitable the sins and woes of their less wise and less fortunate fellow-men. This was before philan-

thropy appeared as an active force, and before voluntary societies were established to do the work for which,
logically, the church was all-sufficient. But philan-
thropic societies were not organized until the tension of
fore-ordination and kindred doctrines had begun to relax.
In this matter a surprising spectacle became visible to
the world a few years later: no less than a total change
of basis and of method,—a change of spirit, a new-born
sympathy, an attempt to realize the brotherhood of
men by mutual effort, as well as by the "appointed
means" before relied on; while yet the creed remained untouched. No heresy was preached in Quabbin or its neighborhood. The Shorter Catechism
continued in diligent use. There was nothing positive
to indicate that Calvin and Jonathan Edwards were not
still the pillars of the New England church. But if
doctrines in their essence had suffered no change, and
if the character of the sermons, and the methods of
work among ministers and deacons had remained what
they were, the narrow and dull provincial Yankee of
sixty years ago would have been a narrow Provincial
still. In the tone and temper of theology was the key
of the situation.

So although New England "orthodoxy" is nominally
what it was, practically it has been changed from pin-
nacle to foundation-stone. The change consists in ignoring certain doctrines which run counter to the sense
of justice and the nobler instincts of mankind. From
a lifeless formula, religion has become a practical force.
By co-operation with lay societies, with education, and
with schemes for social enlightenment and beneficence,
the church regained its ascendency, with a just title to
gratitude and reverence.

Are we to hold the venerable first minister responsible for not establishing in Quabbin a Total Abstinence Society, an Anti Slavery Society, a model school, or a Society for Foreign Missions? By no means. The time for them had not come.

CHAPTER VII

PATIENT EMILY

QUABBIN was not a fertile ground for romance. There were few social inequalities, clandestine marriages, or startling events. The rich men were never numerous, and, after the time of the three courtly brothers mentioned in a former chapter, there were few who, if faithfully drawn, would make attractive figures in a story. The general character, to the casual observer, was humdrum, and as void of prominences as a turnip. There was not in the town an author, wit, cynic, or recluse ; nor had there been a murder or a suicide. Such a lapse as the presence of a child unaccounted for did not occur five times in a century. A tragic or romantic scene in Quabbin would have been as improbable as a Spanish bull-fight. But life has both anxiety and charm, even for the most commonplace of men ; and in his own view the trials of each man may be as momentous as those which beset King Lear. Few have the power, like the rustic Yankee, to batten under hatches any revolt of feeling, and to walk the deck with an air of unconcern. The city Yankee (as Dr. Holmes has observed) differs from his country cousin chiefly in flexibility of facial muscles, and capacity of varying expression.

George Haskins was habitually "shut up" like a

box-turtle (if a change of figure may be allowed), and the few words that escaped him came grudgingly, like coins from a miser's pocket. George had good height, a robust frame, and a dark complexion tinged with rose, and was sufficiently active in movement; but either heredity or Puritanic discipline had rendered him silent, and deliberate in action, and had made a mask of a face that might have been mobile and attractive. Seldom was a muscle relaxed about his shaven lips; so that when, on rare occasions, a fit of laughter seized him, his features were totally upset and unrecognizable. The only constant sign of life was in his wily brown eyes. Sometimes even the eyes were motionless, like still pools; and again there were slight gleams in them, as if microscopic gold-fish were playing in the aqueous humor.

He was a well-to-do farmer, and lived in a good old-fashioned house sheltered by a couple of noble elms. His widowed mother had the care of the house and of all domestic affairs. She was above medium height, and, though slender, had the wiry muscles, the bold features, the resolution, and the complexion that belong with the bilious temperament. Nothing escaped her eye. Her cheeses were renowned, and her stamp upon pats of golden butter made them current as coin. Yet, like her son, she had little to say. The purchase or sale of cows or other live-stock was considered and decided between her and George by fragments of phrase, and by looks and nods untranslatable by others. It is not to be supposed, however, that she did not keep up a deal of thinking of a practical sort.

No persons were more constant at meeting than Mrs. Haskins and her son. They had an old-fashioned chaise (" shay " they called it) that carried two, and no more, drawn by a sedate animal called a " colt," but already past middle-age. The colt jogged on with due gravity on " Sahberdays," but could " let out," and throw gravel with the swiftest, when George drove in his wagon to store or mill.

Mrs. Haskins was firmly grounded in Scripture, and could follow all the texts cited in the longest doctrinal sermon. She held to the views of the first minister, and had but a moderate opinion of his colleague. It was her delight to hear again and again the doctrines of election and reprobation, and she never considered a discourse complete which did not end with a representation of the endless woe of the finally impenitent. She chewed upon these dogmas, as she chewed her sprigs of caraway ; and her head, overtopped by a high-curved green silk *calèche* (calash), moved slowly backward and forward with evident satisfaction at the emphatic points of the sermon.

One day, when this linked array of doctrines had been brought out with unusual effect, Mrs. Haskins chanced to look up at the gallery, and there saw John Foster, a man who seldom came to meeting, and who was known to be far from orthodox. He was a wool-sorter at the mill, and had time in his solitary work to think. He was a pale man, with a nimbus of light hair, reserved in manner, blameless in life, and not in the least capable of making money. Content with little, he pleased himself with the company of his children, and with his few books. His horoscope for the human race was quite different from that which was announced from the pulpit. On this occasion his eldest daughter, Emily, was beside him in the pew, and drew all eyes in the vicinity, especially in the choir, where many lively young fellows sat.

The service ended, John Foster and his daughter rose to go out. "Em'ly," said he in a firm undertone, "I sh'll never hear thet old man agin, with his gospel o' hate."

Mrs. Haskins kept her keen eyes on the pair. The daughter's beauty was striking, but the ideas of old people are fixed upon race, stock, family; and nothing good, in her opinion, could be inherited by the girl from an ungodly, freethinking father.

George, also, was looking; it had never occurred to him that the school-girl he had so often seen, with clear blue eyes and glossy braids of auburn hair, would blossom into beauty like that. This may have been the substance of his thought, but not his way of expressing it. He much preferred to look, and say nothing.

The chances to court a girl in Quabbin were few, unless the parties were intimate; it was only at a singing-school or a sleigh-ride that there was an opportunity to break the ice. In approaching such a matter the youths went as soft-footed as if shod with Indian moccasins. Now, George knew that a sleigh-ride was in prospect, and he thought that Emily would suit him for a partner, at least on that occasion. How he managed to communicate with her was not known, and it was certain he would never tell. But it was done with due secrecy, and without breach of the proprieties recognized in Quabbin; and the father's consent was duly given.

One may be sure, however, that Mrs. Haskins had not been consulted. George went about in his usual way, silently making preparations, his wily brown eyes downcast, so as to reveal nothing of his anticipations to his mother.

The appointed day came, and the party began to assemble in the broad space between the meeting-house and the new tavern. As the sleighs had no "tops," or hoods, the couples were in full view, and there was no longer any mystery about preferences. Every youth had the most stunning "team" he could obtain; the horses were groomed to a nicety, and sleighs and harness shone. At last the tale was complete, — some thirty odd, — and the chosen leader took the road, all following in single file. There was snow enough, well-trodden, and not "hubbly." The horses felt the keen, bracing air, and, tossing their heads, went on with emulous strides, excited by the movements of so many competitors. At the sound of the merry sleigh-bells all the villagers rushed to their windows.

"My! ef thet ain't Marthy Laurence 'long 'o Hi Smith!" — "An' there's Jerush Stebbins 'ith lame Joe Wheeler!" — "Lands sakes! what on airth's she wearin' that red feather fer?" — "But *du* yeou see that yaller sleigh, an' thet harness all silver?" — "George Haskins an' Em'ly Foster, ez trew's I'm alive! Wonder what his mother'll say naow!" — "She don't mean ter hev no young missis a comin' inter *her* haouse, not ef she knows it, she don't; not 'z long ez *she* lives!"

So, with "Du tell!" and "You don't say so!" and many more ejaculations, and with friendly nods and waving handkerchiefs, the people saw the long procession glide through the village.

The old-fashioned sleigh-bells were hollow globes of copper, each with a loose piece of metal inside, arranged like a necklace upon a leather strap. They had a deep sonority, and were chosen so as to give an approach to harmony; and in sleighing-time every farmer was recognized from afar by a well-known tone. Horses were proud of them, and showed it by the way in which they carried their heads. No such pageant was exhibited in Quabbin as the annual sleigh-ride, — the smart turnouts, the young men with fur caps and white woollen comforters, the girls in bright hoods and mufflers, the horses generally keeping step, and the multitude of bells making a merry din. The "pairing off" for such an occasion was generally thought prophetic. Every one looked on with pleasure, excepting youths who could not afford the expense of such an outing, and damsels who had not been invited. Something of heartache lingers behind joy, as shadows lurk behind light.

Emily Foster, without a mother, and with a kind but unprosperous father, was for this day demurely, coyly content, and willing to be altogether happy. Her escort gave his attention at first to his horse, and both were absorbed in the exhilarating course over the long winding road. But propinquity has to be reckoned with. Two kindly disposed young people, warmly clad, packed closely in a well-cushioned sleigh, and protected by a buffalo-robe, inevitably become cosey; then, with the sense of contact, tender, trustful, talkative; and then, perhaps, silent; for feeling may be beyond speech. It is only among the gifted beings created by the novelist that the "subjective" comes into play. George and Emily would not have attempted to express their "feelin's" except in simple words. Nor, doubtless, did it occur to them to admire the green pines with white background, the few russet leaves shivering upon the oaks, the stretch of snow-covered fields, or the softly rounded hilltops. Scenery with its phrases, its sentiment, and associations, had not been imported. Nobody in Quabbin had heard of such a thing. A flower was "pooty," a tree might be "hahn-some," but what was a "landscape"?

For a while George's talk turned upon the past harvest, — the yield of corn and rye, and of potatoes, pumpkins, and apples. After a long pause he said, "Ther' ain't nothin' much livelier than a sleigh-ride on a fine day, when ther's good comp'ny an' good teams."

"An' the bells ringin' all together," said his partner, "sound sunthin like Miss Grant's pianner."

"But it's the comp'ny Em'ly; I go aout in a sleigh 'baout every day, but, when I'm alone, I don't mind nothin' 'baout the bells. But naow" — and without finishing the sentence he settled a little nearer, looked at the girl over his shoulder, and said, "Enjoyin' yer-self, Em'ly?"

There was a faint affirmative that sounded like a blissful sigh.

"Hope 'tain't the las' time!" said George with significant emphasis.

"I sh'll allus be pleased to go 'ith yer — ef my father an' yeour mother don't object."

His mother! The word struck him like a dagger, and he relapsed into silence. Apparently a similar thought possessed the girl. How was she to win that woman's good graces? Both were lost in conjectures, but George easily persuaded himself there would be time enough to bring things around. Only he was beginning to dread the meeting that must take place next morning.

The route of a dozen miles was soon finished, and

the party alighted at a tavern, where an entertainment had been made ready. Among thirty young men there is sure to be some bumpkin, and when it came the turn of George and Emily at the door, they saw Lije Bates holding a pillow-beer of oats he had brought for his horse, and facing the jeering hostlers. The provident youth was endeavoring to mask his position.

"Wal, you see, I don't kaer 'bout one-and-six, or two shillin' for hoss-feed; that ain't it; but th' ol' man (his father) tol' me I'd better bring 'em, 'cause hosses, sometimes away f'm hum git pesky mean fodder, an' 're ap ter git distemper, er broken wind, er sunthin'." Derisive laughter followed him into the house.

At the table were steaks and broiled chickens, with pumpkin-pies and mince-pies to follow; but the *pièce de résistance*, was a huge dish of stewed oysters. In the days before railroads, to get oysters in prime condition at such a distance from the sea was not easy. From its rarity the flavor was wonderful, transcendent. The oysters were cooked to a nicety, as shown by their daintily curled ruffles, and were seasoned and buttered with judgment. There was abundance for all. And how those healthy young people ate! Never afterward would anything taste so exquisite.

The tables were cleared. A self-taught fiddler struck up some dancing-tunes with spirit, and a good number of the merrymakers went through cotillons and contra-dances; not the majority, however, for most of the girls were under maternal injunction; and not George and Emily, for he did not wish to offend his mother unnecessarily.

Some fumes of principe cigars came from the bar-room, and there were suspicions of port-wine sangarees (wine, hot water, sugar, and spice), but these were in moderation, and confined to a few.

The sun had gone down, and the moon was beginning to diffuse its mystical light. The teams were brought out, and the jolly procession re-formed, to return home by another route. The sleigh-bells rang loud and clear in the still air. It was a night which conveyed an impression of the illimitable.

> "God makes sech nights, so white an' still,
> Fer's you can look or listen;
> Moonlight an' snow on field an' hill,
> All silence, an' all glisten."

The stanza had not been written, but the moon was shining on New England snow-hills, and on lovers, as it will for ages to come.

Like *Zekle*, George felt his veins "all crinkly, like curled maple;" but the pretty scene of Lowell's idyl did not follow. He was thinking of his mother. But he pressed closely his plump partner, and she leaned upon his stalwart shoulder. Mere nothings were spoken, in which tone and suggestion were eloquent. A well-reasoned dialogue from a novel would have been absurd. From the weighty hints it was understood that George was to come next Sunday evening, "arter folks was gone to prayer-meetin'." He did not commit himself further; he knew his mother.

Emily was safely landed at home before midnight, and found her father waiting for her. Half an hour later George reached home, and after putting up his horse, went into the house, where he found a good fire; but his mother had gone to bed.

At breakfast there was a passably hostile interchange

of views, after the manner of Indian warfare that is carried on from behind trunks of trees. The wily brown eyes and the steady gray eyes glanced at each other across the table, then turned aside, or looked down; then blazed again with sudden eloquence. The words of mother and son were few, but their tone was regretful rather than ill-natured.

"Might a' let yeour mother a' known."

" 'Tain't nothin' to take a gal to a sleigh-ride."

"Folks don't think so."

"Folks kin mind their business."

"But fer yeou to go a-courtin' John Foster's darter 's *my* business.   He don't b'lieve in nothin'."

"I ain't a-courtin' *him*."

"The Scripter says He will visit the iniquity of the fathers upon the children."

"I ain't argyin' Scripter."

"Wal, yeou might hev regard fer yeour mother's feelin's."

"So I hev."

"We sh'll see."

It was a mere skirmish, for the combatants did not come to close quarters; but each had found out where the other stood.

Some years passed, and all that was noticeable in the conduct of George Haskins was that he neglected the Sunday evening prayer-meetings lamentably. What further interviews he had with his mother, who can say ? People of strong will do not talk much : a word and a look are enough.   Perhaps there was needed only a little more openness and courage on his part ; perhaps, knowing her convictions, and her desire to remain mistress in the house, the dutiful son or faint-hearted lover forbore to press her.

She was growing old, four-score at least; her son was nearing forty, and Emily was no longer as fresh as on the day of the sleigh-ride. " Hope deferred maketh the heart sick."

John Foster, who had long been feeble, passed away. He had kept his word, and had gone no more to hear about election and reprobation ; but he had taken rather kindly to the new minister, although he made no move toward uniting with the church. He died as he had lived, a gentle being, without a creed, but fully per- suaded of the mercy of God. Mrs. Haskins evidently wished to talk about his death, but her son always eluded her.

And so time went on. The house was a miracle of neatness. The dairy was cool and sweet ; the cheeses were golden like harvest-moons. In all that concerned his comfort George had nothing to ask for. But was his conscience at ease ?

Poor Emily Foster ! After the death of her father she had the care of a brother and sister. All the girls of her age were married, or had accepted, with such resignation as was possible, the lot of old maids. She was cheerful in her melancholy way,— a late flowering but still lovely rose. Why had not her lover courage ? Or had he done his utmost in vain ?

Time went on. George's Sunday evening visits were regularly made, but the courtship had become an old story in the village, and people ceased to talk about it. One evening Emily plucked up courage to say something decisive, even if it should bring about a rupture. The great struggle was painfully visible in her face.

" George," she said, while her eyes brimmed with

tears, "yeou can't say I hain't ben patient all these years. I've gin up my youth an' every futur' hope fer yeour love. Seems ter me yeou hain't hed the grit ter meet yeour mother ez yeou orter. The Scriptur' says a man sh'll leave his father an' his mother, an' cleave unter his wife. Did yeou ever repeat tu her that verse?"

"No,— not 'xackly."

"Hev yeou ever asked her what she hed ag'in me? I know she didn't like my father, but he ain't in her way any more."

"No; she wouldn't never say. She was allus offish."

"Wal, I've a'most come ter the conclewsion that I'd ruther be alone, an' continner alone, than ter go on this way, neither married ner single."

"Don't talk so, Em'ly; I'll try ag'in. But mother ain't well, an' I hate to cross her. It'll all come aout right."

"Du yeou mean 't yeou think she ain't goin' ter live? Ef that's what yeou mean by its comin' aout right, it ain't Christian. Much ez I love yer, I don't wanter put my happiness on the chance of any woman's dyin'; I'd ruther the thing was ended right here."

"No; but, Em'ly, jest yeou wait. I'll 'gree ter bring ye mother's consent, or I won't ask ye to merry me."

"Wal, on that promise I'll wait a while; though I'm clear wore aout 'ith hopin' an' dreadin'.'"

A few weeks later some children were picking berries on Great Quabbin, when suddenly they heard two strokes from the meeting-house bell. One stroke denoted the death of a man, two of a woman, and three of a child. The bell then began the strokes for the age, and the children counted. It seemed they would never end. Sixty was passed, then seventy, then eighty; then one, two, three, four, five; and there was silence. Eighty-five.

When the children got home, a boy said, " It must be that the bell was tollin' fer the death of Mrs. Haskins."

"No," said Aunt Keziah; "the bell was ringin' fer Em'ly Foster's weddin'."

George had kept his word. He and his Emily were beside his mother's dying-bed, and they had received her blessing.

This happened long ago. The patient couple are no more, and their children live under the shadow of the ancestral elms.

CHAPTER VIII

JUDAISTIC LEANINGS

IT is a singular and perhaps unexplained fact in the history of Christianity, that, so long after the lapse of the "old dispensation," there should have re-appeared among the Puritans such a marked preference for the Old Testament Scriptures and names, and such a sympathy with the Mosaic jurisprudence and traditions. During the seventeenth century the minds of the Puritans, and of most British dissenters, seem to have been less impressed by the divinely simple Gospel narratives than by the dealings of God with the patriarchs, — by the terrible splendors of Sinai, the translation of Enoch, the audible call of Samuel, and Elijah's chariot of fire. Their stern natures sympathized with the grandeur and awe with which the prophets and psalmists enveloped His throne, and with the unchangeable rigidity attributed to His moral government.

In public worship at Quabbin the Old Testament was drawn upon for texts of sermons, and for reading lessons, far oftener than the New. Prayers were elaborately inlaid with the poetical phrases of David, some of which resembled the grovelling addresses of slaves to Eastern despots; and the phrases were so constantly repeated that every hearer knew their sequence, as he knew the route to his own home. There came a time when the people of Quabbin heard prayers to God marked by a tripping familiarity that would have been discourteous to a county judge. The unseemly levity and the slavish prostration might have been equally avoided, if care had been taken to follow the precept and example of Jesus: "Thus ought ye to pray."

In discourses and exhortations, references were constantly made to the favor shown by the Creator of all men to "His chosen people." It is not to be supposed that the disciples and apostles were not reverenced, but there was far more heard of Moses, David, and the prophets. The bush that burned and was not consumed was as often in mind as the pathetic symbol of Christ's death and man's redemption. The sonorous names of Semitic warriors and kings were familiar to the lips of the early ministers; the syllables of Ze-rub-ba-bel gurgled like water falling over stones; Jehoiada, Jeroboam, Ahasuerus, Ahab, Hezekiah and Sennacherib, how well they were known! But Augustine, Ambrose, Chrysostom, Clement, Ignatius, Irenæus, and Polycarp, were never mentioned except once a year, in the course of a thundering attack upon the Scarlet Woman of the Apocalypse.

Baptismal names showed a similar drift. Of course, a few old English names were represented; but most children wore appellations laboriously sought out from the Bible; and they were often ponderous enough to make the toddling wearers top-heavy. The names were not necessarily Hebrew; they might be Greek or Roman; but they had become hallowed by being imbedded in a biblical text. Aquila, Epaphras, and Theophilus flourished, though less frequently than Abijah, Eliphaz, and Ichabod. A father who had been christ-

ened Moses had three sons, Moses, Aaron, and Josiah.
In Webster's Dictionary there is a list of Scripture
names, and, in running them over, about one hundred
and eighty were found that were well known in Quabbin
and vicinity. Many were beautiful, but more were inharmonious. Ridiculous associations came to be attached to
some that were originally noble. In hearing the names
Hosea and Ezekiel, one seldom thinks of the majestic
prophets, but of " Hosy " the shrewd and comic hero of
the Biglow Papers, and of " Zekle " of the Yankee idyl.
What young lady in modern society would willingly
own to the name of Jemima, Jerusha, or Tabitha? There
were twin sisters not many miles from Quabbin named
Tryphena and Tryphosa. One bright-eyed matron was
named Tirzah; another, fair and delicate, had been
called Zeruiah. What angelic patience must have been
required to bear such burdens for life !

In common speech all names were clipped and vul-
garized; and among school-boys and young men the
actual designations were "Eph," "Bije," "Ez," "Hi,"
"Rast," "Josh," "Lije," etc. Poets must find it hard
to fit these docked and ill-used names into pastoral
verse; and even when the line is made, the reader is
apt to be disgusted by some unromantic association.
Lowell's ballad of "The Courtin'" is almost perfect in
beauty ; and yet, in some moods, at the mention of
"Zekle" and "Huldy" a sense of vulgar comedy comes
in to overbear the poetic feeling.

Oddly enough, there was never a man or boy named
Paul in Quabbin, or in the region. Was there some
half-conscious sympathy with the Judaistic distrust and
dislike of the great apostle to the artistic and lettered
world ?

The manner of keeping Sunday was Judaistic; and its sacredness was defended as by the lightnings of Sinai; it being disingenuously claimed that the substitution of Sunday for the Jewish Sabbath was made by Divine command. Of the blessedness of reserving in every week a day of rest for body and mind, and of the propriety and duty of maintaining the beautiful Christian custom of making that day a glad and solemn religious festival, no reflecting man can have any doubt. But when it comes to the question of regarding the gathering of a few sticks on that day as a crime worthy of death, any man of common-sense might well pause.

Some few persons — not more than two or three families — adhered to the literal meaning of the verse in Genesis (mistranslated in King James's version), "The evening and the morning were the first day." In the revised version it reads, "And there was evening, and there was morning, one day." Such persons began their preparations in the afternoon of Saturday, and their devotions at sundown. The children regarded this as an encroachment on prescriptive rights, as the "Sahberday" stretched quite beyond twenty-four hours. When they asked on Sunday at what hour they might go out to play, the answer was, "When you can see three stars."

The original purpose of encompassing the first day of the week with the awful denunciations that once guarded the seventh is obvious. It was an indispensable part of the plan for keeping the control of the people in the hands of the ministers. With this end in view, the express words and the bold example of Him who was Lord of the Sabbath were silently disregarded, or ingeniously glossed over. For a specimen of clever

juggling with the "middle term" of an implied syllo-
gism, the reader is referred to the Shorter Catechism,
in the part relating to the Fourth Commandment.   If a
"worldly" logician should venture upon such a falsifi-
cation, what would not be said of him?

A few words upon the daily life and occupation of an
old gentleman who lived in Quabbin sixty years ago
will give a better idea of the prevailing tone of thought
than any description.   He became incapable of physical
labor in middle life, and devoted himself for more than
thirty years thereafter to reading and study.   As his
collection of books was scanty and little varied, and as
he knew his Bible by heart, the time often hung heavy
on his hands, and he took to writing.   Had he thought
to have written his memoirs, the book would have been
invaluable.   He was five years old when the battle of
Bunker's Hill was fought, and remembered the hurried
ride of the farmer, who, in shirt-sleeves and without a
saddle, came to rouse the neighborhood (Woodstock,
Conn.) and call for volunteers to go on with General
Putnam ("Old Put") to fight the British at Boston.
Of course he remembered the events of the Revolutionary war, the formation of the Constitution, and the
war of 1812.   He must have had, also, a store of traditions of the settlement of Quabbin, whither he came in
1793.   But, instead of setting down these recollections,
he wrote *sermons !*   They were generally upon Hebrew
themes, and were written merely as literary exercises,
for he never thought of preaching.   Just as if the air
were not full of them!   Then he wrote a long rhymed
essay upon Melchisedek! in which he undertook to
prove, that as this personage was styled a "priest of the
Most High God," and was said to be "without begin-

ning of days or end of time," he could have been no other than the second person of the Trinity, appearing in the flesh on earth in that ancient time, as he did long after in Judea. This old gentleman was the only literary layman in town, and such was the work to which he devoted many years of his life ! He was a keen and quick-witted man, and in a literary atmosphere might have accomplished something. Later he enlisted in the anti-slavery crusade, and his energy found a practical field for exercise.

The gloom which characterized the life of the Puritans and over-shadowed some generations of their descendants, was largely due to the prominence of Old Testament ideas, to the awful traits attributed by Hebrew writers to Jehovah, to the solemnity of their poetry, to the ominous "burdens" of their prophecy, and to their materialistic philosophy, ending in rayless night. While under the influence of such ideas and feelings, one might think Christ had died in vain. In time the clear effulgence of Christianity dispersed these shadows.

In this chapter have been noticed only such Judaistic tendencies as survived in Quabbin ; but at the beginning of the two colonies on the Bay, the opinions and acts of the rulers in regard to liberty and equality, and religious toleration, as well as in regard to law, considered as the basis of society, were broadly Jewish and theocratic.

CHAPTER IX

DRESS, MANNERS, AND SPEECH

MANY of the early settlers of Quabbin were descendants of the Pilgrims, and came from the Old Colony of Plymouth. In the time of its first minister there were heard in the outlying districts, and quite commonly in the village, the tones and inflections used long before by Governor Bradford and Captain Miles Standish. The quality of voice, the vowel sounds, the elisions and the accent, now characterized as Yankee, were heard, beyond doubt, though with some variations, in the preaching of Bunyan, the talk of Cromwell's men, and the debates of the Long Parliament. Of course, this statement is conjectural, but the known facts leave little doubt as to its correctness. It is probable, however, that during an age of more ardent faith and deeper emotion there was a prevalent tone of voice which was easily turned to ridicule -- as is seen in Hudibras — and which in more worldly times began to disappear.

The old speech has been imitated by many writers, as in Lowell's "Biglow Papers," [1] in Mrs. Stowe's "Old Town Folks," in passages of the "Autocrat of the Breakfast Table," and in stories by Trowbridge, by Rose Terry Cooke, and Mary E. Wilkins. Undoubt-

---

[1] In the introduction to the second series of the "Biglow Papers" is the most complete treatise extant upon this subject.

edly there have been, and still are, local differences in
the dialect, for in none of the books above cited is there
a resemblance *in all respects* to the speech once heard
in Quabbin. In most of the specimens which the world
justly admires there has been imported something
modern, which makes an impression like that of a
knowing city youth masquerading in a farmer's frock.
Such is the feeling of a native of Quabbin who recalls
the measured, kindly, and habitually reverent tone and
phrase used by the people he knew. It was only among
the worldly or the openly wicked that one would have
observed the biting shrewdness, or the bantering with
texts of Scripture and sacred things, which have been
attributed to the representative Yankee. Such an
expression as

> " An' you'll hev to git up airly
> Ef you want to take in God "

would never have been used by a Yankee in Quabbin,
except among the irreligious and profane. Yet the
concluding stanzas of the ballad just referred to show
that *Hosea* was animated by a noble and God-fearing
spirit. It would not have helped the matter — in
Quabbin — that St. Augustine, Fuller, and all the
divines in the world, had taken similar liberties with
the Creator. Those people *could not* have spoken so ;
for the Great Name was never mentioned but with awe.
All this may have been different on the seaboard.
And it must be admitted that those godly and slow-
speaking men, whose ways and speech are a part of the
life of all Quabbin's sons, would not have been half as
amusing as the keen fellows who have figured in dialect
story and poem.

An abiding sense of the reality of spiritual things, and of the nearness of the judgment-day, tempered every utterance. Ejaculations and passionate emphasis had no place; the movement of speech was partly like a ploughman's measured tread, and partly like the flow of a gently murmuring brook. Their archaisms were as "nateral" as buttercups to a meadow.

A farmer, during the Millerite craze, about 1840, said to the village blacksmith, in a simple, level tone that no types can express, "Why, Cousin Rozzell," meaning Roswell, "they du say the world is nigh about to come 'pon an eend." — "Wal," replied the blacksmith, "I guess th' airth, an' the housen tu, 'll last out your time an' mine." What was the notion of the end of temporal things, and of the nature of the unseen world, that lay in the mind of that man in the blue frock?

Familiar allusions to the powers of nature were regarded as sinful. There had been a tornado that had demolished houses, and cut a swath through a forest of stalwart trees in the Blue Meadow district, a few miles west; and one of the farmers, whose store of rye had been scattered, coming to the village shortly after, said, " — — — ef I don't think there's a fresh hand got a hold of the bellers!" People laughed, but, on reflection, tne speech was considered as blasphemous. The comparison to a pair of bellows was breezy, but the covert intimation touching the power of the breath of the Almighty was deplorable.

If names of towns in Massachusetts furnish any decisive indication, there must have been settlers in the colony from every part of Great Britain. It is known that in a great many instances companies of immigrants bestowed the names of their old homes upon the new towns rising in the wilderness ; and, if this were not always the case, there are other reasons for believing that there was a general representation of the mother country in the colony. The early native population was the result of a fusion of the British people from many districts. Peculiarities from some of the rural counties of England, and, in less measure from Scotland and Ireland, may be detected in the old colloquial speech, but one never hears from a native New Englander anything resembling the pronounced or obtrusive dialects, as of Yorkshire, Lancashire, or Somerset; still less the Londoner's odious omission or misplacement of *h ;* although some Yankees drop the final *g*, as do the ill-taught upper-class English people. Somerset is represented by the Yankee's double negative, as " I hain't got no dog." The Yankee's tone is more like that of Yorkshire. It is doubtful if there is any district in England where one would hear a connected sentence wholly in the dialect or tone of Quabbin. The nearest approach to it, in the opinion of the writer, was in the talk of a tram-car driver and some hostlers at Moreton near Oxford, upon a badly-fitting collar that was galling one of the horses. There was, moreover, a tone of consideration quite unusual among stablemen ; a decent farmer in Quabbin would have spoken in much the same way.

The various English dialects brought together in the colony remained distinct, probably, for one or two generations ; but, after a time, attrition, usage, and sympathetic imitation, produced a new composite, which now appears like an original, albeit with slight local peculiarities.

The nasal tone in New England, it is said, was caused

by the severe climate and the prevalent catarrh ; but those were not the sole causes. Catarrh debases speech, both in quality of tone and in distinctness of articulation ; but the disease is more prevalent now than formerly, while the general speech is probably less nasal. Australians are said to have nasal voices, and they are not afflicted with catarrh. The New England drawl and the nasal tone were probably derived originally from the meeting-house and the prayer-meetings ; both defects became fixed by habit, and, of course, have been greatly heightened by climatic conditions.

The virtue constantly insisted upon in the old times by parents and religious teachers was humility, self-abnegation. In repeating passages of Scripture, or of the Catechism, the tone was subdued. The religious spirit was manifested in awe and reverence, seldom in cheerfulness, and never in exaltation — except in such exaltation as was accompanied with moistened eyes and "tears in the voice." It was "a dying world" in which our fathers lived ; the expression of their ideas and feelings would not require the expansive lungs, nor heave the deep chest, of a vigorous and well-developed man. The *noise*, no less than the manner, of a burly fox-hunter and athlete, would be abhorrent to one whose soul was melted in penitence, and who in his daily devotions *intoned* in dragging minor intervals the prayers that he dared not address to the Dread Majesty of Heaven with steady eyes and manly voice. There was a good deacon in Quabbin whose words, when he prayed, were joined, as by a singer's *portamento*, with *ah* and *er*, and with indescribable sounds, like the final hum of a nasal *m* and *n*. The words were hyphenated, and each sentence was a close-linked, long-drawn chain. Let such usages of speech go on for generations, and the infection will pervade the community. The child will be soothed by a nasal lullaby, and will drawl from the time he leaves his cradle. He will drawl at his lessons, and make catarrhal yells in the playground. As a lover he will drawl to his mistress, and repeat love's litany through the nose. When his duet with her is finished, and his snuffy voice extinct, he will be drawn (slowly) to his grave, to drawl no more.

It appears to be certain that the nasal and drawling tone is in a large measure the result of two and a half centuries of Puritan training; just as the peculiarities of language, including local and obsolete terms, half-articulated contractions, and clipping of words, are the result of the fusion of many illiterate British dialects. The bucolic speech is dying out, for school-teachers are uprooting it, as farmers do thistles, but the tone hangs on, like the scent of musk in *Hosea Biglow's* " draw."

Manners belong equally to mind and body. On the one hand is the friendly or courteous intention, and on the other the spontaneous movement, accompanied by the look of kindness or deference.

In Quabbin it was the custom to salute on the highway or in public places ; to pass even a stranger without some recognition would have been considered rude ; but the graceful bow and the expressive look were not often at command. Hard-working people are strong but not supple ; ease of movement comes from lighter modes of exercise. And as for the friendly look, how could it be worn by a man whose whole life was within, and whose face was habitually drawn to its four corners ? So, when two farmers met, their greeting might seem to a stranger gruff or surly, since the facial muscles were so inexpressive, while, in fact, they were on most friendly terms. It was one of the reasons which made city people so disliked in Quabbin that they never bowed, or "passed the time o' day."

The chief of the minor virtues, or rules of conduct, was self-command. The faces of the people on the Lord's Day might have been cast in bronze. Except in the rare case of some impulsive brother, whose varying feelings were visible from afar, there was small change in the expression of a godly countenance from the time it was set Zionward until it returned to encounter the Sahber-day pork and beans. The psalms, the Scripture readings, the prayers, and the sermon were all heard with immovable solemnity, tempered, perhaps, with a "half tone" of mournful penitence.

Men of firm mould came to acquire this fixity of visage in permanence : it was not only on Sunday and at prayer-meeting, but at the store and the mill, and in the field. In traffic, such as swapping horses or cattle, it was not without its advantage; for the dealer who does not show his thought to a sharp adversary is not taken unaware. It is, of course, an irreverent and most unlikely suggestion ; but if the game of poker had then been known, and one could conceive the enormity of a Puritan playing it, the impassible countenance of a deacon over a "full hand" or "four kings" would have puzzled and baffled the most experienced gambler; for poker is not so much a game of cards as of men.

As before intimated, neighbors met each other solemnly, but, doubtless, with as much of good will as is felt by the more effusive or more courteous people of larger communities. This constraint was evident in the intercourse between the sexes. A steadfast look and a pointed word from a young man meant as much to an observing girl as the most elaborate compliment from a city beau. In such matters, what girl is not observing? The representations of Yankee courtships in popular novels and stories are almost always false, if Quabbin throws any light on the subject. The words are really few and disconnected, each pointing to separate vistas of thought, or indicating separate pulses of feeling, and each interpreted by looks, secret pressures, and fond breathings. Set down as they were spoken, they would be as unintelligible to one not "to the manner born " as an Aztec inscription.

Married couples, whose life-long affection no native could doubt, moved as if in different though dependent orbits, like double stars, and never (in public view) jostled into tender familiarity. In the presence of the family the head of the house spoke of his wife as " Marm," or " Mother," or " Your ma ; " and to others as " Mis' So-and-so ; " and always in a tone of *distance*, as if there were some dim mystery in the relationship. Years might pass, and the faithful souls would go on with work and worship, wearing all unconsciously the masks which custom had prescribed ; and the onlookers who did not know the secret might think them cold and indifferent. Strangers and Kiplings could not enter into this. But if there were a sudden accident, as from a runaway horse, a mad bull, or a falling tree ; or if there were a dangerous illness, or the death of a child, or other calamity ; then would break out the long-covered fires ; — then the eloquence of the heart would be heard from the stricken father or the bereaved mother, and sobs and tears would show the depth and intensity of

the love that had fused the family group into one
golden ring.

Lord Macaulay's well-known sketch of the Puritan,
in his youthful and glowing essay on Milton, may have
been artistically true for the Cromwellian period, but
the Puritan of Quabbin (and elsewhere) was less gran-
diose and less theatrical. In the course of nearly two
centuries the ardors of the church furnace had abated.
Among men there was less strain and *pose* in attitude,
less amplitude and fewer figures in speech. Perhaps
the men were more common-place, but certainly the
spiritual temperature was cooler.

It is probably a revolving of truisms, but it ought to
be clearly understood that the people of Quabbin, as
well as Yankees in general, did not wear their hearts
upon their sleeves for critical daws to peck at. The
springs of their conduct, their beliefs and prejudices,
their humors and eccentricities, their homely proverbs
and dry witticisms, are rarely comprehended by people
who have not passed a good part of their lives among
them. The "Biglow Papers," except in some minor
details, is a complete mirror of Yankee life and character; much of its wit is so salient that all the world
chuckled over it; but no reader who was not "one of
the family" ever really appreciated it. It is much read
and quoted in Great Britain; but the people know nothing of it, — no more than Englishmen know of Burns.
The customs, the names of common objects, and the
subsidiary vocabulary, to say nothing of merry twists
and allusions, together form an impenetrable barrier.

There had been changes in dress since Puritan times,
such as the use of trowsers and braces instead of knee-
breeches and knit hose, and the disuse of broad linen

collars and steeple-crowned hats; but top-coats, cloaks, and capes defied fashion, and apparently outlasted their wearers. The outer garments of most old men were characteristic in form and color, and, like their wives, were taken for better or worse until death parted them.

In some way there was a distinguishing mark for all the people. It was a double-cape coat of sheep's gray, or one of greenish brown with great horn buttons; or it was a full, wadded, dark-blue camlet cloak, with standing collar, fur-lined, and fastened by a copper chain and clasp; whatever it was, it was peculiar and recognizable. Black was seldom worn, except by women, and by those in mourning. Garments were often enough "sad" in color, but were generally indecisive, as if faded and weather-beaten. It is perhaps superfluous to say that the tailor's art was seldom conspicuous; neither symmetry nor wrinkles were of much consequence, provided the garment was easy and comfortable. Before fashion brought about uniformity, there were strange freaks in costume. A bridegroom in Quabbin once came to meeting wearing a blue coat with brass buttons, buff waistcoat with gilt buttons, and wide trowsers (it was in summer), made from the same material as the bride's dress, — a rather lustrous piece of fawn-colored silk; and the skirt rustled audibly against the trowsers as the pair, each carrying a flower and shod with kid slippers, walked up the aisle.

The vagaries in bonnets, "scoops," and calashes were ingenious. There were silks, straws, chips, crapes, navarinos, leghorns, in endless variety. One hat comes to mind, of which the crown stood out straight behind the head, while the front was raised nearly perpendicular, like a misplaced halo, its upper edge nearly a foot above the forehead. The intervening space was covered with smoothly stretched satin of such a vivid red that it burned the eyes like a red pepper to look at it. The damsel's face seemed to be in the heart of a flame, and her features could never be recalled afterward apart from that fiery background.

There was one grave and silent old man who was a type of a class. He was poverty-stricken but decent; dingy but clean; yet what he wore — of what material was his long coat, or what its color — no one could say. The man and his raiment were one; nothing was more decided in hue than the back of a toad, yet the entity was *sui generis*, distinguishable from all others. His features were grotesque in ugliness, yet wore a look of patience, as if fate could do him no further harm. His ways were solitary, and on Sunday he sat by himself in the gallery, his quaint, bushy head — neither gray nor black — resting against a pilaster on the west wall, whereof the white paint kept an enduring impression.

One day, in sight of all the village folk, he was carried away to the county jail, tied with a cord about his wrists and body — a prisoner for debt. The deputy sheriff not unfrequently carried away prisoners, but they were usually drunkards or cheats, while this old man was sober and harmless. There was no unwonted melancholy upon his face — neither anger nor tears — and he said not a word. For a time he was missed from his post in the gallery, poor old man!

From the beginning of the present century there were improvements in vehicles and tools. The old jolting wagons were relieved by "thorough braces," leather straps supporting the body, and later by elliptic springs of steel. Chaises with bonnet-tops were affected by well-to-do people, as their motion was easy ; but they were back-breaking for horses, and have long since disappeared. Ploughs used to be made of wood, cased and pointed with steel, but were supplanted by those of solid iron with steel lips many years ago.

Dress and vehicles are important so far as they concern beauty and comfort, but they are not the life of a people. The connection with the past was in (a somewhat softened) religious faith and practice ; in traditions of town and parish government ; in the usages of domestic life, and in the old and homely speech. The descendants of both Pilgrims and Puritans adhered substantially to the ways of the fathers as they were from, say, 1620 onward.

A traveller who, sixty years ago, proposed to alight at a farmhouse in Quabbin, would have found conditions nearly the same as those which existed among people of the same class in old colony times, and among the rural English of the same period. The domestic conveniences would have been such as have been described in a former chapter, — the great chimney and open fireplace, the splint-bottomed chairs, the spinning-wheels and loom. He would have been offered a mug of cider or a canakin of rum. At dinner would be seen a boiled leg of salt pork, or boiled ribs of salt beef, with mustard or horse-radish, pickles, and hot vegetables ; the service of plain delft, with steel knives and forks, and without napkins. Rye-and-Indian bread would be served on a wooden trencher. Pumpkin- or apple-pie, doughnuts, and cheese would follow.

If he should pass the night, and it were in winter, he would go up to a freezing attic, undress while stand-

ing on a braided woollen mat, and get into a feather-bed,
which rested on a sack of straw, and that upon cords
stretched crosswise in a solid bedstead of maple.   Over
him would be spread home-made blankets, and a blue
woollen coverlet of a rude, checked pattern, that had
been woven in the family loom.   In the morning he
would go down to the "sink" in the lean-to, next to
the kitchen, fortunate if he had not to break ice in
order to get water to wash his face and hands, or more
fortunate if a little warm water was poured into his
basin from the kettle swung over the kitchen-fire.
After using vigorously the great coarse linen towel
that hung upon a roller near by, he would be ready for
a preparatory nipper of cider, and then for a substantial breakfast.   This might be of ham and eggs, or of
salt fish prepared with cream, or of bean-porridge (for
which a ham-bone furnished the stock), or of cold corned
beef, with hot potatoes, and usually hot bread (called
"biscuits") resembling muffins; and with sauces,
pickles, and other provocatives in plenty.

CHAPTER X

HOW THE POOR WERE CARED FOR

THERE were not a great many people in Quabbin who were not poor, as the world considers poverty, but there were seldom any paupers.[1] Destitute foreigners in Massachusetts are taken to one of the State almshouses — deplorable aggregations of humanity. Each town in its corporate capacity is under obligation to support only such paupers as were born within its limits, or have "acquired a settlement" therein. "Acquiring a settlement" is something not easy to explain. As we shall see, a woman, not being a holder of taxable property, might live in a town half a century and have no legal relation to it ; and it would be the same in the case of a man who had not held public office, or paid taxes for some consecutive years. Instances have been known when wily town officers have silently omitted from the tax-list the names of men, not being natives, who they thought might sometime require public aid. The law is somewhat intricate, and need not be dwelt upon.

Quabbin, like other towns, had its poor-farm, which

[1] There are very few to-day. The almoners, under a bequest for aiding any deserving poor not assisted by the town, have some difficulty in conscientiously distributing the annual allowance. One man to whom the bounty was lately offered said he didn't think he ought to take it : there must be some poorer family than his.

was town property, and was managed by some man in
pursuance of an agreement with the Overseers of the
Poor, who were annually chosen by the people. When
friendless and destitute persons, legally entitled to support, were, in common parlance, "flung upon the town,"
the keeper of the poor-farm provided for them in the
house he occupied. There were a great many years
during which the keeper and his wife had no guests.

Two stories follow, in which the prevalent ideas upon
charity may appear.

AUNT KEZIAH

It was Aunt Keziah who said the bells were "ringin'
for Em'ly Foster's weddin'." Poor woman! no wed-
ding-bells had rung for *her*. She was old and com-
fortably feeble, and had many strange "feelin's," which
she thought it important to detail and illustrate; but,
though she was well past seventy, she was likely still
to hold on for a score of years. From her movements
one would think that her joints had been badly adjusted at first, or else had got out of gear by long use.
Her lower jaw at times had a sidewise or wabbling
motion, like that of some ruminants; and, when her
chin rose and fell, the soft white skin below it seemed
to be the flexible envelope of a bundle of cords,
stretched and wrinkled by turns. Upon scanning her
face attentively, there were evident traces of former
good looks, if not of beauty. Her nose was straight,
her forehead regular, and her blue eyes, behind a pair
of silver-bowed "specs," had still a fine depth of color,
although their forlorn and piteous expression was at
first more obvious than their contour and hue. Some
effort of imagination would be necessary to bring back

any youthful charm to her shrivelled face and figure, but there was no doubt that half a century before she had been an attractive woman. She was neat and cleanly, except for the browning of her lip by snuff. Like all elderly women at that time, she wore a lace or muslin cap; and hers was generally trimmed with slate-colored or black ribbons. Her dress was plain and poor, and her spare shoulders were covered by a small shawl. Needless to say, she was always accorded a warm corner by the fireplace.

She was the neighborhood's aunt, everybody's Aunt Keziah; and much more the aunt of those who were alien to her blood than of her own nephews and nieces. Strangers compassionately gave her shelter, when her kinsfolk had cast her off and appeared not to care what became of her. Probably she would not have been wholly agreeable as a permanent member of a household, for her conversation was not generally cheerful. With her experiences, how could it be? But if her relatives had been considerate people, with a little family pride, she would have been saved from the humiliation which fell upon her.

Her industry in knitting was remarkable. The play of needles in her poor, stiff-jointed fingers ceased only when at intervals she explored the mysterious folds of her dress for the snuff-box, or wiped her "specs," dimmed by contact with her watery eyes. She inclined little to gossip, for her "subjectivity" was intense; her own past griefs and present ailments were of more importance than the affairs of neighbors.

One day, having finished a pinch of snuff with unusual satisfaction, her face wore a beatific expression quite marvellous to the small boy who stood by her chair. She happened for the moment not to be knitting; her hands were partly clasped, and the thumbs were slowly turning over each other. She was almost purring. "Aunt Keziah, what makes you take snuff?" "O, sonny, it-m-rests-me." The words had a gliding kind of *liaison*, and were enveloped in a swelling nasal hum. It seemed fortunate to the boy that the aunt could get rested on such easy terms.

Aunt Keziah told her story to the carpenter's wife bit by bit.

"I was born on the Cape, in Truro, an' lived ther till our fam'ly moved up here, say fifty year ago. When I say 'our fam'ly,' I mean my brothers an' their families, for father an' mother died daown to the Cape, an' was berried ther; an' I hadn't no sister.

"When I was 'bout nineteen, a young feller came a-courtin' me, — a sailor, an' a smart feller he was. E'enamost all on 'em daown ther is sea-farin' men. Some goes long v'yages, an' some only aout ter Chaleur, or the Banks, a fishin' in summer. My young man sailed sometimes to Europe, an' sometimes 'way raound to Aashy. When he axed me to merry 'im, I said he must settle daown on land; fer, ef he kep goin' on them long v'yages, his wife 'ould be same 'z a widder all her days. He tol' me he'd du 'z I said bimeby, but thet he'd got tu go one more v'yage, 'cause he'd promised, an', bein' fust mate, they couldn't du 'thout 'im. I felt dreffle bad to think of his goin' off agin, for he'd told me 'bout the winds an' waves, an' haow the ship sometimes a'most stood on eend, an' sometimes rolled over so fur 't you'd think she wasn't never goin' to come up agin. Every night I dreamt of some offul hurricane, an' I saw Charles — that was his name — in a boat all

alone on a sea that hadn't no shore; or else a-clingin'
tu a piece of a mast, with sharks a-steerin' raound, an'
makin' fer to bite 'im in two. I couldn't stand it no
haow, an' when he come agin' we had a talk.

"Sez I, 'Charles,' sez I, 'the Scriptur' says, "What
doos et profit a man to gain the hull world an' lose his
own soul?"' An' I say, what 'll it profit you er me ef
you airn a year's wages, an' lay yer bones on 'tother
side o' the world, or at the bottom of the sea? Here
ye air, on yer feet, on land, an' ef yer go ter sea yer
don't know where ye'll be.'

"'Oh,' sez he, 'I've allus got thru', an' I sh'll du it
ag'in. 'Twon't be long, an' it's the las' time.'—'O
Charles!' sez I, 'sunthin' tells me 't yer can't allus
count on luck. I've seen ye in my dreams, an' my
heart stood still like a stone, 'twas so awful.'

"'Naow don't you be talkin' 'bout dreams,' sez he;
'bad dreams is only f'm eatin' mince-pie.'

"'I can't help it,' sez I; 'ef you go 'way naow, I
don't never 'xpect to see ye agin. Naow *du* be persuaded!'

"He was tender-hearted ez a man, but trew grit ez a
sailor. I c'd see that his feelin's pulled him one way,
while his dewty gripped him 'tother. We had a long
talk, but 'twas pooty much the same thing over an' over.
At last sez he, 'The wages fer this v'yage, 'ith what
I've got in bank, 'll jest make up enough to pay fer the
haouse of the Widder Snow, that's for sale.'

"'It's a pooty house,' sez I, ' an' I ain't goin' to deny
that 't 'ould suit you an' me to a turn; but I'd rather
live 'ith yer under a whale-boat turned up-si-daown on
the beach, then to hev yer go on a v'yage for a pallis.'

"He just kinder laafed an' kinder smiled, an' looked

at me so sweet! 'Twa'n't no use. While he looked at me so, I couldn't do but one thing. You know what I done: I hung on his neck, an' kissed him a hundred times. I k'n see this minnit jest how he looked: blue roundabaout, an' duck trowsis, black neck-han'kercher, low shoes, an' flat top cap. Haow his black eyes seemed devourin' me, praoud an' soft by turns! Ah, he was a man 'ith a look an' a step; a man fer a woman to look twice at, an' to think abaout ever arter. Our partin' was pullin' heart-strings, an' when he'd gone, I was in a dead faint.

"His vessel was baound to Chiny, an' we sh'd nat-erally be 'thout hearin' from him fur nigh a year. But the year went by; an' then month arter month there was nothin' but waitin' an' dreadin', no news. In two years the owners gin up all hope, an' I wanted ter put on mournin', but the folks wouldn't hear on't. What I suffered in them two years, nobody but God knows! I wonder I'm alive.

"Wal, there was a storekeeper daown thar, a decent enough man, who'd lost his wife, an' he come an' axed me to be a mother to his little childern. But when I thought o' my Charles, my heart riz right up agin this man. 'Who knows,' thought I, 'ef Charles ain't naow on one o' them cannible islands, livin' on bananas an' cokernuts, or waitin' in some strange corner 'v th' airth for a chance to git hum!' I thanked the storekeeper an' sent 'im 'bout his business; I couldn't be mother to any man's childern but Charley's.

"I hed another offer, but thet didn't take no time to ahnswer. So father sez to me, sez he, 'Keziah, yeou'd better not go mournin' all yeour days. Arter I'm gone yeou'll need somebody to take keer o' ye. Don't throw 'way all yeour chances. Good men air skurce.'

" I ahnswered kinder lightly ; — I was so baound up in Charles that I couldn't think of another man.

" I might 'a had a hum o' my own to-day, instid o' bein' tossed about from pillar to post, like a piece o' worn-out furnitur'. I might 'a ben some darlin's mother instid of bein' everybody's aunt. Seems ef God oughtn't let folks come inter the world thet he don't mean to take better keer on. He oughtn't to 've gin me feelin's, jest ter torment me a while, an' then hev 'em dry up, like a last year's hollyhock.

" Howsever, I'd made my bed, an' I hed to lay in 't. I wouldn't merry the men that wanted me, an' bimeby I come ter be so peaked with my sorrers, thet no man wuth lookin' at would 've had me.

" Fust mother died, then father. He hadn't much money, an' my brothers said, ' Let's go up in the west part o' the State an' buy a farm ; an' you kin live with us.' I let 'em do what they wanted, an' went with 'em. I didn't much keer fer anythin' in life.

" They bought land, an' part on't ought ter be mine, but 'taint. They built a couple o' haouses, an' worked hard. An' I worked hard, year arter year, slavin' myself fust fer Harmon an' his fam'ly, an' then fer Joe, who, 'z yeou know, lived alone. Ez Joe hadn't nothin' better to du, he took to drinkin', an' bimeby he got so bad 't I couldn't even go inter his haouse. Then Harmon's wife died, an' he got another. Yeou know her. I needn't say what she is. In which of the two haouses there was the most deviltry, I couldn't say. What I onderwent with that wife o' Harmon's I couldn't tell ye in a week ; an' in Joe's haouse there warnt *nothin'*. He lived like a man who pulls the clabberds off 'm the outside of his haouse ter burn fer ter heat the inside with.

"Them forty year! The time's like a night-mare when I think on't. I hope the Lord 'll give me credit for 'em when it comes to my reck'nin'.

"When I had the rheumatiz, naow 'bove five year ago, an' couldn't do nothin', Harmon's wife put him up ter fling me on the taown, — send me ter the poor-farm. I couldn't walk nor help myself more 'n a child three days old. But Harmon, he packed me inter the waggin, an' druv me ter the poor-farm, an' left me thar.

"The overseers was notified, an' they come, an' sez, 'Yeou can't stay here.' 'Wal,' sez I, 'I don't wanter stay here; but, ef I *should* wanter, I sh'd like to know *why* I can't.' ' 'Cause yeou haint no settlement in this taown,' sez they. 'Yeou was born daown on the Cape; an' ther yeour father lived an' died, an' ther's yeour settlement. So yeou see, ef yeou're flung on the taown, we sh'll hev to send ter Truro; an' the overseers ther 'll hev ter come ter kerry yeou off, an' take keer o' yer.' 'But,' sez I, '*I* don't know anybody daown ter Truro; it's forty year sence I was ther. I don't wanter go 'mong strengers. It's bad enough ter go ter the poor-farm when yeou know the folks.' 'Wal, that's the law,' sez they, an' off they went, an', I 'spose, writ the letter.

"Nex' few days I didn't du nothin' but cry. I couldn't eat, though Mis' Thurstin, the wife of the keeper, got me all the nice things she c'd think on.

"Then come a strange man a-drivin' up t' the haouse, an' when he come in, sez he, 'I've come fer yeou.' 'Wal, I ain't goin',' sez I. 'Yes, yeou be,' sez he. 'S'p'osin' I won't?' sez I. 'Then I sh'll make yer,' sez he. Then I gin a yell 't yeou might 'er heerd way over to the Widder Peasoe's place. I oughter ben ashamed, but I couldn't help it. I got the tongs an' the shovle, an' I dared that man to tech me. But my strength didn't hold aout. I was full o' rheumatiz, an' my poor hands let the shovle an' tongs drop. Then I dropped tu, — clean gone. Then Mis' Thurstin, she put me ter bed, an' Mr. Thurstin an' the strange man went tu the village ter git the doctor. When the doctor went back, arter seein' me, I've heered he made some talk 'bout kerryin' off a woman of my age in that way; an' there was considerable stir. The man from Truro finally went off, 'cause Reuf Wadley and Reub Newman they said they'd be ahnswerable for any 'xpense, an' that the taown o' Truro shouldn't hev any damage on my 'count.

"Yeou know how I've lived sence. Some o' the time I haint lived, but jest ben distriberted in morsils raound the parish. I stay a couple o' weeks 'ith Reuf, — he's a good man even ef he's a leetle flighty, — then a couple with Reub. Then I come here; then I go to yeour uncle's, an' then to ol' Squire Hobson's, an' so on. All I hope is, the Lord 'll call me afore I wear aout all my welcomes; fer I ain't a-goin' t' Truro.

"Yeou don't ketch me a talkin' hard 'bout the way my brothers treated me; there's enough to du that, 'thout me. I'm sorry for 'em. They're gittin' ter be old men. Harmon's older than I be, an' Joe, by his drinkin' ways, hez made himself actilly older'n Harmon.

"I haint got ter trouble 'em any more, nor any that was willin' to see their flesh and blood carted off ter the poor-farm. I hope none on 'em will need sech a hum in their ol' days."

Such was the story of Aunt Keziah. She continued to make her rounds, not like Edie Ochiltree as a "sturdy beggar," but as a modest friend and depend-

ent. She knitted, darned, and mended, solaced and
" rested " herself with snuff, and wiped her dim
" specs " until her weary eyes ceased from weeping.

THE WIDOW CARTER

One frosty afternoon the blacksmith set his two
sons and hired man to sawing and splitting firewood.
Farmers used to bring wood in lengths of four feet ;
and people who used cooking-stoves, then recently
introduced, had it cut in lengths of a foot before putting it away for use.

After sundown on this day (one never said sunset)
the smith's boys were told to bring out their sleds, and
pack them with the neatly prepared wood ; and besides
they loaded a pair of sleigh-runners, having a cover of
boards (in effect the bottom part of a sleigh) and,
between nine and ten o'clock, when the hired man had
gone, the father and sons made their way in silence
through the village, drawing the three sleds over the
polished road. They passed the tavern and stores and
came near the common.

Not even in the fulness of summer nor in many-hued
autumn have the elms and maples of Quabbin such an
effect as when on a still winter's night they stand leaf-
less under the moon, and cast their network of shadows
upon pure and unbroken snow. The moonlight lends a
glory to common objects. Groups of white houses and
dark bushes seem like composed pictures ; the steeple
becomes a marble shaft, and moving objects are like a
succession of instantaneous photographs.

As the party passed under the great trees, there was
not a cloud, nor a breath of wind ; and the shadows of
the main and lesser branches, and then of longer boughs

and slender twigs, down to the minutest ramifications were imprinted on the snow as blue lacework. The beauty of that blue pattern on dazzling white could never be forgotten.

The boys wondered where they were going, and began to ask questions; but the father, who could be peremptory if occasion required, briefly ordered them to make no talk, but do as they had been told. "Poorty bright night," he added, "for what we've got t' dew; an' yer mustn't make the least mite o' noise."

They were near the house of the Widow Carter, and the party stopped to reconnoitre. There were no lights visible in front or rear, and it was probable the inmates had gone to bed. The sleds were drawn into the backyard without a word being spoken, and were unloaded under the shed without noise. The snow muffled their feet, and the pieces of wood were laid down gently. When the last sticks were taken from the old sleigh bottom, the boys saw a bag of meal or flour, and a few small packages. These were placed near the back door, and then, after a look at the windows, the smith and his sons returned home.

"Ye see, boys," said the father, while they were on the road, "Widder Carter, ez long's her husband lived, was used ter good livin' an' good company, — 'long o' college folks an' city folks, an' not 'ith workin' men sech ez I be. Arter he died an' left her a widder, 'ith nothin' to live on, she's had to come daown a bit; an' she's come back here where she lived ez a gal, — she 'n her two darters. They can't airn much a sewin', even ef she allus got it ter dew; an' Mis' Faben, who's ben there callin', tol' me yisterdy she's afeard they hain't a mite o' wood nor meal.

"She puts a good face on metters, the widder doos, an' her darters come to meetin' ez spruce ez two pine saplins. She wouldn't hev no cherity, not she; but I've felt bad all day long, a thinkin' on her.

"When she was a gal she used ter be often enough at your gran'ther's, for he was a master hand to tell stories an' sing ol' songs; an' a nice, bright gal she was. One day he wrote on his slate some vairses 'bout her, — the widder that is naow, Sally Cotton she was then, — an' she larfed, I k'n tell yeou. She called him an ol' beau, an' run on sech a rig that he actilly blushed. A lively gal she was."

They had reached their own door, and while the smith's hand was on the latch, he stopped, and said in a serious tone, —

"But she's praoud, y' know, the widder is; an' she'd feel hurt like all nater ef she sh'd know who gin her that air wood an' meal. Sech wimmin air techy ez nettles 'bout takin' favors, speshily f'm workin' men. So y' air not ter tell on't, not ter anybody. An' don't ye ever go ter hintin', nuther, nor lookin' knowin', nor wistful, at her darters. When you see 'em to-morrer, or any day, at school, jest you act naterally, an' look ez ef nothin' had happened. Some little chaps k'n tell all they know, an' more tu, 'thout sayin' a word."

Later, they were sitting by the kitchen-fire, the boys eating apples, and the blacksmith with his chin in his grimy and calloused hand; — his "baird" of two days' growth anxious for the razor. Memory was bringing pictures of long-past gayety and bloom that made him forget present poverty and toil. The sons observed his meditative air, and wondered if the widow was ever half as pretty as her youngest daughter, Sarah. They thought that if the mother had resembled the favorite of all the village boys, the firewood and their afternoon's work had not been thrown away.

The secret was kept by all concerned; by the widow and her daughters from pride; by the household of the blacksmith from instinctive delicacy. Once, in the course of a *spat* among the school children, when Sally Carter for a moment lost her temper, and said a spiteful word, the eldest boy came near "splitting" upon her — which would have been brutal — but he recovered himself, remembered his father's injunction, endured the stinging epithet, and held his tongue.

This slight story, sad to say, will not have any romantic termination. Whatever may have been the blacksmith's motives or memories, his heart was heart of oak. But it was a case of doing good by stealth under circumstances that were almost pathetic. For of all the men of his class in the village he was least able to do what he did. He worked hard, saved little, and trusted to Providence for the future. There were people who could have helped the widow at her need without feeling it; but it might not have occurred to them to treat her with the chivalric delicacy which seemed so natural to him.

The Widow Carter, not long after, made a rich marriage, at which everybody, including the anxious contingent of old maids, heartily rejoiced. She did not need any more sacrifices from the humble friend of her youth.

On the Sunday after her marriage she came to meeting, of course, with her husband and daughters. The richness of her silks and velvets, though sober in color, was the talk of the women of Quabbin for at least half a dozen quilting-bees. Her demeanor was little changed; since her girlish days she had always been reserved. The daughters were not at all lifted up; there was no need; they had always considered themselves born in the purple. They looked at the blacksmith's boys, and bowed with their eyelids. The boys looked at each other, and the thought of a certain moonlit night flitted on the glances between them.

After service was over, and while the congregation was moving slowly through the vestibule, the blacksmith chanced to pass near the newly-married pair. He said simply "Good-mornin'," nodding to both, "I wish ye both joy." The new husband mumbled something indistinctly, drew up the sharp corner of his standing collar, and looked away. The new wife with a painful politeness of manner, said "It is hardly the time, is it, for worldly compliments, just after such a sermon? However, I thank you, and — I wish you well." While she spoke she looked at him as if she would have him remember her altered station, and his own, and then slowly went out, leaning on her husband's arm. But she did not fail to hear the reply, that might have had a throb under it: "'Pears then 't our Lord wasn't right when he said 'twas lawful to du good on a Sahberday!" But the blacksmith's wife pulled his sleeve and the scene ended. His boys thought that if the great lady *had only known*, she wouldn't have been putting on airs to their "old brick" of a father.

Sally Carter, the adored of Quabbin boys, at the age of twelve was round-faced, chubby, and rosy, with soft brown hair, and great, laughing, blue eyes. But after her kittenish days there was no romantic sentiment to interfere with her practical views of life. She developed in intellect as in physical frame, and became a solid, self-centered woman. Her undeniable beauty and talents were turned to good account in securing a husband and a position. At forty she was a leader in society, plump and stately, and with the *aplomb* of a duchess.

It would have been something for her to remember in her days of splendor, if she had chanced to look out of her bedroom window on that moonlit night when the sleds were unloaded.

CHAPTER XI

CHARACTER

A FARMER of the better class in Quabbin knew that his farm had been made productive by the labor of generations. His fathers had uprooted stumps, dug out or blasted bowlders, picked off loose stones, cut water-channels, kept down useless " brush," and made more and more lines of stone wall to replace rotting fences ; and he followed in their steps, keeping what they had gained, and adding new conquests to grass or grain fields. He had a big barn and a comfortable house ; he knew the points of cattle, and drove a good horse. Had you asked him, he would have assured you that he held religion to be man's chief concern, and " eddication " next ; but the truth was he believed in Work first of all, so that every human being should stand in his own shoes, indebted only to his own efforts for his living and his place in the world.

That was the eternal condition and basis of character, without which the church, the school, and all other blessings would have been naught. Not that he ever reasoned about it, for the notion was born in him ; it was something as unconsidered as air, yet as vital ; something taken for granted, like gravitation, and, like that, immutable and not to be trifled with ; else, like a wall out of plumb, the man would come to the ground.

The blessed doctrine of work, it is true, was held in other parts of the world. Where were workers more industrious than in rural France, in England, or in Scotland? Yet the New England farmer stood up in his simple dignity as did no other working-man on earth. Others toiled and saved; others were godly and brotherly-affectionate; others saw in the school the hope of their offspring and of the state; but his spirit had attained a high serenity, and possessed an unobtrusive force, unknown before.

If Carlyle in the time of his poverty had accepted the invitation of Emerson, and gone to live in Massachusetts, his experience would have changed the Old-World doctrines of his books from door-sill to ridge-pole. He would have seen in what way the true dignity of labor was possible, and that in Great Britain, for the overwhelming majority, it was not possible. It was seen long ago by Sir Henry Wotton, when he wrote, —

> " How happy is he born or taught
> Who serveth not another's will."

It was felt by the Puritan leaders, when grants of land were made, of reasonable size, in severalty, and in fee-simple to all freemen; when there was no lordly estate, no entail, no possessor of a " feu," no rent-charge, no menial service to render, no one to look up to between the working owner and the blue sky. A man so based can no more be overturned than a pyramid. One needs to have been born under such a system to appreciate its influence on character. Few in Great Britain understand this, because they have been reared under feudal influences, and at present they look more at the economic aspect of the land question.

The owners of the bulk of the land in the United Kingdom could be assembled in a good-sized concert-hall, an anomaly of more importance than any inequality in the British constitution. In Great Britain the city warehouse and the seaside villa are said to belong to the occupier, but it is not a possession in fee-simple. The nominal owner has built upon land which was not sold to him, and, though he holds it in perpetuity, it is upon condition of a perpetual annual payment, called ground rent in England and feu duty in Scotland. That is a burden from which he can never be free, and which will rest upon the latest of his descendants or representatives. It can seldom be compounded by a lump sum of money, either on account of an entail, or because the proprietor wishes to assure to his heirs an income that will not be affected by vicissitudes in trade, or by fluctuations in the money market. Let commerce, agriculture, or banking perish, the owner of the feu is untouched.

British people often say to an American " We are as free as you, and in some things more so." But that is not true as to one of the prime conditions of freedom, the right to own land. That is not within the reach of fifty men in a million.

A similar inequality prevails in regard to taxation for municipal or local purposes, at least in Scotland. The proportion borne by landed proprietors is ridiculously small ; and in cities it is not the " superiors," nor the leading financiers, nor the great merchants, who are burdened by taxes, but the shopkeepers, mechanics, and middle-class people.

To recount the inequalities of British municipal taxation would appear to be wandering far from the story of Quabbin; but, in considering the foundations of character in New England, it is necessary to contrast the condition of other people of our race who are nominally free, but who can never be really so while the eldest son robs his brothers and sisters, and while landowners and farmers are distinct classes by law or heredity. The rent of farms in Great Britain is adjusted according to the product of the soil under good management. The "superior" runs no risk of falling prices, of fires in ricks, or of tempest, flood, or pestilence; and any one of these calamities may ruin the tenant. The industrious and saving farmer knows that his labor and self-denial are not primarily for himself, but for his "superior." He may, by the exercise of patience and other Christian virtues, come to a state of resignation and even of content, but he will never be the man he might be if he toiled on his own land. For the sake of character, better the poorest of farms with independence than the most productive with servility.

What has been said of farmers in Quabbin was true, though perhaps in less degree, of mechanics. The smith or the joiner who owned his house and shop was on equal terms with the farmer, his customer, and could hold up his head with the best. The families of mechanics were quite as intelligent, because more given to reading. All these sturdy workers would have been worth the study of an observer like Carlyle; for he would have seen that there were attitudes more manly than dependence upon the great; and that consideration and condescension on the part of superiors, so much insisted upon in Past and Present, would be superfluous if there were free dealings in land, and if the effects of feudalism in society could be got rid of. It is not cosseting, nor soup kitchens, nor the encouraging smiles of Lady Bountiful, that Hodge needs, so much as to be allowed to stand up.

> " An' that's the old Amerikin idee,
> To make a man a Man, an' let him be."

The fact of personal independence is momentous and far-reaching. Manhood is the first of values. It does not matter that lands are more profitably worked in Great Britain ; nor would it matter if it were true that tenants realize more from hired farms than they would from land of their own. A man, if he chooses, has a right to earn less; and, whatever he does, he is richer in his poverty, if there is no one over him to whom he must *lout*.

The independence of citizens in towns like Quabbin was further assured by having a share in the management of town and parish affairs. In theory the right of a tenant-farmer in Great Britain may be similar, but in practice it is wholly otherwise. Public business is entirely out of the control of the people, and perhaps wisely so in the present state of things. The men of Quabbin formed a little democracy. In the thought of Daniel Webster (bettered afterward by Theodore Parker, and then repeated by Abraham Lincoln), it was "a government of the people, for the people, and by the people."

Having seen on what ground these men of Quabbin stood, and what manner of spirit was theirs, we can understand the invincibility of the "embattled farmers" during the war for independence, and appreciate their tenacity of patriotism, and of the undying memories bequeathed from sire to son. We see that Quabbin, and towns like it, have been nurseries of manly virtues, and that, with this basis of character, men's accent and gait are matters of small consequence. We can be patient with a ploughman's walk, and with his drawling equanimity, which a rain of grape-shot could not hurry; and we need not mind much the texture and slouchiness of a frock, when the wearer is sober, self-respecting, and just. The man who makes us smile with his naïve look and tone when he ejaculates " Du tell ! " " I want ter know ! " and " Yeou don't say so ! " may be one who governs his house wisely, educates his children, goes to meeting and enjoys a sermon with "meat " in it, and is a good neighbor, and (according to his light) a public-spirited citizen.

The immediate descendants of the Puritans were not consciously unsocial, but their serious views, self-denial, and determination made them appear so ; and the isolation of families, all bound to unremitting labor by the necessities of an unproductive soil and a rigorous climate, was in marked contrast with the friendly familiarity which prevailed in Virginia and in other colonies, where fox-hunting, racing, and merry-makings enlivened every rural neighborhood.

In New England the home, the church, the school, and the town-meeting formed the whole of life, with its duties, its training, its pleasures, and its hopes. The head of the family was much alone ; and, while he toiled upon the bleak hillside, or wrought in the workshop, his thoughts were upon the last sermon, or upon some other grave topic. Although without scholastic training, he was generally able to take a firm hold of Calvinistic theology, and with the aid of faith to survey its related doctrines with a certain sense of mastery.

In geometry the mind is satisfied when the Q. E. D. is understandingly reached ; there is no need to review the steps of reasoning in a proposition that has been fully wrought out ; but the Puritan was never weary of repeated demonstrations of Calvinistic theorems ; they were the objects of daily contemplation, — his meat and drink and solemn joy.

Some were continually probing themselves, with a restless and almost agonizing anxiety, to know if they could really acquiesce with the Divine decree, and still praise God, if it should happen that by that decree they were included among the damned.

They did not relish mere exhortations, or vague generalities in sermons ; they hungered for the deep things of God, and loved to ponder upon the awful obscurities of the Divine purposes. They admired the preaching which taxed their faculties to the utmost, and which led them to rest on faith, and to wait for the light of eternity to make clear the problems that confounded human reason.

So, chief among the elements of character and training, must be reckoned the influence of a stern theology, which, in silence and loneliness, sobered thought, stiffened the mental fibre, and set up Duty above every personal advantage. If the sons of New England have any one great heritage, it is this.

Along with grave qualities there were some which were provincial and parochial, — whimseys that were as firmly rooted as the others ; so that the Quabbin man was an odd bundle of high convictions, with grotesque notions and prejudices.

The Quabbin man of the better sort believed the Bible to be inspired, in mass and in detail, from Genesis to Revelation ; that Unitarianism and Universalism were doctrines of devils; that Methodists and Baptists were well-meaning people, but blown about by winds of doctrine ; that the cross was a symbol of popery, and Christmas a superstitious observance ; that the Federalists inherited the wisdom and virtues of Washington, and that John Adams and his son John Quincy were his worthy successors ; that Jefferson was the father of infidelity, and that, if every Democrat was not a profane rascal, at least every profane rascal was a Democrat ; that Daniel Webster was the greatest orator of any age (" He kin *talk*, this Daniel Webster ; he kin talk, I tell *yeou ; he* kin ") ; that Napoleon Bonaparte was expressly pointed out (by a calculation of heads and horns) as a monster of some kind in the Apocalypse ; that Dr. Grandley was the greatest surgeon and physician living; that in a great city there were few honest men and fewer virtuous women (to say that a woman had " city ways " was to intimate something greatly to her discredit) ; that any man possessed of more than twenty thousand dollars had come by it dishonestly (" It stands to reason that he couldn't 'ev made it by his own hands ; an', ef other folks airned it, it ain't hisn. Ef he's ben honest, an' gi'n all their deau, he couldn't hev no sech pile o' money ") ; that a bank was a kind of thing he did not understand (" Ef it lends money at six per cent, how du the sheerholders git twelve ? that's what I sh'd like ter know ") ; that the young men to be helped in " gittin' college larnin' " were those intending to preach the gospel (" Ez fer helpin' on young lawyers, let Satan take care of his own!"); that a lawyer was necessarily a dissembler and cheat; that " old-fashioned schoolin'" was good enough; that a man who wore a beard was a Jew, or a dirty fellow, or both; that kid gloves were worn only by dandies (" Ef it's cold, a good woollen mitten's good enough fer *me!*"); that the tune " China" (" Why do we mourn departing friends?") was divinely appointed to be sung at funerals, and that " Coronation" (" All hail the power of Jesus' name ") will be sung in heaven; that the good old days of samp, hulled corn, bean porridge, barrelled apple-sauce, apprenticeship, honest work, and homespun clothes were gone, never to return. In natural philosophy, the things he did not know, and those he thought he knew, but were "not so," were so many that to set him right would have required an enlarged and annotated edition of Sir Thomas Browne on " Vulgar Errors." It must (regretfully) be added that his necessary economy too frequently trenched upon sordid meanness.

Two co-existing institutions, the church and the town-meeting, were shaping character and creating the body politic, and were, to some extent, at cross purposes. For a long time the church had the upper hand, but, meanwhile, political education was going on by means of the town-meeting. When the authority of the church in civil affairs came to an end, the people were ready to govern themselves. It is freely admitted that theocratic rule put back civilization and an enlightened Christianity for more than a century, but the time was not wholly lost. In Great Britain there was no

Puritan rule, — although Scotland had something very much like it, — but there were no town-meetings, and therefore no general and efficient political education. Will it be pretended that artisans and agricultural laborers in Great Britain are to be compared in any respect with mechanics and farmers in New England ? If Parliament had set up " Village Councils " two and a half centuries ago, the case might have been different.

The institutions of New England have been often and ably discussed, and it would be quite beyond the purpose of this book to dwell upon their history or development; we are looking more at concrete results than abstract theories. And it does not matter greatly, — from Quabbin's point of view, — whether those institutions were developed from British models and ideas, as has been generally held, or whether they were brought by the Pilgrims from Holland, as has been recently argued by an able and learned writer.[1] The differences between the population of a typical English county and that of a group of Massachusetts towns covering a similar space are striking enough ; whether those differences are mainly the results of evolution under new conditions, or have sprung from the experience gained by our ancestors in another land, is not important in this simple sketch.

As to the character of the New England people, he who knows its complexities best will be most chary in generalization. It was reserved for a clever story-writer from abroad to give an authoritative exposition after a residence of a few weeks. The subject which had

[1] " The Puritan in Holland, England, and America," by Douglas Campbell,

tasked the powers of life-long observers like Hawthorne, Mrs. Stowe, Lowell, and Holmes, appears to
have been a mere trifle to the oracular young man from
India.   British editors and readers who have exulted in
his swift and condign judgment are to be congratulated.

CHAPTER XII

THE QUILTIN'

CO-OPERATION is a modern word, but the thing is as old as civilization. The benefit of association is at once recognized in a new country, where work has to be done for which the labor of one person, or of a family, would not suffice. In felling trees, co-operation takes the form of log-rolling, in which the neighborhood joins; and one man's land having been cleared, he in turn assists all who have worked for him.

The metaphorical use of log-rolling in politics is obvious, but it is often employed in British newspapers with vague knowledge of its meaning.[1]

Co-operation among the women of Quabbin took the form of an afternoon quilting followed by tea. Before woven white coverlets were introduced, and while woollen blankets were dear, a part of the bed covers were " quilts."

A quilt was made by placing a layer of soft cotton wadding between two sheets of cloth; an upper one with designs in color, and an under one as a lining.

---

[1] So in Great Britain one reads of " Bunkum " instead of " Buncombe," the name of the county in North Carolina where lived the " spread-eagle " orator, for whose flights the term was invented. So, one reads of " jerrymander " instead of " Gerrymander," the editor being ignorant that the word was derived from the name of Elbridge Gerry (G *hard*) whose device for a tricky division of the State into electoral districts has given him an unenviable immortality. But to spell his name, and he a governor of Massachusetts, with a little *j* is rather too much !

The stitching, which went through and attached the two surfaces, was done in an elaborate pattern of needlework. The face of the quilt was composed of pieces of printed cotton (calico) of all colors (arabesques or flowers, or what not) cut in squares, lozenges, rhomboids, hexagons, and the like, and arranged and sewed together in a way to make a symmetrical pattern, or group of patterns, as to form, and a regular distribution of colors.

But artistic perception, and the power of creating pleasing effects with heterogeneous materials, are not given to all; and some quilts were as tawdry and grotesque as the edifices that children build with colored blocks. The choice of materials was generally limited to the skirts of the calico gowns worn by the female members of the family since the last quilting.

Laying out the plan, and sewing together the pieces, occupied the women and children in odd hours for months. When the patchwork was completed, it was laid upon the destined lining, with sheets of wadding between, and the combined edges were basted. Long bars of wood — the "quiltin' frame" — were placed at the four sides; the quilt was attached to the bars by stout thread, and the bars fastened at the corners with listing; then the whole was raised upon the backs of chairs, one at each corner, to serve as trestles.

Around the quilt, so stretched out at a convenient height, a dozen (more or less) might be at work, seated at the four sides, all following in their stitching the pattern laid down. The pattern was fanciful, — in zigzags, parallels, octagons, or concentric circles.

When the width of a foot was completed on any side, so much of the quilt was rolled upon the bar;

and as the work went on, the visible part of the quilt diminished, like Balzac's *Peau de Chagrin.*

A more favorable arrangement for a social afternoon could hardly be imagined. The work demanded no thought on the part of those who were familiar with it ; and the women, all facing inward as at a square table, and all in best gowns, cambric collars, and lace caps, could gossip to their hearts' content.

Mrs. Kempton had invited some neighbors to a quilting, and, together, there was an even dozen of them. Mrs. Kempton was tall, slender, and dark, and had fine, expressive eyes. She was quick in speech, sensitive, and at times appeared restless. She was oppressed by the dead weight of the moral atmosphere of Quabbin. The rule of society was absolute. There were only two sets, — saints and sinners. For a church-member there was an endless number of unwritten laws, not to be transgressed. Mrs. Kempton did not transgress, but seemed always on the verge of doing it. She was like a dancer in leaden shoes, a tomboy in a nunnery ; and sometimes she feared she was an intruder in the church, so little sympathy she felt for the unnatural gloom that overshadowed everybody. A better-hearted or more exemplary woman never existed ; but she had lively faculties, a sense of the ridiculous, and longed now and then for a frolic.

There is a kind of freemasonry between those who find society a tyranny, and a village a prison. Those who wear the invisible ball-and-chain know each other. Three of Mrs. Kempton's friends shared, in different degrees, her qualities and sympathies, — Mrs. Stone, the carpenter's wife ; Mrs. Hale, whose husband owned the saw-mill ; and Almira Marble, spinster. Whenever these women met there was sure to be a merry time.

The quilting-frame so nearly filled the sitting-room that there was little space behind the chairs. The rays of the September sun streamed into the west window, and without the air was filled with reflections of yellow and crimson from the wealth of maple leaves about the house.

Among the women there had been the usual complimentary scrutiny of caps and ribbons, and the exchange of information in regard to measles and whooping-cough ; and, these topics having been exhausted, there was a pause.

After the needles had gleamed a while in silence, Mrs. Fenton, a stout and dull-looking woman, broke out with : —

" Did any o' yeou hear 'bout the bear ? " [1]

Several, speaking at once, said, " Where ? "   " When was it ? "   " Whose bear ? "

" Why," replied Mrs. Fenton, " 'twas a black bear, up'n Cap'n Davis's pastur', on the nor'west hill, week 'fore last."

Said Mrs. Stone, " Why, Mis' Fenton, there ain't ben a bear in nor abaout Quabbin for forty year! There's bears up'n Vermont, — my mother shot one 't her back door, — but they don't come daown here."

" The Rickett childern 've seen 'im, just afore dusk," replied Mrs. Fenton.

" *Now* we *know* 'taint trew," said Mrs. Kempton.

" The Rickett childern can't tell the truth ef they would," said Miss Marble.

" And their parents wouldn't ef they could," added Mrs. Hale.

---

[1] Quabbin women, with very few exceptions, spoke in dialect, but one *never* heard " bear " pronounced " bar." That is a Western usage.

"What was the bear doin'?" asked Mrs. Stone.

"They thought he was braowsin' on the berries."

"Most likely 'twas the minister out a-blueberrin' in his black gown," suggested Mrs. Kempton.

"Couldn't tell him f'm a bear — in the dark," said Mrs. Stone, laughing.

"Yeou sh'd be 'shamed ter liken the minister tu a bear," said Mrs. Fenton, while a sudden cloud of solemnity settled upon her face.

"P'r'aps 'twas Sat'n a-praowlin' raound," said old Mrs. Aldrich, with a shiver.

"O pshaw!" said several voices at once.

"Wal, yeou may *shaw's* much ez yeou please," said Mrs. Aldrich; "but my granny told me that when she was a gal in Brookfield, she was a-ridin' hossback over ter the north perrish of a dark night, an' she see a bear runnin' 'long side of her in the road" —

Here she was interrupted by two voices: —

"Wal, there *were* bears in that day."

"Ef 'twas dark, heow did she know 'twan't a dog?"

"Jest you hark," said Mrs. Aldrich. "She went on, a-whippin' up her hoss, an' arter a while she felt rather queer, an' her flesh seemed ter creep and cringe, kinder like goose-flesh; an' sech a feelin' at the pit o' her stummick! An' then she looked behind her. She *had* ter look behind her; she couldn't help it. An' what d'ye think she saw? That ere bear or some black critter was on her saddle-cloth, a sittin' up on his hind parts, an' his black nozzle just at her ear."

"Did he say anything imperlite?" asked Mrs. Kempton with sweet gravity.

"Naow, yeou're not to poke fun," said Mrs. Aldrich, looking over her spectacles. "Did the bear *say* anything, indeed! I wonder at yeou, I du!"

"Wal, the horse mightn't 've liked it, unless 'twas a very little bear," said Mrs. Hale.

Mrs. Aldrich paid no attention to the interruption, and went on: "She jest said the Lord's Prayer, and she felt the critter tremble; an' when she come ter the words, 'Deliver us f'm evil,' it jumped off, an' run away."

"That ought to be in a Sunday-school book," said Miss Marble.

"Wal," said Mrs. Thurstin, an ally of Mrs. Aldrich, "there's strange things happen in this world, laaf ez yeou will. Naow, yeou know the tahvern-keeper died arter he was kicked by a hoss. Wal, Mis' Shumway, who's a woman o' trewth, tol' _me_ thet she was ther' washin' an' scrubbin', an' thet an ol' clock that hedn't ben runnin' fer a year suddenly broke out a strikin'. They _caounted_, an' it struck forty-four! Jest the dyin' man's age."

"Was it the clock's strikin' that killed the man?" asked Mrs. Hale; "I thought you said the kick of the horse killed him."

"Wish you c'd a seen Mis' Shumway's eyes when she told me the story," continued Mrs. Thurstin. "They stuck aout like two moons."

"No matter 'bout _her_ eyes; they go moonin' easy," said Mrs. Stone. "Somebody who had eyes should a looked arter the clock."

"Yes," added Miss Marble, "I've heard there was a clock pedler 'bout the tavern at that time, and he may have been playin' a joke."

"But haow did it strike forty-four, Almiry? Tell me _that_," said Mrs. Aldrich. "A clock _can't_ strike more'n twelve times. 'Twas agin nater for it to strike forty-four."

"Ef the wheels air wood," said Mrs. Stone, "a man has only to cut off some of the little teeth or cogs, and then, when it begins strikin', 'twill keep on till it runs down."

"'Pears Dr. Grandley couldn't do the tahvern-keeper no good," said Mrs. Fenton.

"'Twas because bleedin' couldn't do him any good," said Mrs. Stone. "The doctor's as handy with his lancet ez a butcher. Poor Tirzy Powers! I sh'll never git over her death. There wasn't nobody like her. To think of her bein' in a pleurisy, an' bled till she couldn't hold up her head nor hand. The last time he bled her, her eyes set afore he could git the bandage fastened on her arm. There'll be a time when doctors won't dew so. 'The life of the flesh is the blood,' so the Bible says, an' it stands ter reason."

"Aour doctors don't bleed," said Mrs. Pomroy. "Doctor Thomson says ef God hed meant to hev blood taken aout o' the veins, he'd a made a hole and stopper."

"No, Mis' Pomroy," said Mrs. Kempton, "Thomsonians don't bleed, but they dose ye with lobelia an' 'composition' tell ye hain't any stomachs left. Jest you keep on, an' see where yeou an' yeour child'en 'll be."

"O' Doctor Salmon hed a bad han' to du up," interrupted Mrs. Aldrich. "Ye know James Johnson, he that's ben away to sea so long. Wal, Josh Wheldin 'ad a sore han', an' he went inter the store t'other day to git sunthin' fer it. 'Show me yer han', says Johnson — he was standin' 'hind the caounter, the side nex' the med'cines — so Josh he drawed off his mitt'n an' stuck out his han' An' then Johnson he reached fer

a bottle, and poured on thet sore han' — what d'ye
think? — *aquy fortis!* Why it smoked, and went burnin'
right inter the flesh. They was goin' to take him up,
— 'sault and battry they call it, — but he pertended he'd
took the wrong bottle by mistake, an' they didn't du
nothin' tu him. P'r'aps he did, but he's a mean, bad.
natered feller."

"What could Doctor Salmon du for sech a hand as
that?" asked a neighbor.

"Grease it, I s'pose," said Mrs. Aldrich.

"He ain't so good's an old woman," said Mrs. Stone.
"The child'n all die where he goes, jest as ef his
shadder killed 'em."

"Wal, this is gettin' grisly," said Mrs. Kempton.
"Fust we had bears, then the Evil One, then a clock
bewitched, then blood-lettin', and then *aqua fortis.*
Ain't ther' somethin' cheerful? Sometimes I think
Quabbin only needs an iron door to be a tomb."

"There's the Widder Carter, I mean Mis' Spauldin'," said Mrs. Hale. "*She* looks smilin'; an' Mr.
Spauldin' hez straightened up amazin'."

"Speakin' of weddin's," said the spinster, "David
Ramsay — the one that calc'lates the eclipse — is goin'
to be married, an' Joe Chandler is goin' to lend him his
horse an' buggy fer his weddin' tower."

"Another chance lost fer you, Almiry," said Mrs.
Kempton.

"My chance 'll keep," replied the old maid. "I'm
waitin' fer a widower. An' have ye heard that Dr.
Northam is makin' up ter one of the Spauldin' girls?
I didn't hear which, but I think it's Prudence."

"Whichever it is," said Mrs. Stone, "it'll be prudence fer him, fer they'll git a heap o' money, each one
on 'em."

At this point there was heard without, gradually coming nearer, the long, periodic wail of a child that had been crying, and appeared to be tired of it, but did not know whether it were better to stop altogether, or keep on at intervals.

The women looked from one to another with mute interrogation, but in a moment Mrs. Fenton's agitated face showed that she recognized the wailing voice. She rose and squeezed her bulky person behind the workers' chairs, on her way to the door; but before she reached it, the little sufferer appeared, and the sight of him was enough to make a sensitive woman qualmish. Mrs. Fenton applied her handkerchief to his nose, but, alas! that was a trifle; face, hands, hair, and clothing, made an image of neglect.

When she found breath she exclaimed, "Lijah, how come you here? Who told you to come here?" The boy's inarticulate blubbering continued; but at length he answered, with many sobs and heavings of the chest, "Dad sent me out ter play, but ther' wan't anybody to play with."

"What was your dad doin' thet he didn't let you stay in the haouse?"

"He's drinkin' pepper 'n cider. Then I went ter gran'ther's, an' Aunt Lucy said I must go 'way home. So I went, an' dad druve me off agin. Then I went ter Mis' Stone's, an' ther' wan't anybody ter hum; an' so I come here, fer I *must be somewher'*."

The last phrase was uttered in a loud tone of lamentation that produced, on the part of listening mothers, first a titter, then a giggle, and then an honest burst of laughter. They had not read "La Rochefoucault" in Quabbin, but it was impossible not to laugh at the

sorrows of a lonesome, untidy boy, and especially at
the incontestable position he laid down, that he "must
be somewhere."

The hostess tried to make a diversion by proposing to
take the boy into the next room, and give him a piece of
cake ; but Mrs. Fenton, a little ruffled by the laughter,
said she thought she would take him home.   But Mrs.
Kempton said that everything was ready, and she
would not hear of any one going away before tea.   In
the end, Mrs. Fenton remained, and the boy as well.

In the opinion of Quabbin, Mrs. Kempton's spreads
were worthy of all superlatives.   The tea, pale in color,
but really strong, was served in delicate old china, with
flesh-colored figures ; and the fragrance of so many
cups filled the room.

There was bread and butter, hot biscuits (which were
not *bis cuit* at all), waffles, peach preserves, apple-
and-quince sauce, doughnuts, mince-pie, custard-pie,
fruit-cake, sponge-cake, and mellow sage cheese.   The
tablecloth was like satiny snow.   Everything was best
and daintiest.   The simple folk praised everything.
The bread was light and "clean-tasted ;" the biscuits were "jest riz enough ; " the waffles "done to a
turn 'thout burnin'."   As for the pies, — well, 'twas of
no use.   "*Sech* a mince-pie !   Why it's jest beautiful !" with a strong nasal hum on the first syllable,
mbeautiful.

Whoever has not eaten mince-pie in some generous
Yankee house, wherein the tradition is several generations old, has no right to an opinion ; and whoever
dares to call it vulgar, may he live and die unblessed
with the incommunicable flavor !   Dyspepsia ?   Perhaps ; but for a mince-pie such as one remembers, ay,

and for other delectable dainties like those on Mrs. Kempton's table, the fiend might do his worst.

The small Fenton ate his generous slice of cake, then stole to the back of his mother's chair, and from time to time received divers sweet morsels. By and by, what with the original layer of dirt, the channels of tears, and the invasion of mucous fluids, and with the smear of sugary lollipops, the boy's face would have been a model for a *genre* painter. Art might copy, but not surpass. And then he was the author of a profound philosophic saying.

Then Mrs. Aldrich found it was " gittin' late," and, after some honest compliments, went for her " things." Mrs. Fenton and her son followed, the latter not much regretted. Soon all had departed except the intimates, Mrs. Stone, Mrs. Hale, and Miss Marble.

" Now sit down, girls," said Mrs. Kempton, with a burst of gay humor. " Sit down ; we'll have some more tea, some fresh cups, and a good, old-fashioned time." And they did.

CHAPTER XIII

THOSE who are familiar with the excellent roads in Eastern Massachusetts can have little idea of the conditions of travel sixty years ago in the poorer districts of the western part of the State. The original settlers generally selected high ground for the centre of a town, to prevent being surprised by Indians, and therefore most of the old routes are hilly.

Quabbin, a newer town, was built in a valley, but its roads furnished all the facilities for discomfort. There were within its limits no high hills to be crossed, but, to make up for their absence, plenty of sharp "pitches," with sinuosities and angles favorable to overturns, and with projecting points and edges of underlying ledges, so as to give a series of shocks to each vehicle. Other hill-roads were strewn with loose stones of assorted sizes, over which horses stumbled and wagons rattled. One of these was in the centre of the town; a short descent, but rough as the moraine of a glacier; and a man who drove down toward the tavern at a trot was tossed about as if he were in a boat on breakers. Others had a bed of deep clay, into which in rainy weather the wheels sank almost to the hubs. Some of the roads over pine plains and through valleys had a covering of sand, which, while wet, was impacted and smooth, but in dry weather was in yellowish granules, through which the wagon-wheels *squealed* in making their furrows.

To prevent a hill-road from being washed in time of heavy rain, it was the custom to make across it, at intervals, a series of barriers or dams that would turn off any sudden current. These dams, built obliquely, gave an emphatic " jounce " and a twist to a wagon descending, — a jounce of which the driver had his share in a jerk that threatened to dislocate his neck. From the involuntary motion of the head in going over these dams, they were popularly known as "thank'ee ma'ams," although the motion was scarcely conducive to a grateful state of mind.

To adorn the steep hill-roads with these ingenious obstructions, to clear out the rude gutters, and to cover hollows and rutted places with turf, loose soil, and roots of bushes, dug at random from the bank, so as to make the " repaired " section like a newly ploughed field, was the total of road-making science in that day.

County commissioners had paramount authority, in regard to long routes (county roads), but made their authority felt less in former times than now. Grading and macadamizing were unknown, and are still rare in Quabbin and in its region. Neighborhood roads were laid out, repaired, or discontinued by each town within its limits.

Once or twice a year the whole male population was called out to work the roads. If any one so chose, he commuted the service by a payment in money. Notice was given by the highway surveyors for the several districts (officers chosen at the annual town meeting), and the people met at the places designated,

to work under direction.   A poor man took a hoe or
shovel, a farmer his oxen, with plough or cart, according to need.   The surveyors adjusted the *corvée* as best
they could, according to the ability of each one liable.
The surveyors were not paid, and they labored with the
others ;   still, the office was sought for, because the
man in authority would be able to keep the road near
his house in fair condition, and because he would
" have the say " as to when the work was to be done,
and could appoint days that would be convenient for
him.   In winter, after a heavy fall of snow, the roads
were " broken out " by the people, under the direction
of the district surveyors.

Working parties began on the part of the road nearest the centre, and proceeded outward, making repairs
as they went, until they reached the boundary.   Often
they met there a similar party from the adjoining town ;
and then at luncheon time there were jumping-matches,
back-hugs, pulling the stick, tugs-of-war, and other
athletic games, besides the customary banter and chaff.

One day, by chance, the Quabbin men, working
southward, came in sight of a party belonging to Ware,
and, as there were various old scores to be settled between the respective towns' champions, the surveyors
in charge on either side got very little more work done
that day.   The two parties differed little in appearance.
Their clothes were mostly of an indescribable neutral
tint ;   their heavy boots were coated with mud, their
hats without shape, and their hair often straggling and
untidy.   But what was specially characteristic of the
people of the time, was a certain sheepish air, and a
heavy, awkward gait.   It was necessary to see the rustic Yankee in action to know that he could be vivacious and energetic.

After some preliminaries the distances were paced off, and there were races of one hundred and two hundred yards, in which the honors were fairly divided. At the high standing-jump Quabbin won. At the tug-of-war Ware won. At pulling the stick victory came to Quabbin. This was the crucial test of power and endurance. The two antagonists sat on the ground facing each other, their legs extended so that the soles of each were squarely against those of his adversary. A smooth, round stick, some two or three feet in length, held transversely, was grasped by both, and at the word, each endeavored to pull the other enough to lift him from the ground. It was a tremendous struggle, but without visible sign, except in the agonized strain of the muscles of face and neck. Often it was a draw, neither being able to raise the other. Whoever pulled spasmodically was pretty sure to be beaten; it was the long, steady pull that succeeded. The success of Quabbin was due to the aid of a stalwart young man, six feet at least, and with the breast and shoulders of Hercules, newly arrived from Vermont. No Ware man could hold his seat against him.

This was before the temperance reform had made much headway, and at the luncheon new rum was freely circulated. There was one who could not be called anything else but a drunkard, but who, in spite of his well-known failing, was regarded with kindness, for he was good-natured, lively, sensible, and often witty. In the early stages of exaltation he was the centre of merriment. He was doing service that day in place of one Crombie, who had the reputation of being "closer'n the bark tu a tree." Poor Dick had been furnished with luncheon by his employer, and he

opene:l the parcel.   There was a doughnut ("nutcake"
they called it), a hunch of skim-milk cheese, and a pair
of slices of rye-bread and butter.   The doughnut was
tough, the cheese like horn, and as for butter, one
never saw it so thinly spread.   "Wal," said Dick,
"Mis' Crombie's got ter be talked tu.   I k'n munch the
nutcake, I guess, an' p'r'aps worry off a bit o' thet
che:se-rine, but I wish she wouldn't cut my bread with
a greasy knife." [1]

A Ware man, wishing to hear Dick talk, asked him
how Mr. Crombie, his employer, liked being a director
of the bank ?

"Wal," said Dick, "when I went ter school, the dictionary said a d'rector is one who d'rects, an' that ain't
the case 'ith Bije Crombie.   He come home t'other day
f'm d'rectors' meetin' ez praoud's a turkey gobbler, but
tried to keep it all inside.   Ye understand, nobody f'm
Quabbin, that I ever heered on, was a bank d'rector
before.   I see he wanted me to ask him abaout it, so I
said, 'Mr. Crombie, I s'pose yeou see an' handled a lot
o' gold an' silver daown ter the bank.   Du they keep
the coin in piles like grain, an' shovel 'em in an' aout?
Or be they packed in berrils?' — 'No,' said he, 'it's in
a vault, a gret square hole in a wall, cased 'raound 'ith
iron.   They didn't take any on it aout.' — 'Oh,' said I,
'then yeou don't know haow much ther' was?' — 'Yis,'
said he, 'the cashier gin us the statement.'   An' aout he
takes a bit o' paper an' reads, so much in gold, so much
in silver, so much in bank-notes, and then so much

---

[1] Giraldus Cambrensis, in an amusing sketch of his travels in Wales, records
a similar witticism uttered by a peasant, and, unconscious of his own absurdity,
takes the trouble to demonstrate the fallacy in the reasoning by gravely citing the
rule of logic that is infringed.

assets. ' What in the name o' natur' is *assets ?* Ther's *loans an' discounts*, with big figgers, that 'pear to be a leetle mixed, — didn't jest know haow they stood ; but *assets* stumped me ! they did, I vum. Howsever, they gin us a dividend o' ten per cent, an' that's sunthin. Ez I k'n borry all the money I sh'd want at *six*, I don't see haow they k'n pay us *ten*. But I'm glad ter git the money.' Naow," continued Dick, " yeou k'n see ef a d'rector is one who d'rects."

While Dick was talking he took an occasional swig from his bottle, and as he entered with a keen relish into the account of Mr. Crombie's views of finance, his broad, rosy face was overspread with an oozy perspiration, and gilded with a perpetual smile. For the time he was happier than the director.

There was in the neighborhood an old iron cannon which appeared to have no owner, and which had been alternately captured and recaptured by the young fellows of Ware on one side, and those of Quabbin on the other, for many years. It was a six-pounder, bearing on its breech a crown and the letters G. R., and was deeply pitted with rust. It was used for firing salutes on the Fourth of July, and for that purpose was chained upon the axle-tree of a pair of cart-wheels. At the time of this road-party the Ware fellows had it, well hidden away as they believed ; and, naturally, the Quabbin boys were trying to ascertain where it was, that they might make a midnight excursion and bring it off. When the new rum had induced confidence, a youth of the Quabbin party said to one of Ware, —

" Ain't ye 'fraid that ol' cannon 'll bust ? I hear yeou fellers fired it all day las' Fourth o' Jewly. Some of aour folks that was daown tu Bost'n in the last war, an' who was artill'ry men, an' knows 'baout guns, says the ol' thing's jest rotten, an' 'll fly ter pieces some day, like a mouldy cheese." The youth from Ware looked wary, and made only an inarticulate response. The Quabbin youth went on, —

"Th' ol' fellers up ter Quabbin says they're glad it's away ; fer ef it busts it's better that it sh'd kill Ware boys than aourn."

"They are very kind," said the youth of Ware.

"I was on'y wantin' to give ye a friendly warnin'," said he of Quabbin.

"Much obleeged," said young Ware.

"Ef yeou folks air so ferce to keep it," said young Quabbin, looking keenly at his companion, "I wonder yeou let it lay in sech an open place as Lyman's ol' kerridge haouse, daown on the Palmer Road."

"Who told yeou 'twas there ? " was the sudden and unguarded response.

"I heered it." This was a fib. The attempt at location was only a bold guess, and proved true. The Quabbin boy looked indifferent, offered his companion a "nutcake," and changed the subject.

It may be added that not long after the Quabbin boys found the cannon, and drew it home, seven miles. On the next Fourth of July before daylight it was dragged through the thick woods to the top of Ram Mountain, and the slumbering village was roused by the unexpected thunder which echoed along the valley. The following year the Ware boys recovered the gun, but, as had been predicted, it burst, — fortunately without loss of life.

In smaller parties there was talk of courtships, of good places for fishing, of the price of mink and musquash skins, of the ministers, singing-schools, and other matters of general interest. The marriage of David Ramsay, the mathematician, was the occasion of some amusing talk, as he was over fifty, and his wife no longer young. Dick, who was not *very far* advanced in inebriation, told of a conversation he heard between the bridegroom on his return from the wedding-trip, and Joe Chandler, who had lent him his team. Joe asked a great many questions, to which David made few answers. At last he said, "Well, now, David, what d'ye think of matrimony? And how do you like your new condition?" — "Wal," said David, "ez to matrimony, it *depends*, ye see. I don't know nothin' 'bout widders, — but merryin' an' ol' maid's a putterin' job."

A discussion then arose over the pretensions of the two towns. Odds were offered that the new factory village in Ware "was goin' to beat Quabbin all holler." These retorted that land in Ware was so poor that "a rabbit 'd shed tears ef he hed to git his livin' off 'm a ten-acre lot on 't." Ware replied that Quabbin "didn't raise nothin' but polecats an' skunks' cabbige."

Then rose an ancient Quabbin man with a merry blue eye, and delivered, off-hand, a few lines of rhyme, albeit with a slight impediment in his speech.

> "Dame Nature once, in makin' land,
> Hed refuse left o' stones an' sand;
> She viewed it o'er, then flung it down
> Between Coy's Hill an' Belchertown.
> Said she, 'Yeou paltry stuff, lie there!'
> An' made a town, an' called it Ware!"

All laughed, the Ware men included, and then the rhymer was asked to sing. He had a good natural voice (wholly uncultivated), abundant feeling, and a surprising memory. It was said that he knew the words and music of above two hundred songs. When he sang, he sang "to the ends of his fingers and toes." He did not say he was hoarse or out of practice, nor wait to be pressed, but in compliance with general desire sang "Wolfe's Adieu," a sweet, old-fashioned song. The taking of Quebec was not then so very long ago. In singing, every trace of his impediment disappeared.

> " Too soon, my dearest Sophy,
>   Pray take this kind adieu.
> Ah, Love, thy pains how bitter,
>   Thy joys how short, how few !
> No more those eyes so killing,
>   That tender glance repeat,
> With bosom gently swelling,
>   Where love's soft tumults beat.
>
> Two passions strongly pleading
>   My doleful heart divide ;
> Lo, there's my country bleeding,
>   And here's my weeping bride.
> But no, thy faithful lover
>   Can true to either prove ;
> War fires my veins all over,
>   While every pulse beats love.
>
> I go where glory leads me,
>   And points the dangerous way,
> Though cowards may upbraid me,
>   Yet honor bids obey.
> But honor's boasting story
>   Too oft thy swain doth move,
> And whispers fame with glory,
>   Ah, what is that to love !

Then think where'er I wander,
  Through parts by sea or land,
No distance e'er can sunder
  What mutual love hath joined.
Kind heaven, the brave requiting,
  Shall safe thy swain restore,
And raptures crown our meeting
  Which love ne'er felt before." [1]

Hearty applause followed; and then the singer gave the ever popular "Vicar of Bray" with vigor and humor.

The surveyors at length induced their parties to separate. The contingent for Quabbin started homeward, and, as they went, smoothed with hoe or shovel some of the roughest of the work they had done. It was but a few miles they had to walk, and all got home safely, even poor Dick, who had not always such good luck.

A working party on the roads was never a just representation of the people of Quabbin. Few thriving mechanics, and none of the men of influence, did personal service, because it was better to pay the money than lose a day. The force which a surveyor could muster was largely made up of hirelings, and of those who did not count for much in town or church affairs; and that accounts for the hilarity, as well as the easygoing way in which the work was done.

---

1 The stanzas are written from memory, after sixty years, and there may be some errors.

CHAPTER XIV

VILLAGE AND COUNTRY

THE old manners naturally survived longest in districts remote from the village and its modernizing influences. This fact was conspicuous among the folk on the Great Hill at the north-west, which covered parts of the territory of three towns. It was a region where what was oldest and rudest in English rural counties lived on, but under less favorable conditions; for the soil was rough and unproductive, markets were distant, and money exceedingly scarce. Probably there could not be seen to-day on the hilly roads a barefooted driver of oxen, or a farmer in blue frock going to mill; but sixty years ago woollen frocks in winter, and flaxen or tow breeches and bare feet in summer, were common enough. The difference between these people and those in the social centre was like a gulf between centuries; and the rooted antipathy on the part of the hill people toward the better-dressed villagers was almost past belief. There could hardly have been a sharper line of division between Jew and Gentile. The differences had slowly come about from the lack of frequent communication, of good schools, and of a convenient place for united worship. As most of the families on the hill had a common origin, and were nearly all connected by marriage, there came to be a known type of countenance among them. Their ways were painfully coarse, but actual illiteracy was uncommon ; that is to say, it was rare to find a man who could not sign his name, and keep what might pass for accounts, to be sharply disputed over at settlement with the store-keeper ; but the general ignorance would have been charming to those who place the Golden Age in the centuries before the Reformation. There were few books (probably not half a dozen to a household), almost no newspapers, no hints of science, and no knowledge of the world, literally or figuratively. The people spoke their mother tongue as they had heard it, using words long obsolete, as well as Saxon plurals and terminations, wholly unconscious that there was such a thing as grammar. The difference between their speech and that of the village was, however, more in matter than in phrase ; but the universal drawl and *twisting* of accent were considerably intensified on the hill. Literary English is the product of centuries of learned labor ; chimney-corner English is a common and indefeasible inheritance, somewhat abused by Yankees, it must be admitted.

In a religious point of view, the majority in the remote districts were not actively, but passively, ungodly, or at least indifferent to the established worship. Many were too far from the meeting-house to attend regularly, even if they had not such a repugnance to the village set ; besides, they and their horses had need of rest ; and when they heard the gospel at all, it was at a district schoolhouse, where some unlettered apostle of an Ishmaelitish church gloried in non-conformity, and poured contempt upon " book-larnin'," " hirelin' priests," and the " praise of God with choirs and fiddles." Some of these, later, supported the Methodist church, and contributed to build for it a small meeting-house in the centre of Quabbin.

The distrust of the village folks which prevailed in the outskirts was assiduously cultivated by neighborhood leaders, until it became something like that of a British radical for a Tory peer. In any popular assembly there will be parties; and local managers, (demagogues they might be called) make them serve their personal ends. From this source came the long and obstinate resistance to the improvement of the public schools, and to the making of needed roads and bridges. Fierce but bloodless battles were fought at the annual town meetings, where any proposition, of what nature soever, if made by an enlightened villager, especially if he happened to be prominent in the church, was at once opposed by all the outdwellers and dissidents, these always rising to be counted when the "otherwise minded" were called by the moderator.

The drunken and depraved portion of the townspeople naturally sided with the "otherwise minded" in opposing the party of the church and parish; but that portion was not large, and the greater and better part of the opposition were not at all responsible for the conduct of their shameless allies.

It is not to be supposed that the villagers — "townspeople" they were called in the country — were greatly distinguished for reading or general intelligence, for there were scarcely more than half a dozen fairly well-educated families among them, and, judged by any high standard, not so many; but the advantage was, that among the less educated villagers there was no bigoted preference for ignorance. If they were not illuminated, their faces were turned toward the light.

The few collections of books were well known, and, excepting that of the second minister and of the lawyer, it is doubtful if any contained so many as a hundred volumes; few had as many as fifty. It is painful to think of the meagre supply of reading available, excepting religious works. If a boy were looking about for something to read, he would have found Josephus, Rollin's "Ancient History," the "Pilgrim's Progress," and some religious treatises before mentioned; also, "Riley's Narrative," a story of captivity among Arabs, Milton, Pollok's "Course of Time," Cowper, a few lives of celebrated preachers, and the like. If there were any complete copies of the works of Shakspeare, Dryden, Pope, Addison, or Johnson, they must have been seldom exhibited and seldom read. The same may be said of Burns, Byron, Coleridge, Shelley, Wordsworth, and Keats. No "profane" author was ever quoted in a discourse; and every author was profane who did not write upon religious subjects, and on evangelical lines. No instruction was given in literature in the schools; no English poetry was ever used except to be picked to pieces in parsing lessons. Therefore an intelligent lad might get what education the schools of Quabbin could give him, without ever seeing any work of the great British poets (Milton excepted), or of any great writers of English prose (Bunyan excepted), and without knowing the character or even the existence of any "profane" author who did not happen to be represented by a specimen in some reading-book. Sometimes a youth might be favored by a certain generous but "worldly" old lady, who had preserved in secret books of tales like "The Arabian Nights," or romances like "The

Scottish Chiefs," or more recent poems like "The Lady
of the Lake." But the youth could not keep such
books in safety, except in the barn and under the hay,
nor read them, except at intervals and by stealth.

To ignore all literature except their own was the
policy of the religious leaders of Massachusetts. They
did not make an *Index Expurgatorius*, for notoriety
would have defeated their purpose.

If such was the intellectual conditions of the village, what must have been the darkness of the outlying regions?

CHAPTER XV

TOWN, PARISH, AND CHURCH

A "TOWN" in Massachusetts is a small republic, or a corporation erected by statute in certain fixed limits, and exercising powers established and defined by a general law. The existence and functions of towns antedate any legislation. At the beginning, each "plantation" set up its local government as by intuition. "Township" is not a native term, and, so far as it has any meaning in Massachusetts, refers to the territory of a town. The town, as we have seen, maintains within its boundaries roads, bridges, and schools, and supports its poor, if there should be any having a legal settlement. Formerly it was obliged to provide for the military drill and equipment of its able-bodied citizens of legal age. Formerly, also, it elected the minister, voted his salary, and raised the amount by taxation, like other town charges; for in early times the town and parish were one. Later, the notion of the town was that of a corporation for civil purposes, and of the parish, a corporation for religious purposes; and in many cases both corporations covered the same area. If a town was large and became populous, it might be divided (for religious purposes solely) into two or more parishes. A "church" means such persons as have made a prescribed profession of faith and experience, and have united under a covenant. A church-member, unless non-resident, was necessarily a member of the parish, but the reverse was not necessary.

Every inhabitant used to be assessed by the authorities of the town for civil purposes, and of the parish for religious purposes. In earlier times, and while the town and parish were virtually one, there was no exception to this rule; but after a time the law allowed a man to sever his connection with the parish, without changing his residence, if he could show that he was taxed for the support of worship elsewhere. Unbelievers and dissidents, sixty years ago, considered the compulsory support of the gospel an oppression; and there was no end of wrath and profanity about it, until at length the voluntary system was established by law, and the final divorce of church and state accomplished. That, one would think, was the " Emancipation of Massachusetts."

Most well-disposed people paid the "minister tax" whether they went to meeting or not. To withdraw was called "signing-off," — a bull in terms, but a proceeding perfectly understood, — and was considered disreputable, unless prompted by religious conviction. Many members of the parish were not church-members, although they might regularly attend meeting. When the bi-monthly communion was to be celebrated, non church-members usually left the meeting-house after sermon.

The parish and church voted separately upon the calling of a minister, and upon the amount of his salary. Differences often occurred, and, even when the two bodies agreed, there was a third power to be consulted, namely an ecclesiastical council, composed of ministers and delegates from neighboring churches,

whose approval was considered necessary in later times.
A minister's first settlement was an "ordination;" a
subsequent one an "installation."

So Quabbin sixty years ago was a duplex republic;
an organized democracy in civil affairs, and a religious
corporation in its other aspect. In the annual town-
meeting, and in the parish-meeting, every man had his
voice and his vote. There was (and still is) no rank or
primacy except from known ability and worth. With
characteristic simplicity the chief officers of a town
were styled the "Selectmen," and, with a view of re-
straining loquacity and personalities, the chairman,
chosen for each occasion, was termed the "Moderator." There were also chosen each year a School
Committee, Overseers of the Poor, Town Clerk, Treas-
urer, and Surveyors of Highways.

The first business in order was the presentation of
reports of town officers for the year then ending.
These were read, discussed, and acted upon, and their
recommendations submitted to vote. Appropriations
were then made for the various town charges, after
which the officers for the coming year were elected by
ballot. In no legislative body was business more intel-
ligently done, and out of this long experience there
has been made a manual of practice. The moderator
ruled upon the admissibility of motions, and the order
of precedence, in case more than one was made at the
same time. He knew the "p'ints of order," and
promptly decided what question was rightfully before
the meeting. Any one aggrieved by his decision
might appeal to the meeting, which sustained or reversed his ruling by a majority vote. Probably there
is nowhere a body of men better trained to public

service than the voters of New England, and of those
States that have followed the same methods. There
are places in Great Britain in which there is not the
least notion of an orderly or parliamentary procedure ;
as, for instance, where the chairman of a meeting
makes a motion, — which is in itself absurd, — and
where such a motion and a hostile amendment are submitted to a vote at one and the same time. An experienced moderator would make short work of the
confusion that arises from ignorance or mischief, and
promptly show what question is rightfully before the
meeting. The usage was not copied from the rules of
the State Legislature ; on the contrary, the town was
the original unit and model, and the State an aggrega-
tion. The experience of a century and a half in these
primitive assemblies made the working of the State
Legislature under the Constitution an easy matter.

The state of schools, roads, bridges, and the town
accounts, with all that concerns public order and well-
being, were discussed by and in presence of those
vitally interested. Whoever had anything to say, said
it ; and practice made speech pointed and effective.
It was face to face and man to man. Facts and wise
suggestions had weight ; but, when the business of a
year was to be finished in a session of a day, mere talk
had small consideration.

This little annual parliament has some likeness to
the village assemblies of our Teutonic ancestors, and
to the democratic rule in ancient Athens ; but as a
scheme of local administration it is more practical
and efficient than any ever devised. It was and is a
means of education of the highest value.

Something has been said of the effect of political

independence upon character, and of the sturdy spirit that came from the individual ownership of farms, and from the extinction of feudal customs. To these must be added the institution of the "town," as one of the influences that have made New England people what they are.

This simple and automatic machine, with the general education and moral training which then came into being, was the sure foundation of personal liberty and free government. Every voter was in effect a member of a committee of supervision upon all matters which concerned him. By himself, or by a known and accepted proxy, he managed the schools, kept order, repressed evil-doers, and maintained highways. It was to his own nominee that he paid the taxes he had assisted in levying : no stranger came to take his hard-earned money. His trusted neighbor was the justice before whom he could plead his cause. The law was not a distant or distrusted power ; its force was exercised for him in so far as he was just. He was at once ruler and subject, a member of the only true and beneficent democracy the world has seen. Why should he not cheerfully obey, since the precepts were of his own making, and the instruments of justice named by his own voice ?

Under local control the schools have naturally indicated the state of public sentiment. People would have felt less personal interest even in better schools, if they had been directed by some remote or exterior authority. With the general advance of intelligence the schools have been improved, and each neighborhood regards its own with the pride of possession.

Furthermore, the system of town government has

made possible the plan of "local option" as to the sale of intoxicating drinks. A town, by its vote, may permit or deny the granting of licenses for the retail sale of spirits, wine, and beer within its borders. In a very great number of small towns such licenses are forbidden, and the general good order in the villages is believed to be due to this regulation.

Carlyle, who, if his writings had been speech, would have made more noise than any in his generation, has given way to many outbursts of temper upon talk. And, truly, when talkers without knowledge are desirous mainly of hearing their own voices, and have not a heartfelt interest in the thing discussed, nor power to follow up opinion by action, talk may be as dreary and profitless as he represents it. But when it is spent upon topics that come home to men's "business and bosoms," on a fit and necessary occasion, with personal knowledge of the matters to be decided, and with intention to decide them then and there, surely talk is one of the most important and useful of faculties.

New England has been justly reproached as the country of windy oratory. Almost every eminent scholar and public man in times past felt bound to deliver set "orations," and to include them in his published works, but the fashion has had its day. Still, something may be said in favor of a system which enables people to set forth their views on matters of public interest with clearness and force ; especially when they are able to make of thought, fact ; of ideas, institutions ; of resolve, action ; of character, renown.

There are people who are reasonably intelligent, and yet are unable to listen to opinions and arguments which they do not approve. At the appearance of a leader of a party opposed to theirs, and often at the bare mention of his name, they burst forth in imprecations, hootings, and yells, and endeavor to drown the speaker's voice and break up the meeting. Others still more violent use missiles and clubs, so that bandages, eye-shades, and sticking-plaster become necessities for a candidate's outfit. Such men would need some preliminary education before they could take part in the business of a deliberative body. The people of New England have not been without blame in this respect, as all early anti-slavery men well remember ; but in town meetings the decorum observed, even in the sharpest contests, has been remarkable. The self-control acquired in these annual assemblies has done much to preserve the amenities in political gatherings, and has made possible something like dispassionate consideration of public questions.

Quabbin, like other towns, had its stormy meetings ; sometimes it was the town party, and sometimes the country party that won ; but in the long run justice was generally done. An instance of sharp practice may be mentioned : —

A wealthy and prominent citizen, who was a leading church-member, and vehemently disliked by the people of the outlying districts, made a motion at one meeting that the authorities be instructed to close a certain road which was little used. He said nothing in support of his motion, and preserved an impassible look. A leading man in the country party was quick to see that the mover really wanted the road kept open, as it led to his own land. This man, therefore, promptly seconded the motion, looking round keenly at his supporters in tne rear of the hall. They were in full force that day, and the motion was carried by show of hands. The truth was, the mover had found that whatever he proposed was defeated, and, desiring to have this road maintained for his personal convenience, moved to discontinue it, and was caught in his own trap. It was a pity he resorted to a trick by which his influence was so much impaired ; for he had been one of the most liberal and enlightened friends of the public schools, and in favor of most projects of reform.

CHAPTER XVI

THE SECOND MINISTER

THIS young man was ordained as colleague, with a salary of five hundred dollars and the use of a good modern house. The use of "pounds" in reckoning had gone by. At the ceremony of ordination there was present a small spectator, who in after years recalled "the laying on of hands." The pulpit seemed to be black with ministers, — swarming with them; and at a certain time the candidate knelt, with his pale face on the puffy crimson cover of the desk, and then ever so many white hands were stretched out, and rested on his head while the "ordaining prayer" was made.

The new minister was a slender man, of serious yet pleasant countenance, with soft, engaging, deep-set brown eyes, which could flash upon occasion, and a broad white forehead with full temples that showed a network of throbbing veins. He looked fragile, but was nervous and wiry, and an indefatigable worker. There was enough for him to do.

The state of religion, viewed as a ceremony, was much as it had always been; but the life of religion, which is active piety, with soberness, purity, and godly living, had sadly declined. This was seen in every aspect of society, but chiefly in the prevalent habit of drinking, in the dull formality of prayer-meetings, and in the wretched state of the schools. The new minister soon came to the conclusion that no "revival" would permanently benefit the church, and that no efforts could raise the standard of education, until the excess of drinking was restrained. But he found out, as Dr. Johnson did long before, that moderation was more difficult than abstinence; and he set to work to found a total abstinence society, of which a revived church was to be the nucleus.

The drinking habit had been universal, and though there were not many notorious drunkards, true moderation was rare. People who wanted it, got rum at the store, and kept it at home, or in their workshops. As we have seen, it appeared at the pastoral call; it refreshed the ecclesiastical council at an ordination; it was glorious at a house-raising when neighbors came to give a lift, and indispensable at the annual training. When heads were heated, the usual consequences followed: sometimes the machinist talked foully; or it was the shoemaker who declaimed politics while he slit the upper leather in trimming a shoe; or it was the butcher who argued upon theology as he bled a calf; or it was the blacksmith who had grown oblivious of a waiting customer, and let his fire die out on the forge. As has been already stated, the indications of intemperance among the farms met the eye at the first glance, in dilapidation and ruin. There were carts without wheels, and wheels without carts, and all manner of broken tools, cumbering the yards. The grass plots were defiled by geese. Petticoats and old hats were stuffed in broken windows. Fences leaned, gates were off their hinges, and walls were tottering. Lean and discontented cows got into the growing corn. Colts went about with manes and tails full of burrs. Pigs disported in the vegetable garden. Orchards lapsed into wildness, and bristled with useless shoots. Untended pastures were nibbled bare, and dotted with clumps of bushes. Mowing fields were overrun with sorrel and white-weed.

Meanwhile there were accidents, woes, "wounds without cause," falls from wagon or cart, stumbles in ditches, and a sorry show of bleared eyes, cracked hands, and unshaven faces. Voices on such farms were under no control; men shouted, women screamed, and boys replied: there was one from which the high-p'tched voices were often heard for half a mile. Wives struggled long on the downward slope, striving to keep up an air of respectability, but at length gave way to despair, sank to their husband's level, or lower, and became frowsy, loose-haired, and sharp-tongued. Scolding only deepened the common misery. By knitting stockings they procured tea or snuff, if they used it, or a bit of calico. The daughters when they wanted gowns or ribbons paid for them by braiding palm-leaf hats. The boys had a hard time to get their schooling, and were glad to trap muskrats, minks, partridges, or rabbits, and to gather wild nuts or berries, so as to buy hats, boots, and books.

Oh! those farms! what misery did they not witness. Love had flown long before; self-respect was dead, and comfort a rare visitor. Sordid poverty was in possession, with ignorance, ill-temper, and brutishness. But there was always a supply of hard cider and of rum; the store-keeper gave liberal credit, on conditions; and, until the length of the tether was run, the farmer's nose continued to glow like a dull ruby. But the end came sooner or later. The sheriff's officer was no stranger, and sometimes a debtor or trespasser was carried away to the county jail.

What was political independence, or ownership of land in severalty, or the education of town meetings, or the preaching of the gospel, or any other blessing, to men sunk in such degradation?

The minister saw that half measures would not do; he threw his whole soul into the work of inducing the church to take a stand upon total abstinence, and at length succeeded. Intemperate brethren were warned, and, if necessary, excommunicated. To be a church-member was to be an abstainer. The next move promised to be more difficult. He turned to the parish and the town, and after a time got the authorities to discountenance the excesses that had attended public meetings. He had to wait for a chance to attack the people of the wild and drunken district, but at length one came to him most unexpectedly.

There was a meeting of the able-bodied men of the military company for drill or display, which was followed by a tragic incident. The like of this village "training" was never seen except in some burlesque on the stage. The men kept time to the sound of fife and drums, but of erect military carriage, of the manual of arms, and of company-formation, they were ludicrously ignorant. Heads moved automatically from side to side, shoulders rose and fell in a distressing rhythm, and awkward feet struck out right and left. Even the boys, who had never seen any well-drilled company parade, laughed and shouted from one end of the common to the other.

The head-gear was in shape like an apothecary's mortar; the material of shining black leather, with a flat brass chain festooned across the front, and a chin-strap; the whole surmounted by a plume made of small feathers, standing more than a foot high; the lower part white, and the tip bright crimson. The coat was dark green, closely fitting, with brass buttons, and transversely braided on the breast with yellow galloon. The trousers were of white linen. The officers wore red sashes. It was a gay costume. The manœuvres were simple to childishness. The firing of the flint-lock muskets (with blank cartridges) resembled nothing so much as the hap-hazard clatter of the hinged seats in the meeting-house.

When the show was over the soldiers gathered at the tavern, where rum-punch was consumed by bucketfuls; and at sundown the scattering of bewildered men for their homes, swaying in rickety wagons, or staggering along on foot, was something never to be forgotten.

People had come from far and near to see the training; and among them was a man from the wild district, who, not content with the punch, had procured a small jug of rum to take home. He was standing near the tavern door, leaning against a pillar of the veranda, and keeping a tight hold of his precious jug. His disordered hair, the spasms of muscular action in his face, the unsteady movements of his knees, which seemed inclined to double under him, and the alternate come and go of light in his foxy eyes, showed that he had long passed the safety line of self-possession, and was heading for some catastrophe. Two men from his neighborhood observed him, and came near.

"Harv," said one, "where yeou goin'? What ye got in thet ere jug?"

"My name ain't Harv," said the drunken man with a vicious assumption of dignity. "Yeou know *thet!* Wher'm I goin'? I'm goin' hum — when I git ready; an' what I've got in this ere jug ain't nothin' to nobody."

The friend pursued, —

"Naow, don't yer git furus fer nothin', Harvey. I was 'feard yeou was goin' ter try walkin' home alone; an' the road's rough, an' it's goin' ter be dark ez a pocket 'fore yeou git ther."

"Thet's so," said the other neighbor. "Don't yeou start alone. Yeou jest go 'long 'ith us."

"I k'n walk," said Harvey, "an' I know the road. I c'd foller it 'ith my eyes shet, an' my han's tied behind me."

"Naow, Harvey, hear tu reason! I don't say yer can't walk, an' don't know the road, — on'y 't 'll be safer fer ye ter hev company."

But Harvey couldn't be "druv," as he said; and, irritated at the imputation of being unfit to take care of himself, he started off, covering a good part of the breadth of the road as he went. It was a long way he had to go, and it was pitch dark when he reached the hilly region. He called for a moment at the house of an acquaintance, and from there, against all persuasion, started across-lots upon a path sufficiently difficult for a sober man in daylight. The event happened which was expected. He strayed out of the path, stumbled, and fell over a precipice, and next morning was found dead, his stiffened hand still grasping the handle of the broken jug.

The new minister went out to attend the funeral. There was a great gathering, especially of the class to which the dead man had belonged. There were far too many for the small and cheerless house to hold; so, while the family sat in the room with the coffin, the neighbors remained outside, and the minister conducted the services in the open air, standing on a log by the wood-pile. When he came to address the mourners, it was said that never a battery with grape-shot threw a crowd into such consternation. He was by nature sympathetic, but he was courageous, and terribly in earnest. He repeated with thrilling emphasis the woes denounced in the Old Testament against drunkards; and never, perhaps, since the days of the prophets, did they appear so dazzling with menace, so mighty in power. The effect was indescribable. Some were so angry that they threatened violence; but, aside from the respect due to his calling, there was something in the look of the minister that repelled aggression. He told them of their brutal neglect of their wives and children; he described their homes without comfort, their lives without dignity or respect, with the poor-house, the jail, and the pauper's grave before them. He told them of their want of manliness, and the need they had of the sustaining power of religion, and warned them of the wrath to come. Then he painted the delights of home as it should be, when the master of the house is a man, "clothed and in his right mind." He appealed to the women, of whom many were present, and all the tenderness of his heart broke forth. Before he had done there were sobs and groans. Then he prayed. Beyond this point it would not be right to follow him; but the reader can imagine the fervency of that prayer from the simple fact that the children who had heard him pray when he came to visit their school had more than once at the end of his prayer found the seat of the chair by which he had knelt sprinkled with tears. What a glowing heart he had! It is not often that a strong man weeps! Precious tears they were, not unnoticed, perhaps, by the All-pitying Eye.

CHAPTER XVII

THE CAMPAIGN BEGUN

THE death of Harvey, and the startling scene at his funeral, made a prodigious talk in Quabbin and in the surrounding towns. The tragedy had furnished the ardent preacher with the opportunity and the text with which to reach the consciences of men who stood in need of warning. Such an audience could have been gathered in no ordinary way; and up to that time there had been no man ready and able to stand up, with a wood-pile for a pulpit, and set before a set of drunken reprobates a true picture of themselves and their destiny. It was a scene upon which one might imagine the angels of light and the powers of darkness to be looking as upon a life-and-death struggle; for the future of Quabbin and of its people was to be decided there. Would this courageous young man, who stood up before that angry crowd, be able to reach their hard hearts, and gain entrance for the Spirit of God? Time was to show.

There was another "warning" which made a deep impression, though not in such a dramatic way. The tavern-keeper was injured by a horse, and died within two or three days. He was not intemperate, but not a church-member, and, aside from his business, was universally liked. Personally, he could have had little

sympathy with the weak or dissolute people who frequented his bar ; on the other hand, he could not have
had any very warm feeling for the minister and the
leading church-members who were attacking his business, and arraying the moral forces of the town in a
way to push dram-sellers and dram-drinkers into out-
lawry. The reader will remember the story of the clock
in a former chapter. The minister was not superstitious, and perhaps never heard the story ; but he
believed and taught the doctrine of a particular providence, and the sudden death of the tavern-keeper was
" improved " with such earnestness that all the town
rang with the echo.

Gradually the church became a body of total ab-
stainers ; and the drinkers, even if they were not scan-
dalously intemperate, were pushed out of the communion. Before many years there was a great change
throughout the town ; the incorrigible were removed
by death, and others took warning. The town-meetings became more orderly ; the riotous trainings were
given up, and an old race-course, two miles down on
the river road, was planted with corn. After a time
some who had been excommunicated came back, chast-
ened and penitent, and lived godly lives ever afterward.

At these blessed changes all Quabbin smiled with
greener fields, and with brighter and purer homes.
Even the wild north-west district became peaceable, and
the sessions of the justice's court were rare. The
dwellers upon the outlying farms, though necessarily
poor on account of the sterile soil, and not highly educated then or since, became Sunday worshippers and
good citizens. The old savagery was going by.

This was the work of the second minister, for the

impulse came from him, but it was not wholly accomplished in his day.

At the beginning he was almost alone, and year after year there were new efforts to be made ; and at each successive reform that was attempted new opposition and new enmities were aroused. The long struggle was wearing to a man of delicate frame and high-strung nerves.

Among the last to be civilized were the youths from fourteen to eighteen years of age. At the singing-schools, spelling-schools, and other festive occasions, these young savages spoiled the pleasure of all decent people. It was their chief object in life to organize rebellion in the district schools; and where they were numerous it was not uncommon to have a change of masters once or twice in the course of a winter session. They would make the master's life a burden by incessant annoyances, such as filling the house with smoke, by putting a cover on the chimney, or they would lock the door and bar the windows ; and sometimes when he attempted to punish them they would set upon him with fists and feet. The masters were commonly young, and often were college students who were compelled by poverty to leave their studies for a term to earn something. The pay was so small that no one would think of making teaching a profession, and there was usually but one session of thirteen weeks in the year. The master of a country school received from seventeen to twenty-five dollars per month and his board ; about the wages of a farmer's hired man. The board was ambulatory, — a week with this family, and a few days with that, according to the number of pupils in each. "Boarding around" gave a teacher a lively impression of the generosity and meanness of mankind, and of the comforts and discomforts of country life. The temptation to linger where there was good fare and the company of pretty girls was generally irresistible.

A night in a fireless bedroom, with the glass below zero; a morning wash in water from a basin crusted with ice; toiling to subdue a thick shock of hair that crackled with electricity; struggling with buttons while red fingers were stiffened with cold — such were the experiences of many a young teacher. After breakfast he might have to walk, perhaps half a mile, perhaps a mile and a half, through mid-leg depths of new-fallen snow, and would be fortunate if he found the school-room warm. If the fire had not been made, as some-times happened, it would be necessary to cut the wood that was provided,— often green, sappy, and ice-coated, — and wait for a slowly struggling blaze. Then he might have to wedge loose windows to keep out the draughts that cut the faces and necks of those sitting near them as with icy knives. Then pupils were to be given turns near the stove, alternating with banishment to the Arctic corners, where the chattering of teeth was constant and irrepressible. Until the roaring cast-iron stove became red, and the ice-frescoed windows were thawed, any effective study was impossible. Often the softening process occupied most of the morning hours. It will be believed that the task of the master, and of the pupils, was hard enough when good humor, good order, and obedience reigned. What maddening per-plexity was it when a herd of half-washed fellows, with wild hair, bovine odor, and unpardonable boots, broke every rule, destroyed the indispensable quiet, burned offensive matters upon the stove, expectorated over the floor, "sarsed" the master, delighted in making the tall girls blush, and the small ones cry, and finally precipitated a "row," which made further exercises impossible! Sometimes, however, they met their match. There was a school from which two masters had been "bounced," which was nevertheless conquered and held in order by a resolute young woman without the least trouble.

This teacher had the good sense to begin without laying down any rules, so that she was not obliged to take up a breach of order unless it were worth while. Her demeanor showed that she was courageous, and that, if she were to be overcome, it would have to be done by brute force; and the boys did not like the idea of laying hands upon a woman. She was busy with instruction, instead of lecturing upon order; and, as she had the gift of making lessons interesting, the pupils had not so much time to meditate upon mischief. The very first case of deliberate misbehavior was taken in hand, and the offender soundly punished then and there; it was not her policy to wait, so as to allow of a combination of evil-doers. By firmness and tact the turbulent fellows were guided into studious habits, and any outbreak was checked without a moment's delay. After two days of her rule the behavior of the school was such as to leave little to be desired.

The summer schools, also of three months, were kept by young women, generally inoffensive and unburdened by useless learning, and were composed of girls, and of such barefooted boys as were not wanted for hoeing corn or in the haying-field. In such schools no deep problem disturbed the simple course of things. It was a matter of rote in reading and spelling, with a skimming of "joggafry," and some cautious ventures in arithmetic, the teacher taking care not to get out of soundings.

There were other conditions in school life of which it is impossible to write, and which cannot be recalled without shame.

The sweeping was done by pupils in turn, as was the making of a fire. Dusting was unknown. The desks were profusely and deeply sculptured. The walls were adorned with charcoal sketches, and the ceiling with bosses of *papier-maché*, made adhesive by small jaws, and then projected from popguns. For drinking, there was a tin dipper, and a pail containing water brought from a neighbor's house. How nauseous the taste of that warm fluid after standing some hours in pine wood ! and what a smell came from the greasy tin dipper !

The state of the schools, it is evident, was wretched, and the standard of attainment low. Farmers' sons had practically but three months in the year for their education, after they were old enough to help in field, pasture, or garden ; and the limit of age was rarely favorable to the boy. In the centre district, boys attended the summer schools as well; but few of the female teachers were strong in arithmetic, or had the power to give lagging pupils the needful *shove ;* and the summer tuition was, even for girls, a feeble and profitless thing. The methods of instruction were inefficient in all the schools, for the teachers generally were qualified neither by knowledge or experience. The range of study was limited, and, with the constant changes, no real progress was possible. Classification, too, was out of the question. Forward boys of eight

and ten years of age might be in a class with great
hulking fellows of from fourteen to nineteen, — belated
scholars who were striving to escape from utter illiteracy, with but few months in which to accomplish it.
A small classmate would prompt them when they came
to hard words in reading, and help them with their
"sums" in arithmetic. They were untidy, odorous of
the stable, coarse, honest, and dull, — void of mathematical and literary sense. No other scholars fretted
over their tasks as they did, and few to so little purpose. In return for help, they protected their small
friend from the bullying of boys who were larger and
more pugnacious, and now and then brought him a
"broadsword" or a "signifide" apple. The broadsword apple tasted like a rich pear, and the other name
was a corruption of "seek-no-further."

The use of the ferule was so common that under
some masters the best-intentioned boy could not escape
having his hands blistered every few days.

When a boy's early schooling was under so many
different teachers the results were mere shreds and
patches, and progress in a right line was out of the
question.

There was never any provision for higher education
in the public schools. Grammar was a mechanical
exercise without any living links with literary composition, and with small effect on daily speech. The study
of geography was limited to a short treatise with wholly
inadequate maps. The chief instruction was in arithmetic, especially in Colburn's "Mental Arithmetic,"
which was far superior to the books which have succeeded it.

Those who had aspirations for learning got some

light now and then from the private " select schools " opened for a term by needy college students, to which pupils were admitted on payment of a fee. Several masters came to Quabbin sixty years ago, whose memories live in the hearts of grateful youths. In such schools one might begin the Latin grammar, read Æsop's Fables, and study algebra and elementary geometry ; and though the term came to an end all too soon, the good seed was sown which in later years might spring up and bear fruit.

With suitable books it is seldom difficult for an intelligent pupil to master a science unaided. What is needed is the impulse, and that generally comes from an intellectual superior. Very little book-knowledge is acquired, either in a school or university, which could not be acquired at home; so that if the purpose of the higher education were merely to store the memory with facts, the costly machinery might be dispensed with. But the true use of education is to fit a man for action in his chosen sphere, for which special training, readiness, and energy are necessary ; and for this it is of the highest importance that the pupil should receive a forward impulse from contact with some great mind. The chief benefit of a university is that in its staff of teachers and lecturers are included some of the eminent scientific and literary men of the age. More than one naturalist has been determined in his vocation by a current of electric energy from Agassiz. That man's personality was so grand, and such influence radiated from him, that pupils were kindled by his enthusiasm, and ever afterward looked upon the world of animate nature with anointed eyes. Whoever had Child or Longfellow or

Lowell for guides in literature, acquired keen perception and a taste for the best models. A mathematician or astronomer who in his youth met Benjamin Peirce, owed an incalculable debt to that man's soaring imagination, no less than to his masterly expositions. A university that has no great men deserves to have no students. Grinding in classics and mathematics can be done anywhere.

No contact with the immortal energy of genius, it is true, was possible in Quabbin; but the masters of the occasional "select schools" brought something of the light of letters and science into that region; and though the bearers were young and inexperienced, and the light came in fitful and feeble flashes, it was a brilliant change from immemorial dulness and gloom. Pupils who had once begun with liberal studies could never thereafter be content with the old ideas. The glimpses they got of the world of letters and art drew them on irresistibly. The "mute, inglorious" masters in Quabbin and elsewhere probably never knew what a movement they had begun, nor recognized the fact that they were instruments in the hands of Divine Providence in civilizing a State.

While a few pupils — a very few — were reaching up toward the light, the great number were settled in half-civilized ignorance, steeped in bucolic thought and manners, and cherishing an immitigable prejudice, verging on hate, toward all youths with superior attainments and honorable ambition.

Any attempts to improve the public schools were stubbornly resisted; first, by those whose instinct is to oppose all improvements, in which class a great many well-meaning persons are included; secondly, by those

who objected to any increase of taxes. Any talk of
new methods of teaching stirred up old-fashioned people ; and it was obvious that, if schools were maintained the whole year, a much larger sum of money
must be raised.

The second minister visited the schools in every
district ; but inspection, though it may reveal defects,
does not always cure them. He, with the leading men
of the village, made strenuous efforts to begin the
work of reform ; but the country people, aided by the
dead weight of the " otherwise minded," were too
strong. Nothing of any consequence was done while
the second minister and his immediate successor remained. It was some years later that Horace Mann,
Secretary of the Board of Education, accomplished the
work which has immortalized him, — the reorganization
of the school system of Massachusetts; and it was in
the reign of the fourth minister of Quabbin that the
new influences were felt in town-meetings, and the
public schools began to be more worthy of an intelligent people.

The second minister had some disagreeable experiences. The knocker of his front door was often violently pulled at night, and when the door was opened
no one was found there. One day, being a member
of the town committee, he visited the central district
school. A boy young in years, but precocious in mischief, continually disturbed the recitations, and was
daring as well as fertile in expedients. The teacher
seemed unable to keep the little rebel quiet, and at
last the minister was incautious enough to take the
matter in hand. " Come here ! " he exclaimed, with his
eyes fixed on the offender. " Is the examination to be

interrupted by one bad boy?" The boy came into the
centre of the room, unabashed, and grinning like a little fiend. "Are you going to be quiet?" No answer
but a defiant blaze in the eyes. "Will you promise to
be quiet?" The boy was still silent, but glowing with
temper. The minister took him by the shoulder, made
him crouch upon the floor, and then, taking his chair,
put it over the boy so that he was enclosed as in a
cage, and sat down in it. The fact that he could be
easily put under a chair showed how small the boy was.

The lessons were resumed, and there was quiet, except for occasional "snickers" at the grimaces made
by the imprisoned culprit. The minster's hand hung
carelessly at his side. Suddenly he started up and uttered a cry of pain that rang through the room. The
boy had bitten the back of his hand until the teeth met
under the skin, and blood was flowing profusely. The
hand was bound with a handkerchief, and the minister went on with the examination as if nothing had
happened.

There was another trait of savagery lingering in the
time of the second minister, — the wanton destruction
of animal life.

The brooks were full of spotted trout; dace played in
the swirling water below the dam; perch and roach
swarmed in the pond; in the deep and dark places were
horn-pouts and eels; snouted pickerel lurked under the
lily-pads of the cove; and in the West Branch suckers
were speared on spring nights by the light of pitch-pine
torches. Nothing so exciting or picturesque attends
the young fisherman to-day; the streams are mostly
depopulated, and it is sad for the boys.

Moreover, in the old times, minks and musquashes

frequented the rivers, and were caught in steel traps, baited with sweet apple. Expert sportsmen snared pigeons and partridges, and shot foxes, squirrels, rabbits, and wild ducks. There were still plenty of raccoons, and there were traditions of wild turkeys, but few, if any, of the latter remained sixty years ago.

The wanton destruction of life took place in the annual "bird-hunt," generally set for Old Election Day. These were matches between sportsmen ("hunters") of adjoining towns, a specified number on each side. A day was appointed for the meet, to which each party brought a bag of heads of birds and of small wild animals. The creatures might be shot anywhere, but only by members of the company, and on the day or days specified in the agreement. Each large head was counted for so much, according to size and rarity ; the smaller kinds were simply numbered. When the bags had been counted, the losing party entertained the winners at a supper and frolic at the tavern.

When the bags were opened, and the heaps of severed and bloody heads were spread out, it was a sight to make a compassionate man heart-sick. There were heads of bluejays, squirrels, song-sparrows, coppercrowns, orioles, minks, scarlet tanagers, woodpeckers, foxes, robins (red-breasted migratory thrushes), yellow birds, swallows, finches, crows, red-winged blackbirds, wood-pigeons, whippoorwills, hawks, kingfishers, woodchucks, eagles, owls, wagtails, herons, snipe, dippers, woodcocks, wrens, and many more ; every bright eye closed, and the beautiful plumage dabbled and crushed. It was sad for any reflecting person, even a child, to think of the blotting-out of so much beauty, the extinction of gayety and song. And these hundreds

of bright creatures, the joy of field, garden, and orchard, were blown to pieces with shot, to decide which of
two sets of young ruffians should pay for the supper
and drink of the other.

This destruction had gone on for years, and the
region for many years after was not peopled with birds
as in the early days. Longfellow had not then written
"The Birds of Killingworth;" but the humane spirit of
that poem was innate in the heart of the minister, and
he was unsparing in his denunciation of the useless
cruelty. For once the popular feeling was with him,
and the "bird-hunters" found they could not pursue
their sport without reprobation. All kindly people,
even children, mourned the gay minstrels; farmers
missed their friends, the destroyers of worms and
insects in garden and orchard; and most young men in
time were ashamed of the slaughter. Nearly all birds
in Massachusetts are now protected by law, but public
sentiment is a still more efficient safeguard; and in
Quabbin public sentiment on this subject was in great
part the creation of this tender-hearted parish minister.

CHAPTER XVIII

PREPARATIONS for the day of rest were begun the day previous. Farmers made ready, as far as possible, for the care of their animals, and got a supply of wood into the house. Women baked bread and prepared dishes, and attended to darning and mending, so as to leave a minimum of work for the holy day. In the evening the Bible lessons were studied, and at the close diligent children were allowed roasted apples and fresh cider.

In the morning the household was called betimes, and all underwent an energetic scrubbing; after which special attention was paid to frizzled hair, and putting on clean clothing. After breakfast came prayers, and then the young people read the Bible or studied the Catechism for an hour. The morning service was at half-past ten o'clock, and lasted until noon, or a little later. Afterward came the Sunday-school; and the lessons, with comments and exhortations, occupied an hour. Then those who lived near enough to the meeting-house hurried home for a lunch. This consisted of bread and milk, or bread and butter, with a section (60°) of pie, and some fruit preserves or apple-sauce. Those who lived at a distance brought luncheon baskets, and ate (solemnly) sitting in their pews, or, in cold weather, by the stoves. The afternoon service began at two o'clock, and lasted an hour and a half. Then there was a dispersion, for there was nothing more to be done at the meeting-house. Not that the observances were finished, by any means. Arriving home, each family sat down between four and five o'clock to a repast, mostly cold, the principal dish having been cooked the day before. At seven o'clock there was a prayer-meeting in a hall illumined by smoky whale-oil lamps ; and this continued according to circumstances, — such as the number and length of the prayers, and the fervor and fluency of exhortation. There was no rule of procedure, and a favorite hymn might be expected at any moment.

All the intervals between services were occupied by religious reading or study. When night fell at last, it seemed to children that the bell in the meeting-house steeple had been ringing all day ; that services had been going on all day, and that they had read the Bible and Catechism all day.

Besides the four Sunday services, there was regularly a week-day prayer-meeting, and a monthly concert of prayer for missionaries. At this last there were read extracts from the *Missionary Herald*, — being experiences among the heathen, — and the hymn, " From Greenland's Icy Mountains," was always sung with great enthusiasm.

The people, old and young, were kept well up to their work. In strict households Sunday was the most fatiguing and the most wearisome day of the week. It was not in any sense a day of rest. The constant reading of the Bible by young people, as a task, destroyed all sense of its power and beauty ; and in committing texts to memory the only care was for accuracy; the meaning and the lesson of a passage were scarcely thought of. There was not much relief when children turned from the Bible and Catechism to the Sunday-school library, a dreary collection of books kept at the meeting-house. The most interesting of them were lives of missionaries, as they sometimes gave a whiff of spicy breezes, and glimpses of the romance of the East. The most odious were biographies of precocious saints, sickly little sages of the nursery, who, because they had weak chests and spindling legs, renounced ball and marbles, and all the sports that healthy children love; who talked of ecstatic experiences and divine mysteries as glibly as if repeating the multiplication-table; whose consumptive looks indicated a speedy release from a world in which they could never have borne a manly part, and who each left behind a lying tombstone and a pretentious memoir for the affliction and disgust of hearty boys.

Bible lessons were studied in the Old Testament quite as often as in the New. It was a grave error. The calmly indecent stories of Hebrew patriarchs, prophets, and kings were shocking to the moral sense of the young, who had been led to suppose that justice, truth, chastity, and honor were in the past, the present, and future the same. The biblical plainness of speech was revolting. Many things were stumbled upon which were not understood, and in regard to which a suspicion was as gross and foul as the fact. A generous-minded youth naturally sympathized with the dusky Hagar and her son, and not at all with the bigamist Abraham and his hoity-toity Sarah. Like the Quaker boy (Whittier), he could not see why David was a man after God's own heart, since he was a man of war, and full of treachery also. He could not make it right that the Lord permitted a lying spirit to beguile Ahab to his ruin. In fact, there were no end to the queries, the doubts, the incipient rebellions, and the flushes of secret shame that came to an ingenuous boy who read the old books in course, and never skipped a chapter, verse, or word.

Much is said of the license of speech in the drama, but there are few plays in any language which contain as much that is shocking as certain portions of Scripture. The influence of these narratives, never meant for babes, is especially baneful, because it forms base associations in minds wholly unable to relegate things to their proper places.

A boy in Quabbin, some six or eight years old, was being questioned by a spruce country damsel upon the story of Rahab the harlot. "Please, miss," said he, "what is a harlot?"

There were often brambly experiences also in questions bearing on the Jewish ceremonial law.

When the first day of the week, instead of being a blessed day of rest, is occupied with hard work, without a moment for a bright thought or memory ; when fancy cannot spread a pinion, and the eyes are forbidden to look for beauty in bird or flower or cloud, that day is the darkest of the seven. The days, on the contrary, that are not "hallowed" are relieved by buoyant spirits, and "labor meets delight half way."

It is freely admitted how much the people of New England owe to Bible study and religious training ; the noble result cannot be gainsaid ; on the other hand, many got such a surfeit of Scripture in youth, that it required years to bring them to a just appreciation of the poetry of the Psalms, or of the philosophy of Job. A similar distaste was produced by the use in schools of "Paradise Lost" for exercises in parsing. The inspiration and splendor of Milton's lines, after they were pulled to thrums in grammatical analysis, departed forever.

It would be easy to make a book of selections from the Old Testament for the use of families. The material is abundant, and of the highest ethical and literary value. The details of the ceremonial law, and some of the bald narratives, might be left for mature readers. The perusal by children of the entire series of works as they stand is a source of evil for which there can be no compensation.

In those early days the meeting-house was warmed in winter by two box stoves set under the choir gallery, but the greater part of the interior was as cold as the adjacent graveyard. Those who sat in the pews near the pulpit were almost at freezing-point. The rigor was tempered for women by the use of little foot-stoves, which were square boxes of perforated tinned iron, fitted in wooden frames with wire handles, and containing small iron basins filled with live coals bedded in ashes. The foot-stove had not much warmth, but it served as a foot-stool, and kept the feet from freezing. The men disdained such coddling, and boys were supposed to be tough ; but on cold days both men and boys found that the sermon had a great many heads.

In summer the coolness of the audience-room with its window-blinds was grateful, but many hard-working men furtively dozed, suspiciously nodded with sudden, periodic jerks, and sometimes openly snored. To be sleepy during sermon-time was the universal failing. It was the custom on warm Sundays to carry sprigs of caraway, or dill, or coriander, to nibble at when the eyelids inclined to droop. The efforts to ward off slumber were frequently amusing. A man would often be seen straightening up with a surprised look when his wife gave his elbow a nudge. One old man had what appeared to be an automatic alarm. The top of his head was bald, and the long, thin hair at the sides was brought up and braided in a central line from crown to forehead, and, along with it, a something that looked like a shoestring. When he nodded, the ends of the string fell in his eyes, whereupon he waked and restored the equilibrium. Twenty times in the course of a sermon his head fell, and as often the dangling ends of string restored him to consciousness and propriety.

One fat old fellow, who looked as if he would dissolve if he should venture to take a very hot bath, seemed always in luxurious ease, since any part of him would have served for a cushion. His chin ran over in successive folds upon his cravat, and the cravat was pressed down to his broad chest. Meanwhile, his eyes softly closed, then half opened, then closed again, as if controlled by some interior spring independent of his volition. He slept while the choir sang, slept standing while the minister prayed, and seated while he preached. It was not only his soft-lidded eyes that slept; he slept all over; and the gospel rain fell upon him soothingly, like showers on the roof of Morpheus. It was averred that he had been seen to doze in the slow and closely packed procession that moved down the aisle at the close of service.

The old fellow with ugly and grotesque features, he

whose head rested for so many years against the white pilaster in the west gallery, did his share of sleeping. The sharp and grave lawyer sometimes nodded. In fact, there were few, except the deacons and certain alert and sprightly women, who did not occasionally close their eyes after " sixthly."

The choir numbered twenty or thirty persons, and was recruited every two or three years from the sing-ing-school. There was a peripatetic master who came at intervals to teach beginners in the science, and to revive the interest and practice of the choir. Like most singing-teachers, he had one of those perfunctory voices which sound equally forced in every part; but his violin was true and smooth. He brought out fairly good results as to harmony, but of individual culture not much could be said. Soldiers are best drilled in squads ; singers, singly. He had fiery red hair, and the keen enthusiasm which generally goes with it, and for some reason was called "Colonel." It was his custom in his schools to vary the monotony of psalmody by the occasional singing of English glees, such as "Here in Cool Grot," "Hail, Smiling Morn," and others, dear to many generations. Had one of the choir in Quabbin been asked to sing a solo, the attack, the tone, or pronunciation, might have caused a smile upon a cultivated audience ; but when the choir was in prac-tice, the solid harmony was not without charm. It was in set hymns, like Dr. Madan's "Before Jehovah's Awful Throne," that the best effects were produced. The choir had its ups and downs ; singers fell off, either from age or removal ; practice was given up, and the style wofully deteriorated ; then would come a new session of the singing-school, and, at the end of it, the colonel would lead the new flock of warblers into the meeting-house, and the people were astonished with the renewed life and energy.

In remoter times the choir-leader used to give the pitch from his tuning-fork with a brusque " fum, s'la fum-m-m ! " Afterward there were instruments, — a flute, bass-viol, or double bass, and sometimes a grumbling bassoon or serpent.

The choir-leader was chosen or approved by the parish committee ; and one Sunday when a change had been agreed upon, but, by inadvertence, notice had not been given, both the old leader and the new stood up when the morning psalm was read, and gave out each a different tune, and sounded a different pitch. For a moment it seemed that the frame of the universe had cracked ; but the small boys thought it was great fun. The new leader, however, had the battalion with him, and the voice of the superseded and crestfallen one was speedily drowned.

Sixty years ago the music of the Bridgewater Collection, or Billings and Holden, was in fashion, and there were frequent fugues, noisy and perverted reminiscences of Händel, or at times the quaint and melancholy strains of Ravenscroft, or the reverent and tender harmonies of Purcell. After that came the Boston Academy's Collection, consisting of music drawn from all schools and all sources, including gems from operas, symphonies, and sonatas; but all was tempered into monotony by cutting out any melodic ornaments, and by suppressing anything rich or inventive in harmony. It was a joy to sopranos to find melodies without surprises, that would sing of themselves. And the basses, too, all knew what was coming ; their track

was no more intricate than that of a blind horse in a
mill.   Every chord was of the tonic or dominant, with
simple mutations and invariable terminations.   Such
tunes had a cloying sweetness and even flow.   Then,
again, the people of Quabbin had not heard operas ;
and melodies from " The Magic Flute," " Don Gio-
vanni," and " Der Frieschütz," were for them as sacred
as any.   Zerlina's "*Batti batti* " became indissolubly
linked with the hymn, " Saviour, Source of Every
Blessing."   As Wesley said, " It was a pity that the
Devil should have all the best music."

The leading soprano was a broad-chested and buxom
young lady, with a clear and powerful voice, and little
delicacy in phrasing.   She used to run over the high
places, especially when she had a line to sing alone,
like a kid capering over the rocks.   The voice of the
leading contralto was as soft and deep as the cooing of a
dove, — a rich and velvety voice.   When the two women
sang a brief duet,— the chorus waiting to pounce in
with a roar, — what a silence in the meeting-house !
The contralto held her own, without undue self-asser-
tion ; the soprano took the lead with a dash, like the
enterprising person she was, and the people generally
agreed that she was a great singer.

As time went on, although there was less rudeness in
performance, there was a decline in the character of the
compositions sung.   The old music was not refined and
not artistic, but it had spirit and energy ; while the
adaptations which followed were frequently vapid and
colorless changes rung on few notes, with harmonies so
little varied, that the impression made by one tune was
just like that of every other.   The jerky Zeunerian
school had sway in many places, but never prevailed in
Quabbin.

On the whole, modern church music has had the slenderest relation to art. There are well-defined schools of sacred music, — those of the Catholic and Episcopalian services, and the old German chorals. Each is adapted to the required uses. But the patchwork, hurdy-gurdy school, full of reminiscences of operas, negro-songs, revivalist melodies, and instrumental gems, with all manner of unsaintly associations, and with no fitness to any devout sentiment, — that "school" which has long infested New England and Scotland, should now be put under ban. It is not artistic, and it is a libel upon the worship of God.

While upon the subject of church music, it may be well to mention a memorable concert given in the meeting-house during the reign of the third minister, to celebrate the conclusion of a singing-school. A large number of new faces appeared in the singers' seats, for the school had been fully attended, and the drill had been long and thorough. The colonel was in great form, and looked proudly over his forces, among which were some half-dozen instrumentalists.

There were the usual anthems and choruses attacked and carried through with stormy bravery, in which the sopranos and basses (as usual) made the lion's share of noise. There was an instrumental interlude, in which two flutes had the leading part, partly because the hesitation of the other players sometimes left uncertain gaps. And there was an English trio, " When Time was Entwining the Garland of Years," in which the deep, cooing notes of the contralto were delightful. The sensation of the evening, however, was caused by the performances of a double-bass player, imported for the occasion. His legitimate work was excellent, for he produced firm and smooth tones, but his pride was in showy solos. A space was made for him in the front of the gallery, so that he could be seen by the audience below. Those who remember Bottesini will have an idea of the effects produced. The hero of this concert was not a Bottesini, but he was clever and comic. He covered all the range of expression from the serious to the ridiculous, and he imitated various animals, as well as instruments from a great organ-pipe to a picolo. Now and then would come out a passage of masculine beauty, followed by strange staccato leaps and plunges, or by swift, fantastic, or chromatic scales.

In action he was a pantomimist; his body, head, and arms were in violent motion, like those of a jointed manikin in exercise, as he bent far over his huge in-strument, or darted up while his fingers tripped along the strings. The muscles of his face were tense, and he plied the stout bow like a fiend. If hearers were moved to admiration at times by a grand strain, they were sure to laugh the next minute at some tripping dance music, or rasping eccentricity, or grotesque imi-tation; but he always closed with harmonics, round and fine as the highest notes of a violin. Before he finished, he had captivated everybody, and the sense of comedy so overpowered the sacred associations of the place, that there was a universal ripple of laughter.

A tumultuous chorus, with plentiful hosannas, brought the concert to an end. The boys thought the show better than a menagerie.

The minister sat at the communion-table in front of the pulpit, and appeared to be satisfied with himself and the concert. But the deacons were deeply stirred, and they had a short conference as they were leaving the meeting-house. Said Deacon Rawson, —

"Fer my part, I feel 'shamed fer hevin' seen an' heered these goin's on, thet I du."

"An' in the haouse o' God, tu," added Deacon Dodge.

"It hed a'most orter be new dedicated," suggested Deacon Holyoke.

"Haow could we look fer a revivle o' trew religion ter foller sech a monkey show?" said Deacon Rawson.

"An' thet air colonel," said Deacon Dodge, "told us 'twas ter be a pufformance o' sacred mewsic, same ez the singin' on a Sahberday."

"Ef a soul was called on to give its 'count ter-night, arter thet foolishness!" said Deacon Rawson with a solemn sigh.

Deacon Holyoke observed tentatively, "Them air fleutes played well."

"But why," asked Deacon Rawson, "sh'd they go a-tweedlin' like two sparrers, flutt'rin' an' tumblin' raound one nuther in the air?"

"The beatenest thing," said Deacon Dodge, "was that feller 'ith the big bass-viol."

"An' ter call thet sacred mewsic!" said Deacon Rawson.

"He made it beller like a bull, or squeal like a pig, jest ez he'd a min' tew," said Deacon Holyoke.

"An' ag'in," added Deacon Dodge, "'twas like a saw goin' thru a log."

"An' then," groaned Deacon Rawson, "it actilly dahnced a jig — in the haouse o' God!"

"An' he kep' a-wigglin' up ter the top o' the strings, an' then he clipper-clappered all the way daown," observed Deacon Holyoke.

"An' he didn't seem ter hev teched nothin', 'cept ez a fly might a-breshed it," added Deacon Dodge.

"An' he kep' a-bobbin' his head," continued Deacon Holyoke, "an' reachin' 'way over, an' sawin' away."

"An' them noises!" said Deacon Dodge.

"Like a pig under a gate," suggested Deacon Holyoke.

"An' ag'in, like a donkey brayin'," added Deacon Dodge.

Deacon Rawson was silently looking at his brethren with astonishment.

Here Deacon Dodge looked furtively at Deacon Holyoke, suspending a chuckle meanwhile. The thin lips of Deacon Holyoke showed the twisted corner of a smile. Deacon Dodge with averted face was beginning to grin. When he turned his eyes upon Deacon Holyoke, there was a mutual twinkle, and both laughed gently.

Said Deacon Rawson, "Deekin Dodge, be yeou *la'afin'* 'bout this disecration o' God's haouse? An' Deekin Holyoke, be yeou?"

"No," answered Deacon Dodge; "I was on'y a-la'afin' at thinkin' o' that air noise like a pig; 'twas so nateral," and he guffawed again.

"An' at thet air bray," added Deacon Holyoke. "'Twas ez nateral ez yeour voice." And he joined again in the laugh. "Howsever, Deekin Rawsin," he added, "what's done can't be *ondone*. An' then, the colonel don't b'long tu aour church, ner the bass-fiddler nuther."

"Wal," said Deacon Rawson severely, "the colonel orter be talked tu, so 's 't he won't du so next time — in God's haouse; an' ef nobody else won't du it, I will."

Meanwhile the colonel, purring like a great yellow cat, was having a pleasant talk with the minister, who appeared to be pleased with everything. Somehow

Deacon Rawson let the offender pass without the threatened admonition.

As Deacon Dodge and Deacon Holyoke were parting, they looked at each other for a moment, and then Deacon Dodge with a smile said, "Thet pig!" while Deacon Holyoke beatifically replied, "Thet donkey!" and they went their ways.

Said Deacon Rawson, left alone, "Wal, I ra'aly b'lieve Deekin Dodge an' Deekin Holyoke ain't a mite sorry to hev heered that fiddler in the haouse of God! Wal, I must say he *was* funny."

CHAPTER XIX

TRANSITION

THE second minister had fought the good fight almost single-handed, and would have been entitled to adopt as his own the triumphant words of the Apostle Paul. He had accomplished much, and it had cost him dear. The church was awakened from formalism, and was a moral force to be counted upon. Public sentiment was becoming strong against drunkenness, and the sale of spirits had ceased, except at the tavern bar, — a place to which few respectable men ventured to go for drams. The meeting-house bore witness to the general improvement, shining in fresh paint without, and newly decorated within. The advocates of better schools began to take courage, and the main roads were a trifle less stony. Altogether, Quabbin was looking up. Of course much remained to be done. It was only the dawn that appeared, not the new day. But as long as Quabbin exists, those who know its history will do honor to the memory of its brave and devoted second minister.

The strain had tried his spirit and broken his health; in nine years he was "worn out," and he resigned his charge. It might have been poetical justice if he could have remained to enjoy the grateful love of a people for whom he had sacrificed so much. The salary could not have been a temptation, as it never exceeded one thousand dollars. And then a man of decided character is always liable to wound the sensibilities of some, without being aware of it ; and, besides, he necessarily makes enemies by engaging in contests. Those whom the minister had faced with such intrepidity, and whom he had blistered with denunciation, would never have been heartily reconciled to him. No ; after the hard work of the pioneer was done, some milder-mannered and more plausible man, with not one-half of his intellectual and moral worth, would succeed to the territory he had gained, and be far more popular. "Other men have labored, and ye have entered into their labors."

An incident which occurred early in the following reign (Minister III.) showed that the fire of old enmity was still smouldering and not extinct. There had been prosecutions for the illegal sale of liquors, and for kindred misdemeanors, which were bitterly resented by those implicated ; and there were threats of reprisals which would make the people of Quabbin "sorry " But no one thought seriously of the menaces, since angry people often bluster without any fixed purpose.

One Saturday at dusk, a man who was passing the meeting-house observed something unusual, — a small square of darkness in the light-gray foundation. He went nearer, and saw that the end of one of the oblong stones had been pushed in, leaving an opening under the building. A train of thought shot like lightning through his brain, and he went away for a lantern. Upon returning he made an exploration, and found within easy reach a fuse, and beyond it a cask. Keeping the lantern well away, he succeeded in pulling out the cask, and found it contained gunpowder! The horror of the discovery made his good sense forsake him; instead of leaving the cask, and cutting or wetting the fuse, and setting a watch to catch any one who should come to light it, he carried away the evidence of the intended crime; so that Quabbin never knew, and we shall never know, if the purpose was to blow up the meeting-house when empty, or to destroy the congregation during worship, or simply to give the people a fright. Charity would favor the latter supposition, but a malicious or even a murderous intention was not wholly improbable. Before that time the temper of the evil-minded had been shown by breaking gates, poisoning pet dogs, shaving the tails of horses, and the like; but putting powder under the meeting-house was such a mixture of murder and sacrilege, that society was agitated to its centre.

Extraordinary stories flew about, growing bigger by distance. Thus, the meeting-house had been blown up with five barrels of cannon powder; the steeple had leaped into the air, and fallen point downward into the pond, and remained sticking there; a man had been caught with a lighted torch, creeping toward the cavity; a fuse had been found partially burned, and providentially extinguished; a well-known criminal had been seen prowling about under the horse-sheds; and a wagon (presumably for the escape of the Guy Fawkes after the explosion) had been seen waiting in the edge of the village.

The discoverer was at first extolled for his prompt action, and afterward as much blamed for not having allowed the plot to mature, so that the criminals could have been convicted.

The minister, as usual, was calm and smiling, as if entirely satisfied with himself, and with the protecting care of Divine Providence.

This minister (the third) was in early middle-age when he came to Quabbin. He was a man of good stature, agreeable presence, and fluent speech. His voice was high-pitched, musical in quality, and with a touch of sympathy that was very effective. His engaging manner and unfailing good-humor won for him universal favor. It is never easy to estimate the depth of religious conviction without knowing the depth of character, but this man's habitual talk was upon divine things; and in his pastoral visits, as well as in public worship, his sweetly phrased counsels, the tender personal interest shown, and the grace of every utterance, made him appear either the saintliest of courtiers or the courtliest of saints. This is not to intimate conscious hypocrisy, for, as far as he knew himself, he was perfectly sincere.

The first minister's sermons had been methodical if unpretending, and were carefully composed, and garnished with biblical quotation. The second had generally written his discourses, but, as we have seen, he could preach extempore upon a fitting occasion. The third seldom took any notes into the pulpit. He was endowed with such a gift of speech that the love of God and man flowed from his lips in smoothest and finest sentences, and in tones of melody that won most hearts. Some few hearts were not won, because they were associated with hard heads.

But the first sermon after the installation was highly successful, and almost triumphant. The new minister was the only man heard up to that time in Quabbin who had the courage to stand up without a scrap of paper, and who could pour out a discourse, without hesitation, in varying modes of warning, entreaty, and ecstasy ; while in exalted moments a fine, tremulous thrill winged his words, giving them a carrying quality, like the notes of a great violoncellist. For some days nothing else was talked about.

A well-known old grumbler said, " Yis, sartin, 'twas a wonderful power o' words ; they come right 'long, 'thout no coaxin'. Fact is, 't he skimmed over his sub-jec' like a sled goin' daown hill on glair ice. But 'pears ez ef he's laid aout a good lot o' work tu du. The sleepy brethren is to be waked up ; the cold ones is to be het, an' the slack an' feeble ones is to be stiff-ened up. Then the prayer-meetin's is to be med lively, an' he's to go f'm haouse ter haouse, lookin' arter the stray lambs o' the flock. An' he's goin' to hev the schools réformed ; jest ez ef readin', writin', and rethemtic wasn't allus the same; jest ez ef ye c'd réform the multiplication-table, er the A B C's, er the Lord's Prayer ! Howsoever, we shell see. Ef talk c'd du it, I sh'd think *he* might, fer he's a master hand thet way. But wut is 't he means 'baout buildin' a railroad to the fix'd stars ? The railroad daown yander — I hain't seen it, but they tell me 't 's bolted to the airth. Yer *can't* send a injine out 'n the air to a star."

" That was a figure of speech," suggested the school-master.

" Figger o' speech ! 'Pears to me 'twas jest foolish-ness, an' no figgers 'baout it. Yer can't figger on a thing thet ain't common-sense. 'Stid o' talkin' 'baout railroadin' ter the stars, I sh'd think he might a gin us

more Scripter, an' less pooty talk. I felt jest like one
o' my oxen when he hain't hed nuthin' but dry straw
to chaw on. He didn't once tech on the decrees, ner
the elect, ner the lake o' fire an' brimstun."

"But," said the schoolmaster, "there isn't time for
everything in one sermon."

"Wal, 'fore I heerd him I sh'd a-said so tu ; but, I'm
thinkin', he hed time fer 'baout all he knows."

This was almost the only discordant note in the
general chorus of praise. The minister's earnestness,
his beautiful voice, and unexampled fluency, had made
a strong impression.

In the course of an impassioned appeal, he had, perhaps inadvertently, made use of the boldly figurative
language of which the aged grumbler complained.
The passage is here given in a somewhat simplified
form, for it would be difficult to follow it in all its luxuriance of phrase.

"Ah," said he in his high-pitched tenor, "the time
will never come in this mortal life when Christians will
find nothing to do for the blessed service of their Divine
Lord and Master. When the enlightened and reani-
mated church shall have gathered into its bosom all the
people of this land, and the folds of the stars and stripes
shall be mingled with the lilies of the Prince of peace,
waving over a regenerated country ; when our foreign
missionaries shall have dethroned the man of sin, and
carried by assault the strongholds of Mohammedanism
and of Paganism ; when the ancient people of God shall
have seen the light of the Star of Bethlehem, and looked
on him whom they once doomed to a shameful death at
the hands of Roman legionaries ; when the isles of the
sea shall have been cheered by the sound of sweet Sab-

bath bells, and the dusky Polynesian shall have turned from his revolting banquets of the roasted flesh of the heralds of the cross ; when in all parts of the earth the peace of God shall rest like sunlight gilding a beautiful landscape, — ah, then, my friends, even then, there will be no time to repose and fold the hands ! No ; for then the untiring servants of God will look for other and wider fields of labor ; and, if possible, they will build a railroad to the fixed stars " (very high intonation here), "so as to carry to the remotest bounds of the universe the glad news of redemption by Christ Jesus."

The minister apparently moved through the Lord's vineyard with a light heart, and cheerfully fulfilled his customary duties. He made calls everywhere, and greatly delighted women by petting their children and complimenting their housekeeping. It soon became known that he was fond of tea, and every matron hastened to make him a cup on his arrival. While he sat balancing a teaspoon, and looking too radiant for a being of flesh and blood, he had a store of sweet sentences to utter, assorted sizes and flavors, and left the household to wonder at an eloquence which never ran dry.

He visited the schools regularly, and was the most agreeable of committee-men. He listened to the lessons repeated by rote, and never stopped to test the pupils' knowledge. He always had some pleasant story to tell, and his counsels were full of encouragement. He had scarcely need to flatter, since his face and voice were the expression of compliment. Inexperienced teachers were entranced, and the boys said his talk was "ez slick ez grease." Some older pupils were dissatisfied with the lack of critical examination ; they were, a few of them, ambitious of undertaking higher studies, and longed for a helping hand, or a suggestion. Some were privately delving in Latin grammar, in algebra or geometry, and imagined that so learned a man as the minister might give them good advice ; but neither they nor any in Quabbin ever knew of what languages or sciences he was master.

Every day he was abroad, distributing smiles and kind words ; and those who lived near him often wondered when he found time to study. Among his other gifts was an unfailing memory of persons and names ; and in a little time the families were so well known to him that, upon meeting any man, he could inquire as to all the members of his household without ever making a mistake. This faculty, besides being serviceable to a public man, is the most insinuating kind of flattery. People are secretly pleased to be promptly remembered.

The prayer-meetings were more animated, and more entertaining (if the word be allowed), because they were conducted in a smoothly superficial way. There was no "deep ploughing," no searching of consciences with a probe, nothing to make people feel uncomfortable. When the minister asked a brother to "lead in prayer," it was in the gracious tone of a monarch addressing a court favorite. His exuberant style had been naturally imitated ; and the extempore prayers and exhortations of the younger brethren became as flowery as Solomon's Songs. The deacons, however, were too fully committed to old forms and usages to change.

After the lapse of some months, the deacons had a conference quite by chance. It is proper to state that the selection of this minister was not so much due to them as to certain rich and influential men who had no official relations with the church.

"Wal," said Deacon Rawson, "the minister's sartin a ready preacher, an' he keeps a-hold o' the congergation pooty wal, so fer; but haow long he k'n go on 'thaout some new idees, thet's what I don't see. A mill don't grind out flaour onless ther's grain fallin' inter the hopper."

"He hain't never preached any doctrine," said Deacon Dodge.

"He hain't raoused th' impenitunt," said Deacon Holyoke.

"An' haow could he?" asked Deacon Rawson; "it's all one thing over 'n over. It's my 'pinion 't he's a good man ez fer's he knows, — ez fer's he *kin* be. But I'm afeard he hain't no depth tu him, an' no ra'al feelin'. All them fine words don't signify nothin'; he k'n reel 'em off any time. Ef he was ra'ally teched himself, he might tech other folks. His words don't come aout f'm his h'art, but aout f'm his head, an' ther' ain't no grip to 'em. He don't feel 'em no more'n a pump feels the resh o' water in its inside."

"Ain't ye a leetle hard on him?" asked Deacon Dodge.

"Wal, p'r'aps I be," answered Deacon Rawson. "But I was a-thinkin' 'baout a funeral wher' he wan't a mite o' use, — wher' he'd better ben away. It was Levi Pomeroy, y' know, who struck the axe in his ankle; an', ez he was full-blooded, the waound mortified. There wan't no savin' him onless they'd a-cut off his leg at fust. 'Twas an occashun when a ra'al minister 'd 've gin some *livin'*, airnest word o' comfort ter the widder, an' some solumn warnin' to th' impenitunt, he bein' took off so suddin. But the minister, he jest went to spinnin' silk rib'ns; an' when I looked at the widder I c'd see she was jest sick an' tired o' his flaowery stuff, 'thaout a mite o' ra'al feelin' in it, an' her pore h'art achin 'so, — jest a-thustin' an' hungerin' fer divine comfort."

"Wal, naow yeou speak on't," said Deacon Holyoke, "I felt much abaout so tu the fun'ral o' young Thompson. 'Twas a bright, pooty boy, ye know, — his flesh an' bones mangled at the saw-mill, an' he fetched home dead to his mother, an' she a-shriekin' so's ter be heered a mile. Wal, naow, arter sech a shock ez thet, what comfort was't tu his mother at the fun'ral ter hear them strings o' words thet don't mean nothin'? He might 've improved the solumn occashun for her good; an' he might 've showed he'd a man's heart inside of him. Any man thet knows what a mother feels thet's lost her boy in thet orful way, ef he trusts to nater, he'll say sunthin' 'live an' tender an' comfortin'. Seemed 's ef I couldn't set still while he was sayin' them smooth things."

"We ain't goin' ter hev another man soon ag'in like him that's left us," said Deacon Rawson. "Talk abaout feelin'! When *he* went tu a fun'ral he was a trew comfort tu the 'flicted; an' he was a terrer tu evil-dewers tu."

"No; we didn't know when we was wal off," said Deacon Dodge. "We hed orter kep' him."

"Wal," said Deacon Rawson, "I s'pose I've said tu much. I talk tu yeou 'cause we've an int'rest in the church together. Them that was the means o' gittin' this minister here 'll naterally stan' by him. It's aour dewty to wait, an' in dew time the Lord 'll show us his will."

The county newspaper, a few days later, had a report of a "powerful sermon" delivered by the minister of Quabbin at the county town, where he had appeared by an exchange of pulpits. After the preliminary, the report was in these terms : —

"It is seldom that the eloquence of the pulpit has received a nobler or more brilliant illustration than in the discourse on last Sabbath morning at the East Church. The Rev. Mr. ——, of Quabbin, preached to a crowded and delighted audience from the text, 'Let your light so shine,' etc. After touching lightly upon the various points of Christian duty, the orator (for so we must call him), arrayed the vast fields of enterprise upon which the church is now engaged, and pictured the triumphs that are to follow when the kingdoms of this world are become the kingdoms of our Lord; when the valiant missionaries of the cross shall have stormed the strongholds of the false prophet and of Paganism ; when the islands of the sea will be wakened on Sabbath mornings by church bells, and the cannibals cease their shocking banquets of human flesh ; when wars shall cease, and men shall beat their swords into ploughshares, and their spears into pruning-hooks; and all men shall be united in the love of God and of each other. 'Then,' asked he with a significant emphasis, 'do you think it will be time for the faithful servants of God to fold their hands and enjoy their well-earned repose ? No ; they will be looking for new worlds to conquer. They will even try to build a railroad to the fixed stars, so as to carry to the uttermost bounds of creation the news of the unsearchable riches of Christ Jesus our Lord.'

"We do not pretend to quote this magnificent outburst *verbatim ;* but the impression was so strong that some of the sentences are a part of memory henceforth and forever. The high note struck by the reverend gentleman at the end of the first clause of the last sentence was absolutely thrilling. The people of Quabbin are to be congratulated in having set over them as minister a man of such extraordinary and irresistible eloquence."

View of the western part of Enfield. From the Donald W. Howe Collection, courtesy of the Society for the Preservation of New England Antiquities.

Enfield Center in the late nineteenth century. From the Donald W. Howe Collection, courtesy of the Society for the Preservation of New England Antiquities.

The Mill Pond at Enfield. From the Donald W. Howe Collection, courtesy of the Society for the Preservation of New England Antiquities.

Bulldozer pushing down the Old Stone Mill, Enfield, 1939. From Metropolitan District Commission contract books, courtesy of Secretary of State's Office, Archives Division.

Blowing up the Enfield Dam, 1939. From Metropolitan District Commission contract books, courtesy of Secretary of State's Office, Archives Division.

CHAPTER XX

HOW THE TWIG WAS BENT

The Puritans laid down rules of conduct for an ideal society of believers. Such a society as they conceived of could not have held together for many generations, for some of their precepts and customs were contrary to the primal and ineradicable instincts of human nature. In practice, as has been intimated, they placed work at the head of the Christian virtues. There was some reason for this; and, with occasional rest and amusements, the condition of daily labor would not have been intolerable. But they imagined play to be foolish, if not sinful, and the longing for recreation on the part of children to be one of the symptoms of that total depravity which infected every son and daughter of Adam. This, in their opinion, was part of the "foolishness" which was "bound up in the heart of a child," and which only "the rod of correction" could drive away. The model boy was he who toiled from Monday morning to Saturday night, and asked for no diversion. In many families this strictness was not observed; a good many boys had reasonable liberty, and were proficient in sports and games, including ball-playing, swimming, and skating; but very few were allowed to grow up in idleness.

As the housewife had enough to do indoors, and

the husband followed his regular work, the odd jobs, called "chores," fell to the lot of the boys. These were the care of poultry, horses, oxen, cows, sheep, or pigs, weeding the garden, cutting and carrying in fire-wood, doing errands at the store, shovelling paths in the snow, and numberless other things. On farms where animals were numerous, there were usually hired men to attend to the barns, but there were, nevertheless, always tasks for the boys.

The ultra-pious, who went about sighing, and ex-claiming, " This is a dying world!" insisted upon chil-dren's renunciation of toys and games, and strove to plant in their minds the sad resolution and endeavor which had guided their own lives.   It was not an inten-tional unkindness, but rather an attempt to override or ignore the conditions and needs of immaturity.   One would think they would have been instructed by the antics of colts and calves, and by the frolics of puppies and kittens ; but the analogy did not appear to strike them, and they believed they were acting " in the light of eternity " by bringing up serious little old men.

It is obviously a lasting wrong to a boy's physical and moral nature to deny him a fair share in the amuse-ments suited to his age.   Two-thirds and more of the children in Quabbin had a reasonable time for play; but for the remnant the world was melancholy enough. Look at the life of a boy during week-days under such repression.   We have already seen how his Sundays were spent.   His week-days were scarcely less monoto-nous.   While some of his school-fellows were at play, the " good boy " was at work in the garden or wood-yard, or was driving the cow to pasture ; and when his chores were done, he was told he might read.   And such books! He never played marbles, as that was a gambling game. He never had a manageable kite, because a good string cost money, and that was wasteful. He had a sled, because that could be made useful in bringing flour and provisions ; but he was not allowed skates, and so missed the exhilaration of gliding over the ice with the joyous crowds that frequented the ponds. From an unwise caution, he was not permitted to learn to swim. On some rare occasions he found time to take a part in round ball or four-old-cat ; but, owing to want of practice, he muffed the balls as a catcher, and missed them as a batter. In fact, he never learned any game well enough to play it tolerably ; for he was expected to make a sober and godly use of his time, and was counselled to live every day as he would if he knew that his next waking were to be in the eternal world. He had a little pocket-money, but generally earned it by the hardest penance, and, in place of laying it out for " follies," he was allowed to put it in the box at the missionary prayer-meeting. A boy who cannot take part in the sports of his fellows is cut off from comradeship, and the isolation produces an estrangement on both sides, that ceases only with life.

The men of Quabbin showed the effects of unintermitted work. They were mostly well-jointed, strong, and enduring, but were heavy, awkward, and slouching in movement. They walked like ploughmen, with a slow inclination from side to side. There was no flexibility in the arms, no erectness in the spinal column, no easy carriage of the head. Had their work been varied with some light and agreeable exercise, — dancing, pleasure excursions, rowing, or the like, — they might have been equally strong, with a great gain in lightness, grace, and activity.

In earlier days the sinners had the advantage of the saints in athletics, owing in a great measure to dancing, which is a wonderful lubricator of the joints, and the parent of graceful movement. When the sinners mostly came under the sway of the church, and dances and romping games fell into disuse, then the lumbering motion became universal; humility and reverence bowed the head and shoulders, and the feet and legs drawled like the speech. The want of liveliness and of inspiriting exercise was painfully characteristic of Quabbin. A walk that extended beyond the limits of the village was unusual. To go three miles people felt obliged to get a horse from the livery stable. If a man walked five miles he was thought eccentric and pretentious. Whereas, if men, women, and children in such a village had been compelled to walk from three to five miles a day in all weathers, it would have set heads upright, given spring and elasticity to joints, made biliousness disappear, and brightened theology.

Strictly religious people forbade their children to strike a blow, whether in retaliation or defence. This was the severest trial; but boys were assured of two things, namely, that, if they were punished at school, another punishment would follow at home, and that they would be birched if they fought with other boys, even in self-defence. Now, boys have always fought, and always will; and a " good boy " who was forbidden to " hit back " was always the first one to be pounced upon, and so became the butt of small scoffers, and the victim of all the malice and mischief not otherwise employed. However non-resistance may have worked "down in Judee," it is scarcely practicable among the Anglo-Saxons of to-day.

The Puritan enjoined upon his children the duty of being kindly affectioned and helpful. "If any man ask thee to go a mile, go with him twain." A boy so brought up was liable to frequent imposition. One of them met the minister (Number III.) one day, and observed from afar his beaming face. His expansive joy was like the oil that ran down upon the beard, even Aaron's beard, and touched the hem of his garment. The boy was overwhelmed as by an angelic vision. "Sonny," said the minister, in his mellifluous tone, " I want to send word over to Brother Colman about exchanging with me next Lord's Day, and am afraid a letter by mail mayn't reach him in season. Now, I have a nice, gentle saddle-horse; and *don't* you want to ride over and take a letter to him? That's a good boy! It will be a pleasant trip for you, and, in a way, you will be doing the Master's work."

Permission was got from his parents, — who could say "no" to the minister? — and for five miles out and five miles back the boy was jounced and pounded on a hard-trotting beast, to oblige a smooth-tongued diplomatist, who had ample means and leisure to attend to his own affairs. The boy had already all he could do from week's end to week's end, and seldom an hour for play. And what did he gain by the ride that made all his bones ache? The reward of an "approving conscience," and a reputation for good nature that would invite further aggression.

To turn the other cheek to the smiter, to be generous and helpful to the point of self-denial, to regard work as a duty and blessing, to the exclusion of amusements, — these are all doctrines of the gospel. But, according to the same authority, all the lands of a town should be held in common, and all the hoards of money and goods should be divided; there should be no rich and no poor; all labor should be equalized, and all dignities abolished; the lawyer must not be called " Esquire," nor the minister " Reverend." Why were the boys given the "hard lines," when adults disregarded the fundamental condition of primitive Christianity ?

The people in ancient times were said to have been divided into beasts of burden and beasts of prey; and the classification is not wholly obsolete. There are plenty of burdens ready for patient shoulders, and there will never be any rest for the good natured. Without some firmness, and a little pugnacity in reserve, and without a *reasonable* core of selfishness, a man will play a poor part in the world as it is. The domineering and predatory, and the crafty and plausible, are always seeking for victims among the amiable and self-forgetting. It seems altogether ludicrous or absurd to think of preaching the need of combativeness and self-protection in times like ours; and probably there are few places in the world now-a-days where such preaching would not be out of place. But among primitive Christians in Quabbin, long ago, and doubtless in other small rural communities, there were youths who were brought up to be willing pack-horses, and men who were so obliging that they lived and died poor. The majority of the people there, as elsewhere, needed no counsel as to their own interests; but the gentle-natured who went forth to seek their fortunes learned to stiffen their own fibre, and take juster views of the character of the men they met in the world.

With all the care that was taken to strengthen children by holy precepts, and to surround them with good examples, it is strange that, in so many instances, they were allowed to come within reach of the baser sort of hired men. This was sometimes an influence for evil, both deadly and contagious. In an hour or in a moment an impression or suggestion might be made that would poison a whole life. Errors of opinion can be combated, and many sins can be atoned for and forsaken, but the soil of immodesty, — what shall wash it away? Can a cheek once kissed be *un*-kissed? or snow once sullied become like ermine again? The youth who has received the hint of sensuality will never again be the pure-hearted youth he was. Those coarse and vicious farm-hands, and strolling journeymen mechanics, were the curse of some families in Quabbin, and the elders seem not to have suspected it. A father should take heed what sort of a man he admits, even for a day, under his roof.

Few young people know under what severe discipline their fathers were brought up; and to many this account of the trials of youth in Quabbin long ago will appear exaggerated and bitter. But, in fact, it is wholly within the limits of truth. While the recollections of boyhood in the old time include much that is bright and beautiful, there are also impressions of an unreasonable austerity, which are as painful as old wounds. When such impressions are recalled, it is not at the dictate of resentment, but with a view of contributing to the stock of human experience something that may be of service in the education of to-day.

CHAPTER XXI

QUABBIN LOSES AND GAINS

In the part of the village near the dam there were formerly mills and shops that have mostly disappeared, though some dozed into forgetfulness and became store-houses for rubbish. Few of the present inhabitants remember that there was once a saw-mill near the bridge, and opposite to it a tall cotton-factory whose booming "picker" strove all day to drown the noise of its neighbor, the strident saw; or that there was a pros-perous (and odorous) tanyard on the river-bank; or that across the bridge there was a linseed-oil mill, whose high stone wheels turned gayly round each other, like a pair of stout and tireless waltzers. All these disap-peared long ago, and left no trace. In a dull yellow building there were, sixty years ago, dozens of bright, clicking machines, complex as watches, which set wire teeth in leather for carding, and acted as if with human intelligence. The card-factory was the foundation of two fortunes; but the business at last went elsewhere, and the building became as melancholy as the town's poor-house.

In the North Village also, various small industries were in progress. There was a little shop where pearl buttons were made from oyster shells; one in which shoe-pegs were cut by ingenious machinery from fragrant birch-wood, most odorous of native woods ; also a saw-mill, a machine-shop, and a trip-hammer forge for making hoes. None of these now exist. The rights of the water-power were absorbed by the cotton-factory ; while in the lower village they were divided between the factory and the grist-mill.

While all these mills and shops were flourishing, the stores were prosperous, new dwellings were built, and new faces appeared on Sunday in the meeting-house. Quabbin appeared to have what in modern times is called a "boom ; " but it was not to endure.

The town reached its maximum of population, and the height of its prosperity in business, about the beginning of the third minister's term ; but with its prosperity or decline neither he nor his predecessor had anything to do ; the business and population were affected by circumstances unforeseen and inevitable. The deterioration began when the State's trunk line of railroad passed a dozen miles on one side. A great many years later a railroad was built through Quabbin, but it was too late ; its business had been tapped and drawn off, never to flow back. Railroads are sometimes feeders and sometimes drains. Other things were co-operating in the decline, and no shrewdness or activity availed. When flax-growing ceased, the pair of great mill-stones had no more seed to waltz over. When the hills had been stripped of the trees of large girth, the saw-mills were no longer profitable. Against the enormous competition of Lowell, Lawrence, and Manchester, a small cotton-factory in Quabbin had not the least chance. The making of card-clothing, which had been such a source of wealth, could be better managed near the machinery for which it was designed. When "satinets" got out of favor, cotton warps were no longer wanted. One thing fell after another. For a long time the factories were idle; and it appeared that Quabbin, possibly, might some day end where it began, with a grist-mill. But latterly shoddy is made there by Canadian French workmen; and the Gallic invasion naturally awakens some apprehension among the natives. SHODDY! *Absit omen.*

Perhaps something worth while might have been done with the wasting water-power; but with un-stable tariffs, just as fatal when too high as too low, and with alien workers, — for Yankees work no more in mills, excepting " opinion mills," — the prospect of manufacturing in such a remote place was not alluring.

Let us go back for a moment to the old time. Peo-ple never knew how it came about that the three courtly and popular mill-owners, before mentioned, gradually lost their hold upon the property, and began to decline in wealth and influence.

A couple of young, active, and pushing men succeeded the three elderly, easy-going, kindly gentlemen by dint of superior business qualities. There was a slow rise of one side, corresponding with the slow decline of the other. The older party had the whole boundless (and useless) sympathy of the town's-people, who looked on at the inch-by-inch process, and anticipated the end of the drama long before the curtain fell.

After the death of the venerable mother, the son who had cared for her went away to another State. Another, he who lived upon the knoll, went elsewhere to begin the world anew. The elder and most distinguished, he of the orange complexion, whose showy house and Oriental treasures were the wonder of the village, withdrew from active business, retaining but a small share in the water-power, and lived upon the lessening remnant of his fortune. His death was the mellow sunset of an autumn day.

A circle of brilliant associations ended for Quabbin when the places of the three brothers knew them no more. Relatives from the county town, and from Boston, used to enliven the village and the country roads in summer, — charming and cultivated ladies, budding clergymen and lawyers, the usual gathering of people of leisure at hospitable country houses. After the end of the old *régime* they came no more. Neither the balustraded villa near the meeting-house, nor the ancient, sombre, elm-shaded mansion, ever knew again the gayety of former days.

About the same time a number of prominent families in the village were broken up by removal or death, and the village began to lose ground in social qualities. Among the grown-up population there was almost a dead level of dulness ; for the leading men, though intelligent, were not highly cultivated : they were good citizens, public-spirited, and often benevolent, but their strength was in making money. It came about, however, that some of the rich men conferred, indirectly, a great boon upon the community by having their daughters taught in distant boarding-schools. There were places in Massachusetts which had largely the start of Quabbin in enlightenment, and it was a great matter that this small town received a share by reflection. When the half-dozen daughters came back with some knowledge of books, and of music, with the speech of the educated world, and with notions of refinement in manners and dress, the usual consequences followed.   That is to say, every home-keeping damsel declared the talk, the dress and ways of the boarding-school graduates to be "stuck-up" and ridiculous, and then proceeded to copy them to the best of her ability.   Some of these educated young ladies were possessed of more than ordinary talents, and were proficient in many studies, including modern languages ; but, for well-known reasons, an acquaintance with English literature was not possible at that time. Unhappily they did not appear to concern themselves with the improvement of society in the village ; they had outgrown it.   In the course of time they married, one after the other, and went away ; but while they remained they appeared conspicuous, and were thought to be indifferent to public opinion.   Their hats, ribbons, laces, and gloves, and the fit of their robes, the dressing of their hair, and even their folding of a shawl, were marked by an inimitable elegance.   Reserved in their intercourse as they were, their silent example was eloquent.   Their rustic neighbors felt convicted of a whole catalogue of social misdemeanors when they learned the necessity of the exclusive use of the fork at table, and of certain proprieties and interdictions in regard to dress and toilet.   The school-mistresses were piqued to discover, as they all did in time, that in practice their grammar was habitually shaky, and their pronunciation hopelessly vulgar ; and forthwith they began to exterminate Yankeeisms like ill weeds, and to strive after pure English.

Meanwhile, the young ladies whose return had made such a stir walked through the village, and drove about the neighborhood, apparently unconscious of the existence of the people they had known all their lives. The only place of contact was the Sunday-school, in which, upon the earnest entreaty of their parents, they became teachers. The religious instruction they gave, however, was somewhat neutralized by what their pupils thought to be airs of superiority ; for divine grace does not mix well with snubbing or ignoring one's neighbor ; but it was a lesson of value to hear passages of Scripture read with pure tone and correct accent, and to observe how English may be free and idiomatic, without ever becoming ungrammatical. It will be inferred that these young women were cordially hated, or at least regarded with that mixture of awe, envy, and creeping aversion, which is more uncomfortable than downright enmity. But there they were, partly the admiration, partly the reproachful example, of their less-favored town's-folk, who, if they had read Virgil, might have justified their position in learning all they could from " the enemy."

The new influence came too late to benefit mature men and women, but it affected, however remotely, every boy and girl in the Sunday-school. It roused a passionate longing in some youths who had been dreaming of a better training than the schools of Quabbin afforded. It was an element in the general elevation of the community, which became evident in the next minister's reign.

One of these young ladies had a pianoforte, the first that was possessed in Quabbin. It is impossible to exaggerate the sensation that was produced in the village when that instrument was first heard. It was a clear, moonlit evening in summer, and the windows were open. Passers-by lingered in the street, and an admiring row of boys appeared to be impaling themselves on the fence pickets under the poplars, as they leaned forward to listen. With every group of *arpeggios*, and of florid *roulades*, it seemed to them that diamonds and pearls were flung into the air, or that catharine-wheels were shooting fiery little stars, or that a thousand bobolinks had been let loose, all singing at once ; and that fitful winds came in deep gusts to furnish the harmonies. All comparisons, however, are poor and inapt to express the effects of music, and especially of brilliant music with full chords, *when heard for the first time.* Explain to a man born blind the glories of a rainbow, and then you may give words to the sensations of those boys as they listened to the pianoforte. Many of them in after years were to hear that ill-used instrument drummed by school-girls until they were ready to execrate the inventor ; but hardly would they forget that beautiful night in Quabbin, when the tones seemed to have come from angelic harps, while the trembling leaves of the poplars in a soft *susurrus* told of the delight that spread through the air.

The society of Quabbin was at times enlivened by some bright young schoolmaster, who was working his way through college. The village matrons made much of these ambitious youths, for there were often appealing possibilities in their eager faces ; but the accomplished young ladies hesitated about wasting time upon young fellows for whom they would have to wait half a dozen years, and, meanwhile, be obliged to forego flirting, and renounce intervening chances. And if one thinks upon it, it was not equitable ; *they* were at their best, — full-blossomed, diplomaed, ticketed, and ready for the principal event of life, while the student had his course to finish, and then his position to win.

Then there came occasionally some young doctor who fancied Quabbin a good place wherein to flesh his maiden lancet, and gain medical experience *in corporibus vilibus ;* and who departed as soon as possible, to use his skill upon richer patients.

One of these might be dainty and dandified, and, as such, would be useful to young men, by exhibiting late models of tailoring and of neckwear. One might be keen, rough, and amusing, with a turn for local politics. Another might reconnoitre the ground to see if a fortune might be got with a rich man's daughter — not too plain or dowdy. But none of the young doctors remained long ; Quabbin was too small and too conservative. The people did not take to a doctor until, as they said, they had " summered and wintered " him, — which also might include starving him.

With a diminishing population, and with no leaders of mark, the town would have been insufferably dull if it had not been for the " pert minxes " who tried the patience of the old, and who were the envy and the despair of those of their own age. Every fine day there was something new in their proceedings. They made parties to climb the hills, or to row on the river, and always came back with handfuls of water-lilies or wild-flowers, besides those they stuck in their dashing Vandyke hats. They galloped along the country roads, with trailing skirts and flying veils ; and their cheery laughter sounded strangely to the sober Puritan folk. At meeting they joined in all the familiar hymns, but sat in their pews : they would not go into the singers' seats; and yet their voices had such vigor and carrying quality that the sopranos in the gallery were sometimes quite overborne.

Deacon Rawson's mind was becoming painfully disturbed. Mrs. Rawson had talked to him about "them gals' goin's on," and at length he thought it his Christian duty to see Brother Grant, the father of two daughters who were reputed to be ringleaders, and endeavor to have some restraint placed upon them.

When the deacon found an opportunity, it was not easy for him to find phrases. He had fancied himself talking with fluency, like the minister; but Brother Grant was a man of cool self-possession, and his manner, though civil, did not invite intimacy, still less intrusion; and the deacon toiled through his first sentences like a horse in a deep clayey road. Said he, —

" P'r'aps it's comin' pooty clos', tu talk tu a brother 'baout his own folks; but 'pears like 'tis a dewty — when I see — the need on't. Some o' the brethren, an' more speshily the sisters, is kinder troubled by th' irreg'lar walk an' wuldly conversashin of " —

"Whose walk and conversation?" asked Mr. Grant abruptly.

"Oh, it's all in Christyin kindness an' brotherly love," said Deacon Rawson. "Don't think I'd " —

"No need o' beatin the bush," interrupted Mr. Grant. "What is't you're drivin' at?"

"We was a-hopin'," said Deacon Rawson, "thet when yeour darters come back from school they'd set a good example tu the perrish. Ez they've hed more 'vantagiz, they'd orter let their light shine, an' be helpful to the other young folks thet hezn't hed their chahnce. 'Stid of which, they don't seem like wut they was, nor wut was 'xpected. They don't mix; an' they don't see nobody when they meet 'em. P'r'aps 'tain't surprisin', sence they was away tew or three years, an' they might a' forgot."

"Wal, deacon," said Mr. Grant, "is it a matter of discipline or reproof *for me*, that my daughters don't remember everybody?"

"'Tain't on'y thet," said Deacon Rawson. "Folks say they ain't settin' a good example in godly speech an' ways, ner in raiment; thet is, in furbelows, ribbons, an' frills."

"And have I to look after women's clothes?" asked Mr. Grant. "Do you look after Mis' Rawson's? That's a little too much."

"An' thet pyanner, Brother Grant," continued Deacon Rawson; "is it right to be a-playin' dahncin' toones in this ere dyin' wuld? Would yeou be willin' to go to the jedgment-seat right arter hearin' thet clatterin' o' wires, an all thet whirligig mewsic?"

"I don't know that we can choose what we would be doin' when we're to be called to our last account," replied Mr. Grant. "I mightn't wish to go to the bar of God right from a pig-killin'; but you wouldn't say I should do without pork and sahsidge? But, Deacon Rawson, you don't know about the piano. Suppose you and Mis' Rawson come over to-morrow in the afternoon? P'r'aps you'll find the piano's like a good many other things, — good or bad, accordin' to how it's used."

After some parley Deacon Rawson said "he'd see ef he could git his folks to 'gree tu it." It was odd that the term "folks" was often used even when the speaker meant only his wife.

At the time appointed Deacon Rawson stepped down from a solid "thorough-braced" wagon at Brother Grant's gate, and helped out his portly spouse. They went in solemnly by the front door, and were received with simple and charming cordiality. The daughters were "on their good behavior," and were tastefully dressed, without anything to offend censorious eyes. The guests presented a sufficient contrast. The deacon was tall and gaunt, with grizzly hair, small and deep-set eyes, and a long, straight nose, depending from the slenderest attachment at the forehead, and broadening like a trumpet. His legs were thin, and his shoulders were bowed. He *looked* like a narrow-minded bigot, but much of his expression came from his training and experience. When Mrs. Rawson took off her "calash," of green silk arched with rattan ribs, which looked like an inharmonious elliptical halo, there was displayed a tufted turban of lemon-colored batiste, resting upon folds of plain black hair streaked with gray. This was an ornament so imposing as to suggest the head-gear of an Oriental prince. But when she was unswathed from her wraps, the straight lines and sombre color of her robes repelled any association with the affluence of the East. She was round, though not *fat;* her cheeks were dusky red, and a film of down rested on various ivory-tinted curves. The popular judgment of her was that she was "good, but slow." She had no children, but looked motherly and kind.

Mr. Grant was a bit of a diplomatist, and had arranged his programme in advance. He went and opened the piano, a small "square," with turned legs of mahogany, and said to his daughters, "You know I have invited our friends, the deacon and his wife, to

hear some music.   Suppose we begin with 'Hamburg.'
You have a good voice, Deacon Rawson, and you can
carry the bass.   The girls will take their two parts, and
I can sing the tenor by tiptoeing a little."   With slow
and even time that noble tune, based upon an ancient
choral, was fairly well sung : —

> "Kingdoms and thrones to God belong,
>   Crown him, ye nations, in your song."

The close and solemn harmony was well sustained
by the piano ; and it was a wholly new sensation to the
deacon to feel that solid support, while his voice mingled with the sweet tones of the young ladies.   The
moisture in his eyes, and at the tip of his colossal
nose, testified to the liveliness of his emotion.   Then
followed Pleyel's hymn : —

> "To thy pastures fair and large,
>   Heavenly Shepherd, lead thy charge."

Then the deacon wanted " Coronation," —

> "All hail the power of Jesus' name."

This taxed Mr. Grant's "tiptoeing" tenor, but he
managed to get through it.   As usual, this was sung
with a great surge of feeling ; and the deacon's ugly
visage became almost beautiful in his ecstasy.   " Coronation" once roused Yankees to religious enthusiasm,
as the " Marseillaise " raised Frenchmen to patriotic
frenzy.

One of the young ladies next played a romance with
a prominent melody, slow and graceful in movement.
Her tasteful fingering seemed absolutely miraculous.
After that, one of them sang an air then in vogue, " Oh,

had I wings like a dove!" There was no resisting this ; and the deacon was fairly carried off his feet.

Then the entertainment was continued with marches, *andante* movements, and variations on familiar themes. Afterward tea was served ; and the deacon and his wife were profuse in thanks and compliments.

"Ez yeou said, Brother Grant, it's jest accordin' to th' yeuse thet's made on't. Naow th' ol' colonel plays a violin with the choir tu meetin', an' it's all right ; but ef 'twas off at some tahvern fer dahncin', 'twouldn't be a violin, but a fiddle, an' be all wrong."

The "pyanner" had triumphed, and the Misses Grant, instead of being elated, were apparently softened and calmed by the victory.

They inquired of Mrs. Rawson about cheese-making, and promised to go out and see the dairy, the calves, the poultry, and all the delights of the farm.

On the way home Mrs. Rawson said, "Them mother-less gals! Folks calls them high-flyers, an' praoud ; p'r'aps they be, but I don't wan' ter see better-behavin' gals, nor modester dressed than they was this arter-noon." If she could have seen how her yellow turban looked !

The deacon was meditating, and made no reply. Mr. Grant, meanwhile, was patting the heads of his daugh-ters, promising them each a new gown.

CHAPTER XXII

COLLEGES AND MINISTERS

QUABBIN never sent many young men to college, probably less than fifteen, and, up to sixty years ago, not more than half a dozen. Within the ancient limits of Newbury, at the mouth of the Merrimac, there were three hundred graduates of Harvard College between 1642 and 1845. Three men every two years coming fresh from a seat of learning must have brought some quickening influence into the community. Even if, for a long time, the standard of Harvard College was not higher than that of a modern grammar school, the mere contact with learned men, and with the air of libraries, was inspiring and liberalizing. The list of those graduates in Coffin's "History of Newbury," a unique and valuable book, reads like a muster-roll of the leaders of Massachusetts, instead of the eminent men of a town. No other town of like population makes a better showing; and the result is instructive. Educated men create public sentiment, and, reciprocally, public sentiment increases the number of educated men. The full effects of classical culture are not developed at once, nor exhausted in the lifetime of those who receive it. They may not all become authors, — Heaven forbid! — but their existence and influence form part of the circumstances in which genius is born. Leaf-mould fertilizes flowers. The effect of a succession of educated men upon the general intelligence, and, after a time, upon the literary atmosphere of a town, is always increasing, and in the course of two centuries works a transformation.

Among the descendants of families in Newbury were the poets Longfellow, Lowell, and Whittier; the Hales, authors and editors; President C. C. Felton, William Lloyd Garrison; the lawyers Parsons and Greenleaf; Caleb Cushing, diplomatist; George Lunt, poet; B. A. Gould, astronomer; Judges Sewall and Lowell, Rev. Leonard Woods, Rev. S. H. Tyng, and many other distinguished men.

In the course of the rise of Newbury, or of whatever town has borne great sons, and, in a measure, in poor and remote Quabbin, there has been a gradual and total change in original ideas and tastes, in views of life, nature, literature, and art; but in the larger and wealthier places, which are naturally centres of thought and opinion, the change was earlier and more emphatic.

At the beginning, the eastern part of the State had the pick of the incoming settlers; and with that advantage, aided afterward by commerce and activity in business, it easily kept the lead in population, in politics, in the movements of mind, and in literary productiveness. In a handbook of literature published about twenty years ago, there are credited to Massachusetts seventy-five authors, of whom sixty-four were born or resident in the part of the State east of Worcester, and eleven in the western part. The majority of these seventy-five authors wrote in the early and middle part of the present century; very few in the centuries preceding. The inference is, that the bulk of the best literature of the State has been written in the east, and since 1830.

The population of the State in that productive period was fairly homogeneous ; and what in common phrase is called the foreign element is scarcely represented in the literature. It is admitted that the population of the eastern part is far larger, and its superior wealth has given leisure and means for literary work ; but after all due allowances, the west is hopelessly behind in productiveness. Genius may not be subject to any law of averages ; and it always appears unexpectedly, without favoring causes that can be estimated. Why Hawthorne was born in Salem, Emerson in Boston, or Bryant near the Berkshire Hills, might elude inquiry ; but most books, however excellent, are not the work of men of genius ; and the total production of books follows certain laws which can be studied.

No great historians, and few great poets, have succeeded in Massachusetts without the aid of ample fortunes ; no man who has not inherited or acquired property can spend ten or twenty years in researches, as did Bancroft, Prescott, Motley, and Parkman. Our leading poets, with a single exception, were reared and always lived in comfort. But leading poets and historians are few; and as for the remaining authors, who might have arisen in any part of the State, we ought to know why most of them arose in the east.

The answer is not far to seek. It was in the cities and large towns of the east that the movement began against the sterner features of Puritan doctrine, and it was there that the people were soonest emancipated from the rigor of a rule under which no general literature was possible. The casting off of that yoke was followed immediately by a period of illimitable expansion, of eager study, of new and joyous impressions of nature, of new and cheerful views of human life, and of new gifts of expression. What is best in the literature of Massachusetts belongs to that period of awakening, or directly followed it.

This is not to say that the credit of our literature is due to the development of Unitarianism; it would have been due to whatever system had succeeded in loosening the old bonds. The liberalizing influence has continued, and is a present moving force in many religious organizations in various parts of the State. For liberalism is not wholly, not even primarily, a matter either of belief or disbelief, provided we leave out the monstrous doctrine of endless and hopeless punishment; it is rather an attitude or condition of the soul in relation to its main points of contact, — God, our fellowmen, and the world of nature. The particular dogmas that are held are mostly unimportant; the spirit is everything.

It happened sixty years ago that nearly all the eminent authors, except of theological books, were Unitarians, while to-day they are of many denominations. There are many small towns which the liberalizing movement but slightly touched; and the western part of the State is mostly made up of small towns. The shadow of the seventeenth century still hangs over many small communities, where, with the old rigidity of doctrine, are found the impress of old customs and narrow ideas, — ignorance of general literature and science; ignorance of biblical criticism, and of the relative place of Judea in history; ignorance of the tendency of philosophical thought, and of the whole world of ideas with which enlightened men are occupied.

That Quabbin and other small towns send few young men to college is partly cause and partly effect, in relation to public sentiment. Not having been moved greatly by the liberalizing spirit, there is not a public sentiment which inspires a desire for higher education ; and there being among the citizens few who have been highly educated, the public sentiment is upon a low level. It is like a vicious circle in reasoning, illustrated by the biblical aphorism, "The destruction of the poor is their poverty."

The prevalent belief was that a college education, though desirable, was not essential to a physician or a lawyer. "When it comes ter studyin' the Scripters," said Deacon Rawson, "a man wants ter know the identicle words that aour Lord an' his disciples spoke. Some says that's Hebrew, an' some says Greek. Whichever 'tis, it stands tu reason thet a minister's got ter know them air tongues. It's a nawfle 'sponsibility, this ere breakin' the bread o' life ; an' he who doos it orter know every grain it's made on."

It was agreed, then, that a minister was to be educated, and no kind of beneficence was so general and so cheerfully bestowed, even in Quabbin, as the aid to young men intending to preach. Much was done by societies, but more by individuals to whom worthy candidates were known. The results were generally satisfactory, but there were sad exceptions. A well-constructed machine turns out uniform work year after year, but who can say that a mind will remain as it is moulded? In minds of low order there is no danger of change; and some of the noblest are equally stable, because they are so exalted and fervent that they view all things through the medium of a feeling which never cools. The extremes of intellect in a divinity class set an observer to thinking ; brilliancy and ardor at one end, and plodding dulness at the other. A reasoning mind, that perceives, compares, and weighs, must, consciously or unconsciously, take new attitudes from time to time toward any complex system of doctrines. Notice the shifting theories of medicine, the constant stretch or reversal of judicial decisions, the evanescence of philosophical conceptions, and consider if it is to be supposed that theology is unchangeable ? From the time of Arius and Athanasius the debatable ground has been fought over, inch by inch, and the orthodoxy of one century becomes the heresy of the next. The successive developments of dogma (upward or downward), from Cotton Mather to Channing, have been slowly and painfully accomplished ; and it would require a master in dialectics to state intelligibly the precise intervening stages.

Theological students, as well as others reared under the influence of Calvinism, have sometimes found themselves not masters but slaves of their convictions. In spite of a predetermination to abide in the old way, and in spite of the ardor of a faith that seeks to dominate reason, men sometimes find themselves borne on an irresistible current, and landed on an unwished-for shore. The conviction of an unwelcome truth, or what appears to be truth, comes to an ardent man with a physical pang ; and the sudden uprooting of a long-cherished belief is like the wrench of forceps on his jaw. Apostasy is an ugly word, and is generally held to include a wilful sin ; when, in fact, it may be the brave action of one who gives up friends, place, and honor, to follow where truth leads. Where interested motives do not enter, and the mind conscientiously weighs the evidence, the decision reached, however erroneous, can never be morally culpable.   To speak of a mind as *drifting*, is to use an inapt metaphor, for the sanest and most sympathetic minds may move in opposite directions under apparently similar influences. Lowell, the son of a Unitarian clergyman, *drifts* late in life into the Episcopal Church, and accepts a sequence of dogmas he had been taught to disbelieve.   Holmes, the son of an Orthodox clergyman in the same city, *drifts* into Unitarianism, rejects the Calvinistic scheme of redemption, and anchors his faith on the boundless love of God.

As in space, outside the solar system, there are no points of compass, so in pure thought, apart from dogma, there is neither height nor depth, right hand nor left ; all movement being equally free and fluid within the limits of the orbit traced by the Creator of intelligence.

This was not understood or believed in Quabbin, and a change of views on the part of one who had been assisted in college was considered a sin of the deepest dye.   So one young man found to his sorrow.   He had taken his academical degree, and then had to tell his benefactor he was not going to study divinity, because he had become a Unitarian.   The wickedness and ingratitude of that man, and his utter shamelessness! And there was no remedy nor punishment ; he had got his Latin and Greek, and it could not be shaken out of him ; and he could not be made to preach what he did not believe.   His apostasy was for some years a damper to the enthusiasm for raising up ministers by " eddicatin' " poor young men.

People did not think of the struggle and pain which the change had cost *him*, of the imputations upon his honor and manliness, of the thrusts at his indigence, of the breaking of old friendships, and the blight upon his future life. Those who knew him saw by his countenance how he had suffered. His clothes, too, were well worn, and his pockets light, when he went away from Quabbin, never to return.

Suppose he had taken the other course, and patched up a compromise with his conscience, — and it is probable that many have done so, — what a strain would it have been to do what was expected of him! to be silent before a confiding people as to the composition and modernness of many parts of the sacred canon ; to ignore science and history in expounding Genesis, with regard to the age of our planet, the duration of human life, or the origin and fortunes of the Jewish people ; to be silent upon the dual source of parts of the hexateuch, and upon the confounding of two prophets of different eras under the name of Isaiah! furthermore, to ignore the truth that morals is a progressive science, and that the dealings of God with men are probably as intimate and authoritative now as in any previous age of the world. Most well-read clergymen know the facts established by biblical criticism, and know that they are none the less true because sometimes urged with indecent rancor by scoffers.

The scientist does not blindly repose upon the theories of Kepler or Newton, but looks for any new light upon celestial mechanics. The physician admits that anatomy and therapeutics have been developed since Galen and Ambrose Paré ; the lawyer knows that Coke upon Littleton, an excellent treatise once, is mostly obsolete to-day. Why, alone among learned men, must the preacher be held to defend corrupt texts, mistranslations, and false exegesis, and to prove *that* to be stationary which has never ceased to rise and to advance with the advancing and broadening ideas of mankind? We are told that such inquiries lead to infidelity. Do we fear to know the truth in chemistry or in biology? Do we not sift every new discovery in the laws of nature? And shall we conceal what is true in regard to the Book on which the hopes of millions rest?

The experiences of those students who accepted help from individuals or societies are worth considering. In spite of all that is said about reciprocal brotherly love, and of bearing one another's burdens, there is always some risk of injury to the delicate feelings and to the moral fibre of the recipient of alms. When he comes under an obligation, he is no longer his own master. He must be ready to render an account not only of the use he makes of his income, but of his dress, his company, and all his doings. The cut of a coat, the color of a cravat, or a chance visit to the city, may upset him in the mind of his patron. He dares not purchase books, except text-books, though he may be hungering for intellectual food. Then the habit of borrowing in itself does him infinite harm. When an emergency arises, he does not shrink, as he ought, from incurring debt. Getting relief through the pockets of another, like the recourse to the pawnshop, or the use of opium or stimulants, becomes in time a chronic disease, which may take a lifetime to get rid of. Clergymen, whose income in many parishes is partly eleemosynary, are apt to become habitual borrowers. They will pay, but they will always be

pushing loads of debt before them as upon hand-bar-
rows.   By the time one loan is paid they are in straits
for another, and so they go on, forever behind-hand.
Others besides clergymen get into the baneful habit.
Trusting and guileless themselves, they are apt to at-
tribute the same generous feelings to others, and do
not dream that, with every application for temporary
assistance, they are lowering themselves before the
willing or unwilling creditor.

Bursaries and fellowships are legitimate aids to indigent students, but, unfortunately, they are attainable
by few.

Character stands for so much more than culture, that
it may well be doubted whether a collegiate course paid
for by the benevolent is worth what it inevitably costs
in moral deterioration.   A youth who has made a fair
beginning, and has a taste for classical and mathematical studies, will be sure to pursue them, even without a
tutor.   But, whatever he does, even to the renunciation
of his hopes and dreams, will be likely to be better for
him in the end than a college degree for which he has
run in debt.

Young men think that upon graduating they will
have no difficulty in speedily earning enough to pay
back with interest what they have borrowed, but opportunities for lucrative employment are rare, and, with
the increasing numbers of educated men, are becoming
rarer.   The teacher or tutor in our day seldom earns
more than enough to support himself reputably ; and
after some years the thought of his college debts becomes worse to him than a convict's ball and chain.

Besides, at three or four and twenty, his feelings as
a man, long held under guard, begin to assert them-

selves. He meets ladies of his own age, and the voice of nature cannot be always silenced. He may dally and resist; but the chances are that at some unguarded moment he will speak, and that he will find himself bound in honor to some trustful damsel, long before he has attained a position that will enable him to marry. The whole business is thorny and perplexing, and becomes all the worse with the increasing requirements in collegiate and professional courses. The Creator could not have intended that all the years of early manhood should be spent in a struggle with celibacy. There should be some way to begin earlier, and to push forward faster, the higher education, so as to bring the student into working relations with the world before the bloom of his best years has departed, and his countenance, as well as his spirit, is "sicklied o'er with the pale cast of thought." This feverish condition of adolescence is something to be seriously considered, and the youth who is looking forward to seven years of study and self-restraint should be sure that he has the will and the power to carry him manfully through to the end.

One student, a rich man's son, was rather coltish while in college; but he settled down, and became a staid and respectable man, though always of a joyous nature. He was well liked by all classes, and in later years held important public offices. From him and his family and friends came much of the influence that raised the district schools. A diverting story was told of one of his boyish capers. Whether it was owing to his "cutting" morning prayers, — the unpardonable sin in those days, — or inattention to study, or some more signal breach of college rules, he had fallen under reproof, and did not seem to amend. As his marks for lessons and conduct continued to be unsatisfactory, the "Prex" sent for him and told him he had written to his father to state that, if there were not a speedy improvement, his connection with the college would cease. The young man bowed, retired, and reflected. It was Saturday evening, and the next mail-stage for Quabbin would leave on Monday morning. That stage carried an unexpected passenger, who, on arrival, got off at the post-office, waited until the mail was sorted, then asked for letters for the family, received the one that had been written by the "Prex" to his father, and thereupon returned by stage to college, without troubling his family with a call. That pressing danger averted, he did better. The "Prex" doubtless thought the father rather indifferent to the well-being of his son.

He was probably the only college graduate of his generation in Quabbin who did not study for the ministry.

CHAPTER XXIII

MIGHT HAVE BEEN A ROMANCE

HERMAN FIELD taught a select school in the old Masonic Hall in Quabbin one summer during the reign of the third minister. He was not an ill-looking man even at first sight, but whoever looked at him twice recognized the distinctive marks of character and power. He was of good height, well proportioned, with a large head, prominent features, fair hair, and violet-blue eyes fine enough for a woman. It is needless to mention a beard in any description of the time, for everybody, except Jews and foreign fiddlers, was smoothly shaven. For an excellent reason he was not any whit too well dressed; but whatever he wore was neat, and never in the least shabby. His face could not be called handsome; but when he talked he seemed to those who met his eyes so truthful, animated, and kind, that he won all hearts.

He was at the end of his third year in college, and was on leave of absence for twelve weeks. He was born in Northern Vermont, where his father had a small farm. For his education he had had a little assistance from relatives, and had worked a few months each year, except the last, as a lumberman on some of the tributaries of the St. Lawrence. He was a strong and resolute youth, and swung a mighty axe. As he lived and dressed with the utmost simplicity, he had been able up to that time to make both ends meet. Hence it was that his hands were rather large, with stout joints and hard palms. With delicate, well-gloved hands, and a newer suit, he might have been a noted figure anywhere. His complexion, hair, and eyes were Saxon, and there was a tradition that his mother was the granddaughter of one of Burgoyne's captured Hessians.

On his arrival he had called, as a matter of courtesy, upon the minister and Deacon Rawson, both of them members of the school committee, and upon Mr. Grant. Being invited to tea at the house of the latter, he met the daughters, and was dazzled.

Although Quabbin was loath to acknowledge it, these young ladies were both beautiful. Venus herself would have been pronounced ill-favored by the damsels at the foot of Olympus or Ida, if they had imagined her supercilious and "airy." Eliza Grant, being tall, was spitefully called the "hay-pole," and Lois, who was short, was known as the "chunk." Eliza, a slender and fair girl, with dark hair and gray eyes, had a gift that is rare with her sex, a natural talent for mathematics. She was never more agreeably occupied than in geometry or algebra, and it was said she had made some progress with more abstruse branches. In her reading she preferred the logical works then in vogue, such as Paley's "Evidences," and some of the Bridgewater Treatises. Latin she liked to the extent of reading Livy and Sallust, but she did not care for Virgil. In her opinion Æneas was a poor creature, and Dido a silly widow who had not profited as she should have done by one experience. On the side of sentiment she was far from callous : she was intensely feminine and delicate ;

but this side of her nature was seldom exhibited, and scarcely acknowledged to herself.

Her sister Lois had a taste for languages. Virgil was her favorite author. In French she had followed eagerly the adventures of Télémaque, and had wept over the woes of Corinne. Besides, she had read a few cantos of the "Inferno," a thing almost unknown in that day. In her manner she was open and engaging, apparently as playful as a kitten; but in fact she was disposed to flirt, though no one would have guessed it from her innocent brown eyes.

After the tea, at which Eliza presided, and during the music that followed, Herman Field had time to take account of his impressions. He had never in his life been in a city, and had never before been seated at a table with young ladies like these. It was in vain he said to himself that they were flesh and blood like other people; for they were quite unlike any women he had met. Such nicety in the results of the toilet; such style in dress and adornment; such simple and serene manners, and unconscious ease of movement; such graceful hands; such musical voices, perfect accent, and easy, unpedantic English, — all these things came to him in a series of surprises, and made a revelation that never comes but to one who is country born.

Some French books on the table led to conversation, in which it appeared that the visitor had no knowledge of that language except what he had learned from the *patois* of Canadian raftsmen. He admitted also his ignorance of Italian, but gratified Lois by praising her favorite Virgil.

Then by inquiry he learned what were Eliza's studies, and what ground she had gone over, and he saw that she was quite in advance of him. He began to think that a college course which left out modern languages and applied science, — the chief subjects of living interest, — was a mouldy relic of mediævalism, and that a degree based on such a course was a fetish. Here were two young women who were his equals in most things, and his superiors in many, and had spent fewer years in study than he had, and they were not spectacled nor unsexed nor dried up, but fresh and blooming. He was humiliated.

But reflections upon courses of study could not long occupy his mind while he was in such company. For the first time he recognized the power that grace and culture lend, and felt that there was no creature on earth like a woman of beauty and intelligence, with refined manners and speech. It seemed to him, further, that this was a new discovery, made by him for the first time in the world.

He was prolonging his visit quite beyond the usual limit, but seemed fascinated, and powerless to depart. He persuaded the young ladies to sing again, and then rose to leave. Mr. Grant came in opportunely, and a few words of ordinary courtesy were exchanged. Then Field departed, a heavy-hearted man. The fall in his barometer was caused by a complex idea which came in a flash : —

> One year more in college.
> Three years afterwards at a seminary.
> And then? What would happen then? That was the rub.

For he was two and twenty, full of vigor, with not a fibre lax ; and his whole nature, like some perfectly strung and perfectly attuned instrument, was ready to throb with harmonies if touched or even breathed upon.

A few days later Field met Miss Lois Grant on the street, and was intending to pass with a bow, but stopped as he saw she was about to speak. After the usual greeting, she said, —

"Our cousin Harry Lyman is with us for a few days, and we are thinking of a walk over 'the mountain,' as people call our small hill," pointing to the sharp cone behind the meeting-house; "and, as it will be new to you as well as to him, Eliza and I have thought you might like to go with us."

"I shall be delighted, if" —

"If you are at liberty; yes, we thought of that, and have fixed upon to-morrow afternoon, when you have half a holiday."

"You are very kind. I thank you for thinking of me. I will go with you, with pleasure."

About three o'clock the next day, Field, with the girls and their cousin Harry Lyman, started up the North Hill. There was scarcely a visible path, and the bushes were thick and scraggy; but the ascent, though steep and rough, was not long, and the crown of the hill was soon reached. There was not a fine tree, or a spring of water, or a wild-flower on the way, — a most uninteresting little hill; but, as the party went on, the view began to broaden, and in a short time they came to a clearing and a tolerably level path.

Field had not thought of making choice of a companion, preferring to leave everything to chance, and he talked with one or another, as it happened. But after a time Lois, the younger, leaving her sister and cousin to go on before, fell back and walked with Field. It was quite indifferent to him with which of them he should walk, only he had fancied that he might be more at ease with Eliza, who was less vivacious, and nearer his own age. He was not awkward, but rather shy, and willing to let his companion take the lead.

"You spoke of Canada the other day," said Lois. "I should like so much to visit it. Most of the romance of the continent hangs about the old French settlements."

"Yes," he answered, "I have often been in Canada; it is not very far from my home; but there was no room for romance in a lumberman's life. I have been through the Chateaugay, and on the Missisquoi River, and twice I have been to Montreal, though not *as a tourist*, Miss Grant."

Lois thought there was a significant emphasis in the last phrase, and, looking at him inquiringly, said, —

"And if you did not go as a tourist?"

"With a party of men on a lumber raft," said Field simply. "We drifted slowly, and I had plenty of time for the scenery."

"Then this distinguished-looking man has been a woodchopper," thought Lois; but what she said was, "I suppose Montreal is very beautiful."

"It is beautifully situated, with a grand mountain behind it, and it has fine churches; but it has nothing of the boldness or the majesty of Quebec. Upon that high rock, and about its foot, you see what old France was, and what Britain has done with it. But I know Quebec very slightly. I never went there" —

"Professionally," said the girl with a sly look, as if to help him out.

"No," said he with a smile, "not 'professionally;' I

went to Quebec for pleasure, in a steamboat from
Montreal."

Now to hear about Montreal and Quebec was not
Lois's object; she wanted to know about the past life
of her companion. So, taking her courage in her two
hands, and looking quite demure, she asked, " Do the
lumbermen read Greek and Latin ? "

" Not much," replied Field with a laugh. " A little
mathematics, enough to tell how many feet of lumber
a log will ' scale,' is more to the purpose. But I see
how it is. You wonder how a woodchopper became a
student. Confess it now ! "

Lois only smiled; there was no need to speak, and
Field went on, —

" Well, I will tell you. I am a farmer's son. By
chance I got a Latin grammar and reader, and after I
had learned the rudiments I was no longer my own
master. I was so possessed by the desire for knowledge, that I cared for little else. To go on with my
studies it was necessary to leave home, and I was poor.
When I was sixteen I took an axe and went into the
woods, so as to earn enough to keep me at school. You
see it is the reverse of what you thought ; it was the
student that became a woodchopper. There were difficulties and trials, but not worth speaking about, since
they are passed. At school and college I worked as I
had done in the woods. It is strange when I think of
it. I seem to have moved like a young whirlwind, — but
why am I telling you this ! it cannot be interesting,
and I beg your pardon."

" Yes, Mr. Field, it is deeply interesting. I have
never had any obstacles to overcome, and when I hear
you, I fancy myself strong and brave."

A bright flush crimsoned his face as he said, "It was no bravery; I couldn't help myself; it was impossible to stop when I had my fate in my own hands, — in the shape of an axe-helve. Twice, since, I have spent some time with my old friends in the woods. This year I thought I would try keeping school for a change."

"After you had become interested in your studies, wasn't it hard to go back to a logging-camp?"

"Yes, something of a shock; some discomforts."

"And nothing to amuse yourself with."

"Oh, yes; there were sports. We caught pickerel through the ice, and we snared partridges and rabbits. But my main resource was in three thin books."

"May I ask what they were?"

"The New Testament, the Odyssey, and Horace. Pitch-pine knots were plenty."

"I really envy you. My cousin — not this one, not Harry — is quite pathetic over his hard study; but he has never earned a dollar, nor needed one. But you know the saying, *finis coronat opus*, and I suppose you have an object in view, something worth your labor and self-denial." Lois was finding her companion's quiet energy inspiring.

"That is the difficulty," he replied. "I haven't any definite object, except to get the best outfit I can. I hope to find something worth doing."

"And your parents and relatives?"

"My relatives are troubled that I don't make a choice, but I think it is better to wait to see what I am fit for."

"Perhaps they wish you to study for the ministry."

"They do."

"It is a noble profession," she said softly.

"Yes, if a man felt that he was called to it," he answered, with something like a sigh.

"I should suppose a man was 'called' to the profession he was best fitted for."

"I believe that is true ; but some hold that a minister should feel that a personal demand has been made upon him, as upon the infant Samuel. If that is what is meant by a 'calling,' I have none."

"But you have no doubts, — no trouble about doctrines ? There has been lately a painful case here." The young man blushed suddenly to the roots of his blond hair, and after a slight hesitation said, —

"No, I cannot say I have any serious doubts at present ; but suppose I should have, by and by ?"

"Sufficient for the day " —

"That proverb may have two faces. My conscience does not trouble me now ; but now I am free. Suppose when the doubt came I were *not* free ; a change of faith then might mean dishonor."

Just what this usually astute young woman had been aiming at by her leading questions she herself could not have told. Various trains of luminous thought shot through her brain, not consecutively, but commingled like the flashings of fire-flies. Now it was that her father might save this brave man from further trial and anxiety. Her father was rich enough ; still she knew he would not do it ; for he was one of those who had aided Graham, — he who had turned Unitarian. Now it was that four years must pass — and here she involuntarily made the addition of that figure to her own age. Now it was that her interest in a stranger was absurd, that her sympathy, perhaps, was of the imaginative kind, such as one takes in the hero of an unreal drama. "At all events," she said to herself, "he is a man of mind, of feeling, and character; and such eyes! He is to be here twelve weeks more; no, ten weeks only; only ten weeks. We shall see."

They had reached the part of the ridge from which they looked down upon the North Village, immediately under the cliff. At the distance it seemed only a spread of broad maple tops, with here and there a chimney or a bit of a white house showing through the interstices. There was also a factory, whose dull ugliness was relieved by the shrubbery on a brambly knoll, and then by a high hill behind it. The view is so unexpected, and so directly *down*, that it gives a singular pleasure.

Turning and looking westward, they saw successive ranges of wooded hills, that rose and receded in distant undulations.

Field sat down with his companion to enjoy the prospect, and neither of them noticed that the other two had begun to descend. After a while he rose, walked a few steps westward, and, looking down, saw Eliza and her cousin far below, getting over the wall into the road that leads around the base of the hill to the village.

"Come, Miss Grant," he said, returning to the place where he left her. "Come! They have full half a mile the start of us."

He offered her his hand, but with a gesture she declined it, and at the same time made a quick movement to rise. In a moment her face became white; she groaned, but only half-audibly, compressed her lips, and then, staggering, sank back upon the turf, and lay unconscious. Field saw that she had fainted, and knew that there was no water or other restorative at hand, and no house within half a mile. He was naturally in a great perplexity. He looked again for Eliza and Harry, and found they had turned the curve of the road, and were out of sight. One of Lois's feet was left exposed, and he saw a hole in her boot, made by the short, sharp stub of a bush near by, on which was a stain of blood. Evidently she had trodden upon this, as upon a spike, and had, probably, also wrenched her ankle. The sudden pain had caused a shock that rendered her insensible. There was no time for reflection, nor for dallying. He quickly bound her injured foot and ankle with a handkerchief, and, taking her up carefully, carried her like a child down the long slope of the pasture to the road. He never knew how he managed to get over the wall with his burden. The burden had grown momently more precious, and in all his veins "the eloquent blood told an ineffable tale."

He placed the girl upon a grassy bank at the roadside and waited, hoping that some vehicle would pass on its way to the village. None came, and he again took her in his arms and was walking on, when she opened her eyes. They were dazed with surprise, and then wild with terror. "What has happened? How dare you? Put me down, I say!"

"Dear Lois," he said gently, "you fainted from the injury to your foot and ankle. There was nothing to be done but bring you down the hill."

"I will walk," she said with wounded dignity. But when he lowered her from his arms she could not put her wounded foot to the ground, and he was obliged to save her from falling.

"You had better sit here on the bank," he said; "some one may come with a wagon."

He assisted her to a comfortable seat, and stood at a respectful distance. Meanwhile the girl wept, — sincere, maidenly tears; and, between physical pain and offended modesty, she sobbed like an infant.

Before long a wagon came in sight, and the girl, naving been lifted into it by Field, was tenderly carried home.

The injury to the foot and ankle, though painful, was not very serious, and it soon yielded to treatment; but there might be impalpable effects more lasting.

Eliza was usually amiable and sympathetic, but on this occasion, after the doctor's visit, she was quite acrimonious in her colloquy with her sister. Said she, —

"The village people will all be talking of your accident, and they won't spare you."

"What can they say?"

"They will hint more than they will say. They may intimate that a girl might be willing to sprain her ankle, just a little, to be carried in a young man's arms."

"Well, sister Eliza, let *them* say such mean things rather than you."

"I suppose," said Eliza, with a little nervous laugh, "that your hero availed himself of the proximity of a pair of lips."

"Eliza Grant," said Lois with indignation, "I shouldn't answer the insinuation, for my part, but it touches a man who would be too proud to defend himself, however much he felt hurt by it. So, let me tell you that a father couldn't have been more tender to his child, nor an angel nicer to a nun. I am ashamed of you! I know no more of Mr. Field than I have seen to-day, but I think there are few men like him."

"He has a zealous defender."

"He needs none."

"And why did you possess yourself of him, in place of Cousin Harry?"

"You have always 'possessed yourself' of Cousin Harry before."

"Yes; but I might have wished to talk with the schoolmaster to-day. What had you to talk about all the afternoon?"

"He told me something of his past life."

"And his hopes for the future, perhaps."

"Not one word."

"When a man becomes confidential as to his history, it is generally a prelude."

"To a declaration, you mean. Well, my kind sister, let me tell you that no word of love, or even of friendship, was spoken."

"Then all your arts were vain."

"I used no arts."

"O sister, you are known. You look innocent, but you are sometimes 'spidery,' as I have heard you confess.

"If I am ever 'spidery,' it is toward foolish creatures who deserve to be caught. Mr Field would make any 'spider' forego her instincts, and become a vegetarian. You can try him for yourself when he comes again."

"Thank you, sister; our experiences would not be equal. *I* wouldn't sprain my ankle, not even to be carried in arms by a father, or — what was it? Oh, yes, — or an angel."

Lois turned away her head, too much annoyed to

continue the conversation. It was unusual for her sister to show such irritation. There was a *possible* cause, but she did not like to assume it.

After the accident to the "chunk," tongues were busy and eyes were on the watch ; but Field, who had learned from the doctor that the accident was slight, simply left his card at the house, and then kept aloof, that there might be no ground for gossip. Mr. Grant was not the confidant of either daughter, and he naturally was silent.

There are things that cannot be undone, and the arms that had held Lois Grant would not forget the pressure of the form they had enclosed. They had held heaven for a minute ; the thrilling sensation attested that ; whether the heart was engaged was another matter. Field was resolute not to put himself again in the way of temptation ; yet some disturbing influence was all the time confusing his points of compass as he walked, as if his way home were not toward his one-story boarding-house, but in another direction.

Six weeks passed, and he had not called again ; Lois and Eliza had counted the time. Had he been as artful as he was guileless, he could not in any other way have awakened so surely their curiosity and interest. I say "their," because Eliza had proposed that when he called she would look a little closer at the paragon. But he kept away from them, and yet made no calls elsewhere ; so said the gossips, and they knew.

Three weeks passed, and there remained but one more. He began his farewell calls with the minister, who was very affable. Learning that his visitor had some thought of studying divinity, he broke out into an eloquent discourse in his finest phrases, upon the duty and delight of serving the Master, and suggested that even when the whole world had been converted, and the souls of all men were kindled with divine love, the enthusiastic Christians would seek for new worlds to conquer, and would even try to build a railroad to the fixed stars, so as to carry to the remotest bounds of the universe the blessed news of Christ's redemption.

Of any practical suggestion as to the completion of his studies there was not a word. With a charming smile the minister bade him farewell.

After calling on Deacon Rawson and the young doctor, who had, as he said, "reduced the luxation of the joint" on that fateful day, Field thought he must at least leave a card with the Misses Grant. Much agitated in fact, but outwardly calm, he called, and was shown in. Miss Eliza, as it happened, was out of town, and Lois alone received him. A great joy and a great fear fell upon him together. He seemed to float in air, and words came which he had not sought; so that his manner was easily confident while his knees were shaking, and his phrases were neatly turned while he did not know what he was saying.

What he had been thinking about during the nine weeks since he had carried that charming girl in his arms he could not have told. But there were indications of a struggle; his studies had been neglected; he had been moody and silent; and his landlady had told a neighbor that he had become "amazin' differkilt abaout his vittles." But now he thought he was calm. On one point he was immovably determined, and that was not to approach her, but to leave an ample cool space of air between her sphere and his own. Moreover, he would not speak to her except in the ordinary language

of civility. There was but the slightest reference to
the incident that for half an hour brought them so near
together. He was nervous, like most persons acting a
part, but carried himself fairly well. She had half expected some tender words, and wondered at his indifference or singular self-command. Their conversation
was void of all interest, mere banality; yet both were
giddy with excitement. He saw that the scene was
becoming painful, and rose to take leave; and she,
stepping frankly forward, held out her hand. As he
took it, their eyes met; and in an instant — neither
could tell how it happened — in an instant her head was
against his breast, and his arms were around her neck.
The movement was not consciously his.

Then, with a sudden effort, and with something like
the cry of a lost soul, — if souls ever cry audibly, — he
seized her hand, kissed it passionately, tore away from
her, while a flood of tears came from his eyes, and left
the house.

He was gone; he had not uttered a word of love,
and he had not kissed her lips or cheeks. He was a
more inscrutable problem than ever.

Herman Field should have returned to college, but a
new resolution seized him. He packed his trunk to be
forwarded, and, with a light hand-bag, set out on foot
northward on the very evening of the close of his
school. He was, like Bunyan's Pilgrim, in haste to
leave the City of Destruction. Nothing could detain
him. He walked till midnight, and slept in a barn,
then breakfasted at a farmhouse, and went on. So for
two or three days he pushed forward, until he came
upon a route where stage-coaches passed; and by that

line he was carried within a few miles of his father's house.

How he was received by the family, of which he was the idol and the hope, need not be told. After the embraces and the kindly inquiries that follow long absences, Mrs. Field said, —

"Herman, we've some ruther bad news. I'm 'feared Uncle Parkman won't help ye no more, 'thout yeou make up yeour mind ter preach the gospel."

"Why, what's started him in that direction?"

"Ther' was a 'vangelist come along, an' got a-hold of him, an' told him thet all his money b'longed ter the Lord, an' thet he (uncle) was on'y the steward; an' thet ter help edicate a lawyer or doctor was wastin' the Lord's treasure. The end on't was, he made uncle promise thet ef you didn't 'gree to preach, the money should go ter him (the 'vangelist) fer some young man he knows."

"As well as he knows himself, I suppose. Well, dear mother, don't be troubled; I've had three years in college, and that I am sure of. If I don't get any more, I must try to do the best with the education I have. We won't trouble Uncle Parkman. But I say, mother, where's Susy?"

"Wal, Herman, you wasn't to know abaout it, but I s'pose it 'll hev ter come aout. She's ben over to Burlin'ton."

"In Burlington? What is she there for?"

"Goin' tu school. She said she couldn't bear to hev the edication all on one side o' the haouse; so she went over ther' jest arter you went away. She has come home now an' then, but she's ben t' school most a year."

"And when is she coming home?"

" The school was shet abaout a month ago, but she wanted to stay a leetle longer fer her music; an' this last month she's ben doin' nothin' but play the pianner. Her mother's t' git one fer her."

" Mrs. Gilbert buying a piano for Susy! why, it's fairly snowing and hailing wonders! But you don't say when she is coming."

"No; wal, it's naow 'baout five o'clock, an' I sh'd think yeour father 'd naterally git here by six."

" And father has gone for her?"

" Yis, with Mis' Gilbert's wag'n, for aourn ain't a very good-goin' concern."

That was the longest hour Herman Field ever spent. He almost counted the minutes.

At length the wagon-wheels were heard; and he rushed out of the house, hatless, and met the party on the green plat in front. There was a quick "Hullo, dad!" and then Susy was helped, or rather lifted, out. The greeting for the " dad " would keep. He held the rather frightened girl in his arms, she wondering at his impetuosity, and gave her uncounted kisses. Then he held her at arm's length, and looked at her. Then he took her again in his arms and kissed her.

" I'm fairly 'shamed o' yeou, Herman," said his mother. " Du let the gal git her breath. Yeou tumble her abaout jest 's ef she was a cosset lamb."

" Absence makes the heart grow fonder," thought Susy, as she shook herself free from her lover's boisterous caresses. Evidently he had not been flirting with girls down in Massachusetts, but had kept her image always bright in his heart.

The end of this little romance is reached. Susy Gilbert had grown up to be one of the brightest and sweetest of women, even in silent comparison with a nameless person in Quabbin ; and she had developed tastes and aptitudes which were to make her the companion and the pride of an educated man. She had been under refining influences at Burlington ; and she was to return for six months or a year to continue her studies.

Field taught the district school for the ensuing winter, and later, having a solid knowledge of mathematics, fitted himself to become a civil engineer. Uncle Parkman's money went off by the hands of the evangelist ; also various earrings, brooches, and finger-rings, contributed in a moment of religious frenzy by admirers at a farewell meeting. Mrs. Field said of the evangelist, that "she didn't know rightly about his convarting sinners so's ter hev 'em stay converted, but he was a master hand for preachin' jewlry off'm saints."

Field continued his membership in the church, but never regretted the choice he had made of a profession, nor his hurried departure from Quabbin.

CHAPTER XXIV

THE CIDER—MILL

ABIJAH CROMBIE'S cider-mill was somewhat off the main road, upon a bank that sloped toward the river. The outlook from the front of the mill in early autumn was delightful to those who can see beauty in simple things. There was a broad meadow with natural inequalities, never tormented by cultivation, covered with a second growth of thick, dark grass, flecked with white and golden blossoms, and dotted with tall plants resembling spirea, but classed ignominiously with "weeds." Along the farther margin was the familiar ragged fringe of alders, through which was seen at intervals the shining blue-black surface of the river, placid at this point, and lazily moving in dim wrinkles and swirls. So inky was the water one could hardly imagine it to be the same stream which whitened over the dam, and played with the brown and yellow stones in the rapids near the village.

The narrow lane which passed the cider-mill led down to a wooden bridge that spanned the river, — a skeleton bridge made by some carpenter unskilled in geometry, a bridge which confounded lines, whether parallels or perpendiculars, and which appeared to have crouched on all fours, so as to let the cattle cross on its back to the hill pastures opposite, on the side of Great Quabbin.

The lane was bordered by zigzag fences, in the corners of which were brambles, plumes of golden-rod, pink spikes of hardhack, burdocks, with leaves like elephant's ears, and all sorts of useless luxuriance. Leaves were beginning to fall, and the lane seemed to have been carpeted with stuffs from Persian looms for the cows to walk over.

On account of its situation upon the slope, the mill had two stories in front, and one in the rear. Carts were driven in from the lane to unload apples at the upper level, and then taken around to receive barrels of cider at the lower. The mill might have been called a shed without hurting anybody's feelings. Many of the sheathing boards and shingles were split, or warped, or loose ; and little of a burglar's art would have been required to open the rickety doors, fastened by wooden latches and pins. The building had never been painted, and its rough sides had the tone of soft gray, which is so pleasing in pictures, and so melancholy in fact.

The upper story was a receptacle for apples, from whence they were poured through an inclining trough into the grinding-mill below. The visitor who entered upon the lower level saw a pair of upright wooden cylinders, placed near together, and revolving in opposite directions, so as to crush the apples drawn in between them. Teeth upon one cylinder fitted into holes in the other, to facilitate the crushing. The power was supplied by a horse travelling in a small circle, and moving the lever which turned the motor-wheel. The machinery was of the rudest sort, wholly of wood, but easily managed, and efficient. The pomace fell into a large shallow vat (presumably clean), and was scooped out by wooden shovels when a form was made up to be pressed. The form was simply arranged. A sheaf of clean straw was spread out evenly upon a platform, which was grooved with channels, and placed directly beneath a large perpendicular screw depending from a solid frame. Upon the layer of straw the pomace was spread like a boy's jam ; that is to say, considerably more jam than bread. Then a second even layer was spread at right angles to the first ; then more pomace and more straw, until the pile reached a height of two or three feet. A coping board was placed upon the top, and blocks were laid upon it. Then the great screw was turned with long wooden levers, and brought down upon the blocks, very gently at first, so that the pile might retain its consistency, then harder, until the last drops of juice had trickled out.

If the apples were carefully picked over, excluding those that were rotten or wormy ; if all parts of the mill, including cylinders, channels, vats, shovels, and straw, were scrupulously clean ; and if the barrels were well-seasoned and sweet, the cider was certain to be pure and palatable. There were many *ifs*.

Two boys, twelve and fourteen years of age respectively, who had been fishing at the bridge, and were carrying home a pickerel and a hornpout, lingered at the mill to get a sip of the cider, and to watch the operations. All boys were delighted to suck the running juice with straws. They were not too dainty as to the cleanliness of the process, nor could they often be deterred by mischievous suggestions as to the flavor of wormy fruit. Of course the fluid was not intoxicating, but when taken too freely it was apt to work them woe.

Mr. Crombie's hired man, known to everybody by

the name of Dick, was turning the screw by means of a stout hickory lever; and his puffy good-humored face, of a uniform pink, was overspread with a gently oozing perspiration. He knew the boys well, and their relations with him were of the most friendly sort.

"I thank you very much for the neck-ribbon," said the elder boy to Dick; "I wore it at the examination, and I shall keep it for Sundays."

"'Twan't nothin'," said Dick, "but you know I allus liked yeour father, an' I wanted yeou ter look ez smart's any o' the boys. A bit o' black ribbin don't cost much, an' I hev it in my heart ter du a good deal more fer ye, ef I could. Jes' be easy on the cider, 'Ratio," addressing the younger lad. "Mr. Crombie don't mind the vally on't, ef he *is* close, but I don't wanter see ye doubled up, ez ef ye was a worm on a fishhook. Don't take no more'n six or eight leetle sucks, an' then wait a spell, so's ter see ef it ain't goin' to give yeour innards a twist."

"Why does the minister say folks oughtn't to drink cider?" asked Horatio. "It doesn't make *boys* cross, nor their noses red."

"Boys drink it sweet, afore it's worked," answered Dick. "Yeou boys may git a stummick-ache, but, till the cider's worked, it hain't no stingo."

"What's 'stingo'?"

"Stingo's sperrit; sunthin' like rum. Arter cider gits old an' hard, it makes folks drunk, an' it makes 'em bad-tempered tu."

"How does apple-juice get spirit in it?" asked Eli, the elder boy.

"Jes' by fermentin'; it's changed somehaow."

"Couldn't the fermenting be stopped?"

"Not altogether; but ef ye put a pint o' mustard seed in the barril, an' hang in the bung-hole a string 'ith bits o' isinglass, an' then bung it up tight, 'twill be clear in twenty or thirty days, an' 'twon't hev tu much stingo. But, Eli," continued Dick, "don't yeou never drink no hard cider, nor nuthin' thet hez sperrit in't. Take warnin' from me. I was 'counted a smart boy, an' I might 'a' been a smart man, an' hed a fam'ly o' my own. An' yeou see what I am naow. Everybody calls me Dick the drunkard. Don't yeou never du's I've done."

Eli was touched by this sudden outburst, and asked sympathetically, "Couldn't you leave off? You are not old, and you might have a chance yet."

Dick mournfully shook his head, and wiped his eyes with his shirt sleeve. "No, 'tain't no use," he said; "I can't du it. I've tried often 'nough. I allus say arter I've hed a spree, thet it's the last one; but when I'm well over it the thirst comes, an' I can't stan' it. Folks think I've got no feelin's, but *I* know. I see ye, Eli, when I was ter the butcher's t'other day, and the boys hed put my heel in the hook o' the iron chain, and then wanted ter turn the windlass so's to pull me up like a dead critter, 'ith my hed hangin' daown; I see ye, Eli, an' yeou wouldn't let 'em pull me up, an' yeou made 'em leave me 'lone in the chair till I hed my sleep. I see ye, an' I hain't forgot it, an' never shell. But don't du ez I've done. Tell your pa what I've told ye. *He*'ll know why I take some int'rest an' pride in his boys."

Dick went on with his work, shovelling out pomace, building it up in square heaps with layers of straw, and turning the screw with brawny arms. But he said no more. He looked unutterable things, and wiped his red eyes.

The two boys took their fish and poles and left him. They stopped at the rear of the mill where many heaps of apples lay on the grass, and then looked in at the upper story to see Mr. Crombie put apples in the trough that led down to the works.

" Lemme see," said Mr. Crombie, " yeou're Eli an' 'Ratio, the carpenter's boys, ain't ye? Air ye goin' ter skule ? "

Eli answered that they had been attending Mr. Field's select school, but that the term was just over.

" Yeou talk pooty wal; what hev yeou ben a studyin' ? "

" Arithmetic, geography, and Latin grammar."

" Yeou've ben a-studyin' Latin? What air yeou 'xpectin' ter du or ter be ? "

" I don't know. I mean to learn all I can."

"Wal, it's curus what notions boys takes. Ef yeou're a good boy, yeou'll help yeour father when yeou're big enough ; an' ef yeou du, yeou won't have any yeuse fer Latin. But I don't want ter discourage any boy : I hain't hed any larnin', an' 'sted o' studyin' books, I mostly study human nater, — an' here ez wal ez anywhere. In any o' them piles of apples I kin see the nater o' the man thet raised 'em, an' o' his father thet set aout the trees. This one is shif'less an' poor ; thet one is forehanded an' stiddy. This one goes ter meetin' an' fears God ; thet one is wicked or keerless."

" And do you know, then, whose they all are ? "

"Oh, yis ; I could a'most tell 'em by feelin' on 'em 'ith my eyes shet." He went on, " Thet air pile, ye see, is full o' leaves an' bits o' leetle sticks. An' ye see the apples is bruised. Them hev ben knocked off the trees by pesky lazy boys, an' raked up, leaves an' all; 'stid o' shakin' 'em off properly, an' pickin' up one ter time. They air Josh Aldrich's apples. That's the way he an' his boys du. Them red-streaks is Newman's. They're soft, an' orter a ben picked keerful. They air part bruised an' part rotten. Folks says rotten apples make good cider, but 'tain't so; the rotten taste goes clean thru it.

"Them leetle gnurly ones 'ith o'ny one cheek air Sherman's. 'Pears like they're goin' back ter wild apples. The trees air old, an' air run ter shoots an' suckers. They air tu fer gone ever to bear anythin' decent. But though them leetle, one-sided apples air sour 'nough to make a pig squeal, I'd ruther hev 'em for cider than better apples thet is part rotten.

"Them green pippins ther' is Chandler's. He's hed all his trees grafted. They're good, but I shouldn't fancy hevin' all one kind.

"Thet pooty pile layin' on a blanket is the Widder Howson's. She's nice, she is, an' won't hev no cider thet ain't ez clean ez a cup of her own tea. Them apples is all picked over an' washed an' wiped. Ef she was goin' to make a pie or a puddin', she wouldn't a' taken more pains. When she gits her cider she knows what she's drinkin'.

"An' look at thet mons'ous big pile, all sorts, yaller, green, an' red. Them b'longs ter Lijah Hanks. He'll hev ten or fifteen barrels."

" P'r'aps he'll sell some," suggested the boy.

" Not he. It takes a lot o' cider to last him, even ef he doos put red pepper in't."

" You said that the trees which bore those little

apples were too far gone to be good for anything ; now, if the man that raised them should be a steady man and go to the meeting, would his apples be any better ? "

" Not till he hed better trees. But ef he was the right kind o' man all thru, he'd either *hev* new trees, or graff the old ones, or *sunthin'*."

" Do you charge so much a barrel for making cider of people's apples ? " asked Eli, " or do you exchange, taking so many bushels for a barrel ? "

" Sometimes one way, sometimes t'other ; an' sometimes a man pays me so much a day for the use o' the mill. Most folks, who wanter know what they're goin' ter git, hev their own apples (which they've gathered an' picked over) made inter cider, arter hevin' the mill washed."

The ingenuous faces of the boys impressed Mr. Crombie, and he evidently wished to efface the harshness of his comment upon the study of Latin. " I don't want ye ter think I'm ag'in larnin' ; an' though I can't see the good o' Latin, I'm allus glad ter see boys tryin' ter be well eddicated, an' ter raise 'emselves. On'y, allus remember thet the fear o' the Lord is the beginnin' o' wisdom ; an' don't ye never let anythin' come atween yeou an the faith o' yeour fathers."

This earnestness touched the boy, quite as much as had the tender words of poor Dick. He had not realized how the hearts of right-minded people go out in sympathy with a youth who aims at qualifying himself for some honorable career. He had begun to see a vista opening before him, and looked forward to becoming a disciple of the great and wise. The influence of Mr. Field had been stimulating and helpful. He was moved by vague presentiments, and there came a sense of uplifting by some power not his own. His outward appearance gave little indication of the dreamy, soaring mind. His face was striking only for the large and lustrous eyes, and for the shock of bushy hair. His clothes were poor, and evidently often mended, and his feet were bare. He was healthy and solid, but evidently knew nothing of the requirements of the toilet, nor of the manners of society. He was as simple and natural as a savage.

He had taken the first step in a road that was to lead him far from the life of Quabbin. Would he ever forget how he looked in his patched suit, barefoot, and dangling a couple of fish?

"Wait, Horatio," he said to his brother. "Wait a minute." He ran quickly to the lower story where Dick was at work. "Dick," said he in a gentle tone, "if you're ever in want of anything, come to our house. Mother 'll be good to you; and you needn't think that nobody cares for you. It made me ache to hear you talk. There *are* some who care for you, a great deal."

He did not wait for an answer, but ran back to join his brother. "I wish that neck-ribbin could a' ben made o' gold an' di'monds," thought Dick.

CHAPTER XXV

AN EXIT

THE third minister's orbit was not of great extent. His period near the sun of favor was short, and he soon entered upon the long curve which led through cold and gloom.

People began to wonder what they had admired in him, or in his preaching. No one was willing to admit that he had actively favored settling him. The general expression was, " I never was, *myself*, so much carried away by his elerkence, but ez everybody *else* seemed ter be pleased, I thought 'twas my dewty to jine in." We have seen what were the deacons' opinions. Mr. Grant did not say much, but behind his gold spectacles there was a deal of thinking, and his manner to the minister was seen to be " offish."

Certain young fellows learned the trick of pulpit rhetoric, and used to imitate the minister's glittering sentences and high-pitched voice. He was discussed at the counting-room, the post-office, the stores, and the shoemaker's shop. The talk over the lapstone was especially damnatory. The new doctor took him up, and called him sophomorical; and as people did not know what that meant, and the doctor was "a college-larnt man," it was supposed to be something very bad.

No one could say that the formalities of duty were not observed. The sermons were of orthodox length, and earnestly delivered. Fresh texts were brought out every Sunday; but after a few sentences the discourse somehow fell into old ruts of thought, and observant hearers soon perceived that in any half-dozen Sundays he went over all the solid parts of his repertory.

"When sh'll we hev any revivle o' religion?"

"When 'll come forrard the young to fill aour places?"

"When 'll ther' be a-movin' 'mong the dry bones o' the church?"

"Ther's sermons thet's all glitter, like a heap of icicles."

"Ther's talk thet hain't any life-givin' paower in't, more'n a Jinnuary moon 'd hev on a growin' punkin-vine."

Such were the current comments; but most people were backward when a movement was proposed. Ministers were formerly settled for life, and the feeling was still strong that an incumbent had rights which were sacred. In the event of the minister's being dismissed against his will, it was felt that he would be entitled to compensation which might burden the parish.

One day the whole town was startled by the report that a special meeting had been called to take action in regard to sundering the relation between the parish and the minister. In the village there was a general sense of relief; but, when the meeting was held, it was found that the "otherwise minded" were out in full force, and were bent on mischief. They cared nothing for the interests of religion; their only motive was to cross the leaders of the church and parish.

Deacon Rawson stated the case for the church, and was discreet enough to state it mildly, and without any harsh words about the minister. There was no one among the dissentients who could speak with any effect, but they made plenty of noise in interruptions, and were ready to vote as one man. They seldom came to meeting, and their contributions counted very little in the parish treasury.

After some skirmishing, Mr. Grant got the floor, and, addressing the moderator, said, in substance, —

"It does me good to be present at this large meeting of the parishioners of Quabbin. It is a good sign when upon a matter of general concern there is such an unusual turn-out. Our friends from the remote parts of the town have left their farms and their workshops, and have come to give us their counsel in the matter which has called us together. I am glad to see this wide-spread interest, especially on the part of those who come in all weathers to meeting, and pay so liberally for the support of the gospel. You all know who they are. Their zeal and good works are known to all men. They are those who strongly upheld the fearless course of our former minister. Now, if they were laggards in God's service; if they remained at home, or ran after new lights, or helped the Methodists; if they had no heart in sustaining this church, and the doctrines and traditions of the fathers; if they were loose in life, or irreligious at heart, we should consider it a little out of place, a little indelicate perhaps, to come here to take part in a matter in which they could have no real concern : we should say they ought to leave the choice of a minister to those who habitually go to hear one, and not to interfere, for motives which it would be improper for me to state in plain words. But as they are known to have a deep interest in this church, we shall be glad to know what they have to say for its good." (Mr. Grant had a slight Yankee accent, but not enough to justify a change in spelling.)

Said the moderator, " Is the gentleman thru? Supposin' that he would conclude his speech with a motion he was 'lowed to go on. Ez he didn't make one, he was aout of order. There is no motion afore the meetin'."

Deacon Rawson then moved to pass the resolution embodied in the call for the meeting.

The ironical gibes of Mr. Grant had only the usual effect, namely, to harden the temper of the opposition ; but none of the party could make an effective reply, and they took their punishment in silence.

One speaker favored the minister because he did not read written sermons ; he had no patience with " elerkence studied out aforehand." He thought that when a preacher's mouth was opened, he would be told by the Holy Ghost what to say.

Deacon Dodge asked the last speaker if he thought the days of miracles would come back. If so, they might look for the gift of tongues, the healing of the sick, and the raising of the dead ; as none of those things were more supernatural than the power of preaching without study.

Meanwhile, Mr. Grant and a friend had made a count, and had satisfied themselves that, in spite of the noisy demonstration at the back of the hall, the meeting was controlled by the friends of the church.

Having allowed ample time for all to express their views, Deacon Rawson moved that the main question be now put, which was carried. The moderator then stated the question, which was to the effect that the parish officers be authorized and directed to confer with the church and with the minister, with the view of bringing about an amicable separation ; and he added, " This meetin' hez ordered thet the main question be naow put, and this isn't open ter 'mendment ner debate. The thing is to vote yea or nay on this ere resolution. Ef the yeas hev it, ther's an end of the business. Ef the nays hev it, then the way is open ter perpose sunthin' else."

The yeas were called for, and the hands were eagerly counted ; then the otherwise minded made their show, and were clearly in the minority.

The church was almost unanimous for the change. At the conference, the minister said that the proposal was an injury to his reputation and to his feelings ; that he had hoped and expected to pass the remainder of his days among brethren who had received him so warmly, and whom he still loved. He enlarged upon his success in preaching, and hinted at the lustre thereby reflected upon the church ; and he wished to know in what he had come short of any just expectation ?

Deacon Rawson, speaking for the church, declined to be drawn into a discussion, which was sure to be unpleasant, and could serve no good purpose, and said the case for the church and parish would be laid before the ecclesiastical council.

Certain churches were thereupon invited to send each its pastor and a lay delegate on a day named. When the council assembled, the minister asked to be represented by a brother in the Lord, the Rev. Dr.

Windust, who had come a long distance for the purpos[.] of stating his case.

It was a very unusual proceeding, and was unfair, as the church and parish had no counsel; but the great name of the reverend doctor overawed the simple-minded brothers. Within an hour Deacon Rawson saw how matters were going, and whispered to Deacon Holyoke, "We hedn't orter let him in. He's a-goin' to twist the caouncil 'baout his leetle finger. He's goin' in for big damiges, and poor ol' Quabbin 'll hev to sweat."

It was even so. The doctor of divinity had a consummate knowledge of the world, plenty of "cheek," and talent for pushing; and he shoved this way and that among the innocent people he had to deal with, until he became as supreme as the Pope.

It was admitted on both sides that the minister must go, since the breach was irreparable; the only question was as to compensation. On this point the "brother in the Lord" developed as much ingenuity and force as would have done credit to a leader of the metropolitan bar. He flattered the ministers, and put to them the *argumentum ad hominem:* — as much as to say, "How would you like it yourselves?" He smoothed the lay delegates as if they had been tabbies. He poked fun at the deacons of Quabbin, and stigmatized that poor village as purse-proud and pretentious. And when he came to tell the minister's story, that gentleman drew out a great silk handkerchief, blew his nose, and wept. The reverend orator went on, momently scaling new rhetorical heights, and likened his friend and client to Cicero, Massillon, Jeremy Taylor, White-field, and other celebrities. He talked long and well, but his matter was nearly exhausted, when, upon a nudge and a whisper from his heart-broken client, he made a fresh start. He began to tell the council of the minister's wonderful outbursts of eloquence, and said it would be with sincere diffidence that he should repeat even a sentence, as it might be spoiled from want of memory or skill on the part of the humble narrator; but he would try. And he did try. On account of its novelty the passage is herewith transcribed.[1]

"The future glories of Christianity and the high destinies of the human race appeal with gigantic power to the hearts of all enthusiastic disciples. With prophetic eye I see the long generations of men of all nations winding over Syrian sands on their pilgrimage to the haunts in Palestine that were hallowed by the feet of the Son of man. The long strife with sin and evil is coming finally to an end. Pope and patriarch throw down their tiaras, cardinals strip off the scarlet livery of the mistress of the seven hills. The Chinese renounce Confucius. The Indian hermit arises from the life-long contemplation of the mystery of existence as shown in his own umbilical excision.

"The Polynesian abstains from human flesh, and breaks bread under a missionary's roof. The crescents of thousands of mosques are made into sickles to reap the harvests of the world; while sultans emancipate the inmates of their seraglios. Then, when the gospel-car has rolled triumphantly through every land; when

[1] The transcriber obviously shows some disposition to burlesque; but though some passages of the speech may have been tampered with, there will be no doubt of the genuineness of the conclusion.

every ship carries a white flag at her mast-head, and a Sunday-school in her forecastle; when the Esquimaux shall have set up chapels, and raised the gospel banner at the North Pole, — then, my brethren, perhaps you suppose there will be nothing left for Christians to do! Far from that! The fiery zeal of the faithful must then have some other outlet; and they will even try to build a railroad to the fixed stars, so as to carry to the remotest bounds of the universe the glad news of salvation."

"Was not that a sublime conception?" demanded the reverend orator. Here Deacon Rawson tried to say that the people of Quabbin had heard about nothing else but that railroad for some years; but he was no match for the pertinacious brother in the Lord, and could not get in a word edgewise.

Doctor Windust concluded by suggesting that the damages be fixed at five thousand dollars. The minister was still weeping, or at least his face was covered by his ample handkerchief.

Deacon Rawson said the sum named was monstrous; that "the perrish couldn't raise no sech pile o' money;" that they "couldn't squeeze blood aout of a turnip." He and his colleague were very earnest, and showed by the tax-lists that the payment of even half that sum would make it difficult to maintain the regular preaching for the next two years.

The parties retired, and the council deliberated. When the doors were opened it was announced that the council recommended the dissolution of the pastoral relation, and that the minister should have a *solatium* of three thousand dollars.

Then was seen an affecting *tableau* in two parts. I. The minister and the Rev. Doctor embracing with tears of joy. II. Deacon Rawson and his colleague with countenances expressive of disgust.

Said the deacon, " I s'pose we sh'll hev to du it. We kin borrer the money, an' p'r'aps we kin pay it up in four or five year."

And so disappeared the third minister.

CHAPTER XXVI

ROBERT IV

THE fourth minister was one to whom in after times all goodness and graciousness were ascribed. To those who best knew him he was almost an ideal pastor, yet, like many a blessing, he appeared more lustrous in the after-glow of memory. The wonder was how a man of such ability, learning, and character contented himself with the prosaic society and often thankless labor that awaited a minister in Quabbin. It must have been a high sense of duty that led and kept him there; for he was the equal in intellectual force of the foremost orthodox preachers of his time.

He was born in New England, the son of a Scotch clergyman. His accent was purely English; his unassuming manners were those of the best society; while his firm character, no less than his name, recalled his origin. His countenance and voice were impressive, although a careful description would not require any unusual adjectives; for what was striking and memorable in him was the vague something which eludes description. He was rather above medium height, solid but spare in figure, with a large and finely modelled head, regular features, a dull yellowish (but not unwholesome) complexion, and steady gray eyes. The shirt collars of that time were high and projecting, and his broad and bluish chin was sunk between two curving supports of starched linen, while the soft white neckcloth below was a mass of wrinkled folds.

But when he spoke he touched a sensorium behind the organs of hearing, and then no one thought of the high-curving collar-points, the much-swathed neck, or the pale, lemon-tinted skin. For there was something in his penetrating yet kindly look, and in the rich tones of his voice, which awakened instant attention, and won the homage of every auditor. At certain times his face became more than beautiful, — since beauty, power, and tenderness were mingled, — drawing the hearts of hearers in sympathy, while at the same time reason and conscience felt the imperious summons to surrender.

Such effects of soul in the human countenance recall the pictures of legendary saints, wherein the attempts of the masters to portray a spiritual illumination have led to preternatural high lights and emblematic haloes. No one in after years ever thought of that man in the pulpit, with the deep crimson drapery behind him, except with a beam of light touching his noble forehead, and his features eloquent with divine love.

The sermons of the good Robert IV. were direct and practical. Necessarily they were doctrinal, for he was wholly a Calvinist ; but the doctrine was the spirit of the sermons, and seldom their subject. They were never rhetorical, in the sinister sense of the word, but in style they were without fault ; for the minister was a scholar, and wrote with a purity and ease that had become instinctive. There was many a fine touch for an educated ear, but in substance there was nothing above the ordinary comprehension. All classes of

hearers were reached, yet very few knew to what perfect English they were listening. But as few people
anywhere know the rarity of pure, fresh, and idiomatic
style, the imperfect perception of the dwellers in Quabbin is not a matter of serious reproach.

The minister was learned in theology, as far as concerned the affirmation and defence of the dogmas he
held ; but neither he nor any man of his order had, up
to that time, made any serious study of doubts or
denials. The usual way was to set up an imaginary
adversary on an impossible basis, and then easily bowl
him down. Modern inquiry had scarcely begun upon
the character and history of the sacred books ; and the
plenary inspiration of Scripture in every chapter and
verse was never questioned. Nor was "the endless
punishment of the finally impenitent" ever doubted, except by Universalists, Unitarians, and other "infidels."
The upheaval of conscience in the Orthodox Church
against that terrible doctrine had not then begun ; so
that, although the minister seldom ventured to draw
those baleful pictures of the wrath of God with which
Jonathan Edwards shocked the Connecticut Valley, yet
in every discourse and prayer, the "fearful looking-for
of judgment and fiery indignation " was the thing understood as being the background and alternative. He
aimed to persuade, and to lead by tender appeals ; but
every soul knew that the "terrors" lurked behind like
menacing spectres.

He had been distinguished in scholarship while at
college, and afterward as an instructor ; but it may be
doubted whether he esteemed classical studies and
English literature as more than means of mental training and temporary recreation. If he had felt the

abounding joy which fills the heart of an earnest and accomplished scholar, something of it should have overflowed; and there were youths hungering for knowledge, who followed all his utterances. As, in the feeling of the time, the whole of this mortal life was none too long as a preparation for an endless future existence, all studies and recreations which had no bearing upon "the one thing needful" were lightly regarded, or thrust aside.

This minister's reading was broader and more varied than that of the second, — with the third there need be no comparison made upon this or any other subject, — but it would be considered narrow to-day. He doubtless knew something of Shakespeare, but he would no more have thought of quoting him in the pulpit than of quoting Boccaccio or Rabelais. Gibbon's History was probably interdicted for its too celebrated sixteenth chapter; Hume's, for his arguments against miracles; Chaucer and Dryden for immodest license; Pope for the rationalistic philosophy of the "Essay on Man," and for the filth of the "Dunciad." Swift, Prior, Gay, Herrick, Suckling, and many more were set aside for obvious reasons. In fact, an orthodox clergyman would have but a limited selection if he were to read none but unexceptionable books. The works of English divines, with Bacon, Milton, Johnson, Gray, Collins, Cowper, and Wordsworth, and the class of religious books mentioned in a former chapter, made up the bulk of his library.

The reviews which the fourth minister read were "religious," and any discussion of literature in them was incidental, and in the clerical manner. Nor was any purely literary periodical taken in the town. But

the minister was still strongly inclined to reading and
study, and had the habits of a bookish man. Having
inherited a small fortune, he was free from anxiety, and
besides he had no desire for money. He was not indifferent to the temporal welfare of his parishioners,
but he never got the least knowledge of their farming
or trades. Whether turnips grew on trees, or shoe-pegs
were thrashed out of oat-sheaves, were matters of no
consequence. He was not absolutely ignorant of the
world's work, but it did not concern him. A horse was
a necessary evil; a garden was a place for penance; if
he had to harness the one or spade the other, he would
not have accepted either as a gift. He had never been
a gymnast, ball-player, or pedestrian. In the use of
tools, and in regard to household jobs in general, he
rivalled Emerson in helplessness. He lived in his intellectual and moral nature. Although pleasant and
genial, he had no more points of contact with an ordinary man in regard to every-day affairs than a billiard-
ball. If Farmer Sherman showed him his mighty
oxen, the minister never thought to praise them; instead of that, he might be thinking of the Greek terms
for their rolling gait and calm eyes. John Ramsay
wondered that he never gave a second glance at his
"2.40" Morgan trotting-horse. It was a magnificent
animal, whether at rest or in motion; but the minister
thought chiefly of the disagreeable shaking-up one
would get to be driven at such speed, and of the pelt-
ing of sand from the flying feet. He felt the beauty
of the deep green meadows, starred with the gold of
kingcups and cowslips; but never thought of estimat-
ing how many tons of grass they yielded to the acre.
Sheep were picturesque as white dots on the hill pas-

tures, or when massed under the farm sheds; but he did
not know the weight of fleeces or the price of mutton.

The elders of the church knew his devotion to his
work; a few recognized dimly his attainments; all the
parish felt the glow of his piety; yet there were few
houses in which he was really at home, and few people
who felt him to be near. They loved him and reverenced him, but on a pedestal; and, on his part, his
senses were so delicate, and his tastes so refined, that
the contact of many well-meaning persons was almost
painful. Perhaps, also, the relations with his people
would have been more intimate if he had not, with
others causes for isolation, been childless. He always
seemed to have his head in the clouds (figuratively
speaking), even when he walked abroad with his rather
stately wife; with a child to lead them, the world would
have had a new aspect. In making pastoral calls, when
he came where young children were, his manner often
became so solemn that the little creatures fancied
there was some momently impending trouble, and began to whimper. This forbidding austerity arose solely
from his intense anxiety to " win souls to Christ."

In regard to the affairs of the parish and the schools,
he was a vivifying influence rather than a leader and
manager. He made few personal efforts, not because
he was lukewarm, but because he was diffident and un-
skilful. A word from him had weight, and he was not
slow to speak when there was occasion, but he did
not know how to use his parishioners like chessmen.
The rule of total abstinence was maintained in the
church; but, if he had been in the place of the second
minister, he could not have preached that fiery sermon
by the woodpile, nor terrified that drunken circle of

mourners. He had the courage to preach against slavery, and described it as "a cancer eating into the vitals of the nation;" but his sermon, like the common denunciation of the scribes and pharisees, dead near two thousand years, led to no practical result. One old man in Quabbin had for many years cast an anti-slavery vote, amid the jeers of politicians and the insults of the baser sort. The sermon was a comfort to this solitary voter, but brought him no helpers; he continued to cast his one vote for years afterward. It was supposed that Garrison and his friends were trying to rend the churches, and to set up women as preachers. Besides, the chief industry in the mills was spinning cotton; and, without slaves, how could there be any cotton? On that point all the leading men of the village were as dogmatic as the Chancellor of the Exchequer in expounding a budget.

He was very earnest in his desire to raise the standard of teaching, but he was a favoring influence rather than a moving force. During his time something was done to make the schoolhouses decent and comfortable, to increase the annual appropriation by the town, to extend the school terms, and to secure better teachers by stricter preliminary examinations.

On the subject of foreign missions the minister had a profound conviction. In his sermons and in his remarks at prayer-meetings, as well as in his pastoral calls, he represented the need of the perishing world, and extolled the courage and self-denying labors of the missionaries; and he urged that concerted efforts should be made to increase contributions. A systematic canvass was begun by the deacons and teachers of the Sunday-school. The rich were urged to give,

and did give liberally ; but all, without exception, gave
something ; even boys were prevailed upon to open
their tin boxes and part with their few jingling cents.
So thoroughly was the work prosecuted that in one year
the collections amounted to more than three thousand
dollars ; which was rather more than the annual cost of
the public schools, and considerably more than the ex-
penses of the parish, including the minister's salary.
This was not a mere gathering of superfluous cash ; it
came from actual self-denial of comforts, from the renunciation of books and amusements, as well as from the
breaking up of petty hoards ; it represented endless sewing and knitting ; so that the total was not merely money,
but a near and dear part of human lives. This result,
which so much rejoiced the minister, and upon which he
expatiated with just pride, was turned upon him and upon
the leaders of the church in an unexpected manner.

At the next town meeting, when the appropriation
for schools was under consideration, the advocates of
progress and reform urged the raising of a larger sum
by taxation. They dwelt upon the condition of the
children who were growing up with such meagre
opportunities, and showed what might be done if the
committee had the necessary funds. It was getting to
be an old story, for the arguments had often been presented in previous years. At last one old farmer,
Captain Newcomb, arose and " freed his mind."

" Mr. Moderator, I dunno but wut all the gen'leman
says is trew " (it was Mr. Grant who had last spoken),
"though, fer myself, I don't see thet larnin' would 'a
made my life any easier. I kin read the Bible an' a
newspaper, an' I hain't time to read any more. All my
time's took up tu airn a livin', an' ter pay my taxes ; an',

ef they was ter be any higher, I couldn't pay 'em, 'thout scrimpin' my vittles an' clothes. I kin reckon the vally of a hog or a fat ox ; an' ef I hed larnin' to cal'late an eclipse I couldn't make the heft o' ary one on 'em a paound more. My boys 'll hev ter foller me, an' the larnin' thet's sarved me 'll hev ter du fer them. So fer a blacksmith's son, or a shewmaker's ; they kin make hoss shews an' wimmin's shews, ef so be they're willin' ter du wut their fathers hev done, an' grow up stiddy workin'-men. Ef they want ter be lawyers an' doctors an' ministers, thet's another mahter ; an' it stands ter reason thet ther' ain't never room fer but one at a time fer 'em in a taown like this, in a gineration o' men. When a youngster wants ter git up a peg in the world, ther's allus a way, ef he's got the brains an' the grit ; an' I don't see the yeuse o' puttin' all the boys in the way o' gittin' up ter the same peg, ef they hain't the 'bilities. The skule sh'd be fer the evrige, an' not fer one or tew. But even supposin' we was agreed ter hev the skules what the gen'lemen want, I sh'd like ter know ef ther' ain't some way ter du it 'thout pilin' up taxes ? Some folks in this village, they tell me, make more money in runnin' a factory a day than I kin on my farm in a year. Taxes ain't nothin' ter them ; but they're heavy 'nough fer me naow.

"I heered t'other day thet this perrish hed raised more'n three thaousan' dollars fer forrin missions. Three thaousan' dollars in a poor leetle taown, ter keep a set o' well-fed fellers in forrin parts, wher' the people don't want 'em, an' wher' they kin du plaguy leetle good. Thet's more money than all aour skules cost, 'cordin' ter the report jest read. Naow, Mr. Moderator, they say cherrity begins ter hum ; an' ef the sittiwation of aour boys an' gals is so dreffle bad, an' ef we air, all on us, in danger o' becomin' heathens an' savages fer want o' better skules, it 'pears ter me thet a part o' thet air three thaousan' dollars better be spent here fust; an' arterwards, ef ther's any left, it kin be gi'n ter the missionaries."

The hit was felt, in spite of the low tone of the objections to higher education. Many of the country people were in ecstasies, and even the most devout of church-members smiled. The only reply came from a deacon who said, "'These things ought ye to have done, and not to have left the other undone.'"

When the vote was taken, there was only a small increase in the appropriation. Progress was slow for many years, against the prevailing sentiment expressed in the first part of the farmer's speech.

The large contribution was often referred to on other occasions. When an appeal was made for a poor widow, a sick family, or a man in misfortune, the answer would come, "Better take sunthin' from that air three thaousan' dollars ye've scraped up fer the heathen."

CHAPTER XXVII

DAWN

A CASUAL observer would have noticed but few changes in the village from the time of Joshua I. to that of Robert IV. The new buildings were not many, and not in the least imposing ; although there was a more general air of neatness in houses, dooryards, and gardens, and there were more ornamental trees. Several disused mills and shops had disappeared, and, after their sites were levelled and turfed, the open spaces were more agreeable than shabby ruins. Business was visibly declining ; but this appeared to affect the incomes of few, for the general style of living was even more comfortable, and all the appointments of households were in better taste.

In the country, more of the dwellings were painted and in good repair ; scarcely any were so cheerless as in the old time. On the few good farms barns were built from improved plans. The new barn was often a large structure, surmounted by a showy cupola, bearing a gilded vane in the form of an ox or horse. Implements that used to be exposed to the weather were sheltered in convenient out-houses. The old straggling heaps of wood were cut and piled under cover, and yards were raked clear of chips and rubbish. These are prosy details, but they count in life as in landscape.

Among the people an almost insensible change was going on, owing in a great measure to their more temperate and cleanly habits. Few visages seen at the mill or the stores had the old fiery glow ; hair had become docile ; hats were not prematurely beaten out of shape ; and the razor no longer skipped those edges and ridges of beard which told of bleary eyes and trembling hands. The majority of men were clear-eyed and clean-looking, and wore comfortable, well-mended clothing. Fewer barrels of cider were stored, and more apples sent to market. Oaths were rare, except among the dwindling frequenters of the tavern ; and one could count upon the fingers all the flagrant cases of habitual drunkenness.

Yet the farmers were hardly so prosperous, for their produce brought lower prices. There was a market for firewood and railroad-ties, and other timber ; animals, poultry, and dairy products were in demand ; but as to grain, it was seen that with the extension of railroads its price must continue to fall. In raising bread-stuffs New England's day was coming to an end. So, throughout the town, young men arriving at maturity were looking abroad for their future, and in time few who were possessed of good abilities were left behind. Destiny had some surprises for the exiles or explorers ; for one, a place as fireman on a locomotive ; for another, a quarter section of prairie land ; for a third, a desk in a merchant's office in Boston ; for a fourth, a seat in the Stock Exchange in New York. One handsome fellow, moderately educated, and with no inheritance, was taken for a husband by a wealthy woman, and carried off to her "brown-stone front" on Fifth Avenue.

Women more than men are rooted to the soil, *quasi*

adscriptæ glebæ, and, owing to the absence of partners, the number of the unmarried increased; but in one way or another many of them found spouses, and there are few Northern or Western States where there are not daughters of Quabbin now at the head of families. Although now and then a young man became prominent or made a fortune, the influence of the young women was nobler and more pervasive; for they happened to possess a larger share of mind, culture, and worth. Nearly all who were highly educated married away from home, and some of them attained to positions for which there are no titles, but for which the honors given to eminent men would be inadequate. In the case of a mother of half a dozen vigorous and well-trained children, who is foremost in religious work; who sets luxury aside, and uses her wealth to do good; who is the friend of the poor, and comes to be the one person looked up to, reverenced, and loved by a whole town, what rank or honor would be appropriate? Such a woman leaves a memory that is blessed, and God will take care of her reward.

Gay young women, like Eliza and Lois Grant, when the new wine of youth had done fuming, became excellent and notable members of society. Nor was education confined to the rich. During and after the reign of Robert IV. it happened that a great many bright girls from humble families, after beginning with the transient "select schools," found means to attend some distant academy or boarding-school, with marvellous results. It was wonderful to see some budding girl, who a few years before was a freckled and wild-haired tomboy, come back with the calm eyes of conscious power, and with the equipment and manners to shine in a drawing-room. No leveller like education, for it levels upwards.

The presence of cultivated young women, even for a few years each, began to tell upon the old dialect. Perhaps the characteristic tone was not so much ameliorated, but it became rare to hear sentences framed on slovenly models, and rough with contractions. Some of these women became teachers, and were active propagandists; some of them married, and succeeded in toning down the speech of their husbands and relatives. All were active agents in bringing about the coming enlightenment.

As a result of the departure of the young, the people of Quabbin might be likened to a forest which had parted with most of its lusty and growing trees, and consisted largely of old and wind-shaken trunks, with few branches and sparse foliage. Toward the end of the fourth minister's time the congregation on a Sunday was noticeable for the numbers of gray heads. There were a few old couples, but more widowers and widows; there were the local storekeepers and mechanics, the venerable lawyer, the few mill-owners, and others upon whom the frame of things seemed to rest. Besides, there were a few mill-hands, and other "hewers of wood and drawers of water," most of them recent immigrants; but there were very few young men and women of the old stock. Those who still remained were either without ambition and courage, or those whom duty and affection retained at home to take care of the old. Now and then would be seen some native who had come home on a visit, and his appearance at meeting was the subject of much curiosity. But any one who had known the people could reckon the absent of both sexes from the vacant spaces in so many pews. A deeper melancholy, if that were possible, had settled upon many pinched and grizzled faces.

This slow exodus began with the completion of the trunk railroad. It was no longer a difficult thing to traverse the State, or even to pay a visit to friends in Illinois. People were no longer rooted to natal soil, but moved about with a light-heartedness or indifference, strangely in contrast with old custom. In the time of the first minister very few in the village had ever travelled fifty miles, and a visit to Boston was the talk of a lifetime. There were seldom any removals; except of the very poor, who had nothing to carry; — where a man was born, there his lot was cast, and there he toiled until his release came. In one respect this was a wholesome restraint; honesty abides, while villany if discovered is forced to fly. It was strange, too, to see, after this general movement began, how easily occupations were changed. Before, a youth followed in his father's footsteps; and to become some day the owner of the farm, or head of the workshop, was the great prize in life; but when the door was suddenly opened into the great world, the farms and shops of Quabbin, seen over the shoulder, looked mean. A youth when he set forth generally believed that Fortune was waiting for him in some guise, if he could only recognize her; and until she was revealed to him he did not care to what labor he applied himself. For the time being he was willing to be teamster, porter, clerk, or "utility man." This readiness to adapt one's self to anything was a wholly new symptom; and if it was attended by some instability or feverish impatience, it was not without good results. The old fixedness and torpor were gone, and society was full of motion, albeit motion was not always progress.

There were two stations on the railroad, each about a dozen miles from Quabbin, with which there was daily communication. The trade of the local stores was speedily reduced to odds and ends, because farmers drove with their produce to the stations and brought back their supplies, and because well-to-do people went by rail to the nearest large town for "shopping." These frequent excursions served to break the monotony of life in a small village. Then daily newspapers began to appear in the stores and counting-rooms, and in a few residences, and the ideas of Boston and New York, the commercial, political, and literary centres, began to awaken a vivid and continuous interest. This was an epoch. Quabbin became a part of the great world, and felt the universal pulsations of humanity. It could never be solitary again. Many influences contributed to its enlightenment, but the railroad and the daily newspaper were the chief. Home and foreign news, politics, inventions, and discoveries in arts and science, were brought home to people who had never had anything to occupy their minds except neighborhood gossip and sermons. The educational power and stimulus effected an entire transformation; although at first many a reader spelled his way through paragraphs but dimly understood. The appreciation of newspapers rose with the spread of education; but from the beginning there was some notion of the solidarity of mankind, and of the inestimable value of knowledge.

Other changes were in progress. Instead of heavy, rumbling wagons, there were light buggies moving without noise. Clumsy and rusty harnesses were exchanged for newer work, with finer lines and tasteful buckles. In former times a man whose clothes were made at home by the ancient tailoress, who went the rounds of the neighborhood, could be easily distinguished at a hundred yards' distance by his slouchy and baggy outlines. Such a costume was naturally associated with huge, shapeless boots, an old hat with the crown stove in, the nasal drawl of the rustic dialect, and tobacco stains at the corners of the mouth. Such a repulsive outfit was becoming rare, especially in the village; as all, excepting the very poor, were in the habit of going to some large town for their clothing.

Especially marked was the change among women, who are always quicker than men to perceive the beauty and advantages of new things. Little by little what used to be stigmatized as "city ways" began to come in without comment, — neater boots and gloves, tasteful scarfs, better "form" in gait and attitude, a readier and smoother speech, and more composure of manner.

Most important were the changes in tools and implements. It would be difficult to exaggerate the relief that came to working-men, — and almost everybody worked in Quabbin, — when the heavy and awkward hoes, shovels, axes, forks, rakes, and scythes were replaced by new tools, so light, yet so strong, so polished and so perfectly adapted to use, such as are now seen in New England and in the West. They are found nowhere else; those in Great Britain, where farming and gardening are carried to perfection, are generally twice as heavy, and not so effective.

The same is true in regard to mechanics' tools. The Yankee makes and uses hammers, saws, files, pincers, screw-cutters, vices, tailors' shears, dental instruments, and the like, which are fashioned with a precision seldom attained elsewhere.

The children of Quabbin that were scattered abroad gave new light upon countless affairs by their letters and visits to the old people. Travellers came and went, and by this outflow and inflood the small inland pool maintained its level with the distant ocean.

Events and the progress of ideas have been grouped under the reigns of successive ministers; but it is evident that in many instances the ministers, if not passive spectators, were wholly incapable of initiating the changes that took place; they might as well have the credit of directing the weather. The good Robert IV. duly preached his earnest and faultless sermons, made his conscientious visits, and distributed all the sunshine compatible with his duty of warning sinners. He was as worthy of veneration as Goldsmith's village parson. Yet, had it rested solely with him, the people would have long remained in their provincial isolation. And, further, the time had passed when the intellectual character, opinions, and will of the public could be controlled by any one man. In the days of Joshua I. there were not half a dozen in the town who could be said to have self-based character and reasoned opinions. When, in every quarter, men and women were reading for themselves, there was a distribution of power.

CHAPTER XXVIII

MISS WICKS'S TEA—PARTY

MISS WICKS was an only daughter, who kept the house of her father, a widower. It was a pleasant old house, standing on the lot where, almost a hundred years before, the primitive hatters had lived. In the rear a garden with terraces extended down to the river. The broad slopes of the Russell farm and a part of the shoulder of Great Quabbin formed an attractive outlook from the rear windows. There were old-fashioned flowers in the beds below the house, such as roses, pinks, sweet-williams, peonies, balsams, geraniums, lilies, and violets ; and in front a horse-chestnut tree, a feathery larch, and a mountain-ash, with its clusters of pale coral, formed a checkered screen against the western sun.

Miss Wicks had enjoyed all the advantages of education then obtainable ; and, though far from beautiful, she was attractive on account of her delicacy of feeling, courtesy, and tact. No one who came to know her ever thought her plain. Upon a memorable evening she had invited the Grant sisters and two gentlemen to tea. Her father did not join the party until late.

One of the guests was the new doctor, Fletcher by name, who was a bit of a dandy, and conspicuous for wearing patent-leather straps to hold down his strained

"pantaloons." The other was David Wentworth, a
student who was absent from college on leave, engaged
in teaching a select school. The fact that he was so
employed was proof that he was not rich; but he was
neatly dressed, and his manners and speech showed
him well born and well bred. The contrast between
him and the doctor was marked. In the one case you
were earnestly regarding the man, in the other you
were more attracted by the clothes; for, besides the
innovation of trouser straps, the doctor was finical in
regard to linen and ornaments. He had the air of
a cultured man, but one who attached importance
to externals, and who flattered himself upon his
superiority.

The small party was seated around a large table, for
tea was not served in those days on dainty little stands
with trays, and there were two vacant places.

Miss Wicks was asking her guests to admire her old
china. "My father," she said, "bought it in Boston
the year after I was born."

"Now, really," said the doctor, "you can't call that
old china!"

"Old enough," said Miss Wicks, smiling. "Father
drove with mother from here to Boston, and was two
days on the road."

"A delicate and beautiful piece of porcelain," said
Wentworth, holding up a cup to the light. "Happy
the man who will be served by it."

The eyes of Eliza and Lois Grant exchanged a faintly
perceptible gleam.

"I thought," said the doctor, "you were going to tell
me it was brought from China by the old gentleman
opposite, — your relative, is he not? He looks as if he

might have been a mandarin of ever so many gold buttons."

"Our families have some slight relationship," said Miss Wicks, "but the set did not come from him. It is not rare, and I fancy it was made in France. — I was going to ask you, Mr. Wentworth, about your school. I have an interest in the young girls who are coming on. I remember what the schools were a few years ago, and I am glad to know that there are more advantages to-day."

The doctor perceived that he was set aside, and began to give his attention to his neighbor, Lois Grant. They talked of agreeable nothings in a desultory way, but after a while both were drawn to listen to the schoolmaster.

"It is grateful to know," said Wentworth, "that you are interested, for there is need of sympathy. At present it is like lifting a dead weight without leverage. My pupils learn their lessons, but they lack intelligence, or, I should say, they lack general knowledge. I happened the other day to make a reference to geology, and found they hadn't the least notion of it. For very shame I had to stop and make some explanations upon the structure of the earth's crust. That led to questions upon the time that must have been taken to harden the successive formations ; and, after a few seconds of mental calculation, I was asked if, according to the Bible, the creation of the world was not just four thousand and four years before Christ ? I suggested that it wasn't necessary to hold strictly to biblical chronology, for that was only a deduction from uncertain data, and the work of fallible men ; while the testimony of the rocks was evidence which could not be contradicted."

The doctor gave an approving nod to the inquiring glances of his neighbors, but Miss Wicks looked troubled. She said she had heard a sermon by Professor Hitchcock, the great geologist, and thought he showed there was no conflict between Genesis and geology.

"On that subject," said Wentworth, "I say nothing. For the sake of the book, I hope it is so ; science will take care of itself. I was giving that merely as an illustration of the want of knowledge. In literature the condition is worse. I was speaking to the class about Shakespeare, and, to my surprise, saw no responsive light in their faces. On inquiry, I found that not one had ever read a play or poem of his. I said something to show them his place among the world's great poets, and then a girl asked if Shakespeare did not write for the theatre ? if the theatre was not immoral, and if it was Christian to read his plays ? The questions and the faces of the class showed there had been *prévention* from some quarter, and I changed the subject."

"We had selections at our school," said Miss Grant, "but never plays entire."

The doctor looked amused.

"Our Shakespeare was edited, and with notes for the use of schools," said Miss Wicks.

"That 'editing' has been a sore subject," said Wentworth. "There has been sad work done in that way by male prudes. The main question is, if men and women can be called 'educated' who grow up in ignorance of the greatest poet of our race, — perhaps of any race. If my pupils were asked, I fear they would give that place to Dr. Watts."

"Dr. Watts!" cried the doctor gayly. "Methinks I hear —

> ' Let dogs delight to bark and bite.' "

"Ah, doctor," said Wentworth, "the infant rhymes are easily ridiculed; but you must not forget his hymns and his versions of the Psalms. Such lines as —

> ' Sweet fields beyond the swelling flood'

are beautiful and noble, and will be sung for centuries to come."

"It pains me," he continued, after a pause, "when I find an empty niche in a mind where Shakespeare's image should be; but, for most people, ignorance of Scott is quite as much to be regretted. Not to have read the ' Antiquary,' or ' Quentin Durward '! Not to have devoured ' Ivanhoe '! Not to have loved Flora MacIvor! I can hardly conceive it! I hope, Miss Wicks, you were encouraged to read those charming books?"

"I have read most of them. My parents did not approve of reading novels, but these were exceptional, for their history and their healthy tone. But I have no copies. I knew father would not like to have them on the shelves; and I don't think there is a full set in town. What do you say, Eliza?"

"I do not know of any. While at school we read several of the Waverley novels, not exactly by permission, because the rules were against all novels, but our teacher made no serious objection to our reading a few of the most famous."

"Well," said Wentworth, "I don't sympathize with any man who renounces for himself, or deprives others of, the pleasure of reading Scott."

"I wish I could read him a dozen times," said the doctor; "I am sure I should always feel the old thrill."

"The dead past," continued Wentworth, "lives in his pages. It is history visible and real. But do you think, Miss Wicks, that your minister objects to the Waverley novels?"

"I really don't know. I am afraid he does; not so much for anything in them, you know, but because they absorb the mind, and draw it away from serious things."

She was beginning to look solemn.

"Does he object to poetry as well?"

"He dotes on poetry," said Lois Grant. "He loves Virgil and Milton, and Gray and Wordsworth, and a great many more."

"And I heard him read a piece by Mr. Bryant, a recent poet," said Eliza Grant. "I can't think of the title, but it was about death, and as beautiful as slow music."

"'Thanatopsis,'" suggested Miss Wicks.

"That view of death is a fine poem for a youth of nineteen to have written," said Wentworth. — "You have heard of Edgar Poe?"

The ladies all shook their heads. He continued, "I think Poe may go far. He has produced few poems, but they have the stamp of genius, — classic from their birth."

"You seem to lay great stress on novels and poetry," said Miss Wicks.

"Yes; on noble fiction like Scott's, and on poetry of a high order. I wish to bring them near. I don't want scholars to think of the classic authors as so many statues set up in a gallery apart, but as real men.

of whom the latest are living to-day ; and that any of these may be put on pedestals in due time. It is a long stretch from Homer to the poet of your county newspaper, but it is not impossible. But I am preaching. Let me only add that I hope my scholars may be led to the affectionate study of works of genius, as well as to matters of every-day use."

There was a rap at the door, and a moment later the minister appeared, and was duly welcomed. It was evident that he was not wholly unexpected. Addressing Miss Wicks, he said, —

" My wife has gone out on a visit ; and, though I am tardy, I concluded to avail myself of your invitation. I am very fond of a cup of your fragrant tea."

When the usual small talk was ended, Miss Wicks said to the minister, very simply, " We have been talking of fiction and poetry, such as the Waverley novels and Shakespeare's plays ; we should all like to know what you think of them ? "

The minister's face was a study. He paused and looked at all the guests in turn. There was a visible struggle, as if taste and principle were at odds.

" If I were to speak of merits alone, as an abstract question," said he, " I should have to frankly commend them. I have read the Waverley novels, most of them, and Scott's romantic poems, and I have felt their charm. And I read Shakespeare while in college, not only with delight but with wonder and awe. And I admit in advance that his occasional grossness may be pardoned on account of the customs of his age. But I am a Christian minister, with souls in charge, for whom I must give account ; and I should not think myself justified if I were to favor the reading of romances or

poems, when my people have so little time for reading,
and when there is so much to be done for their eternal
welfare. Consider, sir," he said, addressing Wentworth
after a moment's pause, "for you are a scholar ; consider
in what light St. Paul regarded this matter. He could
have read, and probably had read, Homer, Æschylus,
Euripides, and Sophocles; and he may have known
enough Latin to have read Virgil. Do you think he
counselled his converts and followers to read Œdipus,
Prometheus, or the Æneid ? He turned his back on
that noble literature, and said 'for I determined not to
know anything among you except Jesus Christ and him
crucified.' "

"If you put it on the ground of there being no time,"
replied Wentworth, "I would ask if school-children
have not a reasonable expectation of many years ? If
you should carry your principle to its logical conclusion,
you would have them spend all their lives in prayer.
Don't you think, sir, God intended that men, besides
adoring and serving him, should rejoice in this beautiful world, and occupy themselves with literature and
science, and with cultivating a taste for the fine arts?
An all-round man ; one who is learned, accomplished,
and cheerful, besides being pious and good ; is he not
as pleasing in his sight as a filthy hermit crouching in
a cave, or set on a pillar in the Thebaid ? or as an
ignorant fanatic at a camp-meeting ? I don't mean to
be disrespectful. If God is the Founder of the sciences,
the Author of beauty and proportion, the Inspirer of
genius, the Fashioner of our faculties, how could he
wish us to check philosophic inquiry, to repress the
creative instinct, or to dry up the sources of feeling ?
Even laughter is as natural as crying, and a great deal
more wholesome."

"Your propositions have a broad reach," said the minister, "and I should not like to assent to them without consideration. I will say, however, that those who realize their true condition in a dying world, exposed to the wrath of God, will seldom be moved to laughter."

The phrases grated harshly in Wentworth's ears, but he shrank from touching the question of eternal punishment, and was glad to return to St. Paul.

"I think," said he, "there was another obvious reason why Paul did not give more attention to Greek poetry: it was based on the belief in the fabled divinities. What to us are Apollo, Mars, Diana, and Venus? Merely brilliant fictions, poetical conceptions; but as gods or idols they are non-existent. What prevents you and me from looking at an image of Hermes, like that of John of Bologna, with admiration for the artist, and with a clear conscience? In Paul's time it would have been an idolatrous symbol. He would be careful not to give countenance to a superstition which had overrun the world, and which was dying so hard."

"Our ancestors," said the minister, "had some scruples about the Greek and Latin classics, on account of their serving to keep alive a familiarity with false gods."

"I am aware of that," said Wentworth. "It is to be seen in Cotton Mather and others of his time; but when a man is afraid of being made an idolater by reading the fables of early ages, I should think him in a pitiable state of imbecility."

"The divine command is still in force," said the minister.

"True," replied Wentworth; "but I would ask you if it is not to be interpreted in its spirit, and with regard to the light of to-day? How can we conceive of the Almighty as 'jealous' of an airy nothing, or of an artistic image in marble? We do not deify the forces of nature, because we have found out the natural laws. We do not dread witches, as poor Cotton Mather did, for we know that occult practices are impossible and ridiculous. Science has swept the earth, sea, and sky clear of divinities and demons, leaving only the universe of matter, and God, its Creator. But we are not considering the question put by Miss Wicks. I was telling her I felt oppressed and hindered by the want of knowledge on the part of my pupils of the common facts of science, and of general ideas of literature. To know the 'three Rs' may enable people to live, but it is not enough to make them men and women. Don't you think there is need here for a library? for more reading, and on broader lines?"

"Yes, and for the grace of God," added the minister.

"But does his grace," asked Wentworth, "dwell by preference with ignorance and insensibility? It has been said that the church has not looked kindly upon any literature except its own, nor upon science not under its guidance. It seems to me the time has come when neither literature nor science can be fettered. It must be free for masters to teach what is known of the earth, of the people that have lived upon it, and of their ideas and works."

"Religion," said the minister, "is not hostile to science when taught by reverent men; nor to literature, with due regard to other necessary instruction, and to the preparation for the world to come."

"If a man should discover new laws of light," said

Doctor Fletcher, "or a way of utilizing the force of electricity, would you think his discovery less valuable because he happened to be an unbeliever?"

"No," said the minister; "but suppose he were an atheist trying to show that the universe has no need of God?"

"Like Laplace with his 'La Mécanique Céleste,'" suggested Eliza Grant.

"That would not be a question in physics, but metaphysics," said Wentworth. "In geology, for instance, there is no question either of theism or atheism. The geologist simply says that things are found *so*, and in such an order. It seems to me there is no science which may not, and should not, be taught with perfect reverence."

Here Mr. Wicks came in, apparently tired and preoccupied, and the conversation ceased. To judge by countenances, the doctor and Lois Grant had sided with Wentworth, while Eliza and Miss Wicks inclined to the minister's way of thinking.

Soon after leaving the table, Doctor Fletcher and Wentworth took their leave. The face of the latter was still glowing with excitement, and his good-by to Miss Wicks was noticeable for its mingling of admiration with respect. Again the sisters exchanged glances.

The minister's experience was novel and not wholly pleasant. It was the first time that any one in the village, in which his supremacy was unquestioned, had "withstood him to his face." But he contented himself with observing that Mr. Wentworth was a most enthusiastic young man.

"How I should like to have such a teacher," said

Lois Grant. "What a way he has! Why, he fairly takes you up and carries you along with him."

"No," said Eliza, half aside; "it was only Herman Field who could do that."

Miss Wicks heard the reminder; and, as she knew the old story of the sprained ankle, there was a mischievous laugh between her and Eliza. She said softly to Lois, —

"You have a *penchant* for schoolmasters."

The retort came in a twinkling, —

"There is one, I am sure, who has a *penchant* for you."

"I am afraid," said the minister, "he is too much set upon learning. I do not say puffed up by it; too much concerned with the things of this world. We have not talked of doctrine, but trifles are often significant. Did you observe that he said 'Paul,' and not 'St. Paul'? I should not be surprised to find that he is a Unitarian."

Mr. Wicks was looking at his daughter earnestly.

Lois Grant plucked up courage to ask, —

"Did not the saint speak of himself simply as 'Paul, an apostle'? I don't remember that any one is called 'saint' in the New Testament, except in the captions, and I suppose those may be modern."

"It is a matter of long usage in the church," said the minister, "and is not important except as an indication. Ah!" he continued, as he crossed his legs and tossed one foot, in a fit of abstraction, "these high-mettled youths! They mistake their exuberant spirits for a divine afflatus; their ecstasies upon the beauties of nature for worship; their instinctive sympathy for Christian benevolence, and the vague yearnings of an imaginative soul for communion with God. All things in earth are beautiful to them, when we know that sin and death have entered into the world; that there is no one good, not one, and that the heart is deceitful above all things, and desperately wicked. Of all the insidious forms of infidelity, none has wrought more evil than this new worship of nature,—as if it were anything more than the garment of a sinful world, soon to be destroyed by fire,—unless it be the twin delusion of glorifying human nature, which is corruption." After a pause he went on,—

"The plausible phrases of the modern enemies of Christ have seduced many. It is the latest invention of the great enemy of souls. And to think that the college founded by our pious forefathers for the purpose of training up laborers for the Lord's vineyard, the college whose motto was *Christo et Ecclesia*, should have fallen into the hands of those who dethrone Christ and undermine the foundations of his church! Ah, my dear young friends," he continued, looking solemnly at their attentive faces, "better to have the heart right toward God, than to shine in intellect, or to glow with an unchastened enthusiasm. If I were to advise a young lady upon her choice of a partner for life, I would say that a farmer or blacksmith who fears God is more worthy of love and honor than the most brilliant of the graduates of a Christless college."

Mr. Wicks's looks seemed to his daughter to say, "Did I not tell you so?"

CHAPTER XXIX

A TALK BY THE ROADSIDE

ONE Saturday afternoon David Wentworth set out for a walk, intending to climb the eastern hill and descend into the valley beyond. He passed the semicircle of the cove, starred with lilies ; crossed the thin fallow lands that were cultivated only once in two or three years ; then ascended the hillside pasture, bristling here and there with patches of sturdy huckleberry bushes, and soon gained the ridge. There were choppers at work felling tall trees ; and, as he saw one that appeared to be ready to fall, he waited. Blow after blow was struck into the heart of the trunk, while the chopper cast frequent glances at the quivering upper boughs. Soon he stepped aside, for there was a deeper thrill. Then came a wavering motion, an awful leaning, a breathless interval, a gathering rush, and a thundering downfall upon the leafy ground, while the rebounding branches and twigs were violently agitated, like the limbs of a giant in the last agony. To Wentworth the sensation was like seeing the fall of an ox under the blow of a butcher. But the chopper did not appear to be one who would be touched by sentiment, and the schoolmaster merely bowed and walked on. Along his path were piles of corded wood, heaps of chopped twigs, and the tracks made by the logs as they were hauled away. The clearing was thorough, and the hill was soon to have a bald head.

In the road below was a farmer taking the dimensions of a number of logs with a rule. Wentworth thought his face engaging, in spite of the stern lines at the corners of his mouth. Salutes were always exchanged in Quabbin, and it was considered courteous to say a friendly word in passing. Wentworth asked, —

"Is it your woodland that I have just crossed — up there where they are cutting down trees ?"

"I s'pose 'tis," said the farmer. "Be yeou f'm Quabbin ? "

"Yes; I am teaching school there."

"Yeou be, be yer ? Haow come ye ter climb the hill ? Didn't ye know ye could git raound at ary eend on't ? "

"I like to climb a hill; I need exercise. But I don't much like to see a fine big tree cut down."

"Nor I nuther."

"Why do you have them cut ? "

"Got ter live somehaow. Raisin' grain don't pay. 'Less we sold milk, or killed a critter naow an' then, we sh'd starve. Ye see, when we country folks run behindhan', we hain't no chahnce to make it up by spec'-lation. Ef we try spec'lation, we air sure ter git took in. Ther' ain't nothin' for us but hard work an' elbow grease. Some years ago we had a leetle flurry here, an' every man an' boy thought he was goin' ter be rich by raisin' *Morus multicaulis.* I don't know many larned names, but we all come ter know *thet.* Haow the d'lusion got started I never 'xackly knew. 'Twa'n't reason nor common-sense; for mulberry-trees ain't good for nothin', 'ceptin' to raise silkwums; an' everybody orter know this ain't the climate to raise 'em. People said somebody way off was goin' to want the trees — jest ez though they couldn't be raised better where they was wanted. But the fever was up. Folks paid fifty cents a-piece for trees not so big ez yer leetle finger, and not more'n *so* high. They used these to make cuttin's of, and put 'em to sprout under glass. Some used ol' cowcum'er frames, and some built hot-haouses, an' kep' the steam up days an' nights an' Sundays. Some o' the fust ones *made*, 'cause they sold trees an' cuttin's t' others thet was startin' in. But by an' by the thing fell ez flat ez a cold slap-jack. Yer couldn't give away a tree. Some was bit pooty bad. Even sech a smart man ez Wicks. Ef yer want ter make him mad, y've on'y to say, '*Morus multicaulis.*'"

"The experience was salutary, though painful," said Wentworth. "But you won't have any more oaks to cut."

"Trew 'nough. Them air's ben growin' sence afore my father's time; when they're gone, we sh'll hev to du sunthin' else."

"People used to live without cutting off their trees."

"Thet's so; but folks didn't use ter treat their crops an' airnin's like a cowcumber, — eat out the middle and fling away both eends."

"I thought the people about here were economical."

"So they be — some on 'em; an' some is runnin' to new funnitoor an' carpets. The man who must hev new carpets to walk on when he's ter hum won't stan' on his own graass ou' doors but a leetle while."

"What has made the change in the value of crops?"

"Railroads, an' one thing 'n nuther. I kin buy a

bushel o' corn fer fifty cents that I couldn't raise fer less 'n seventy-five."

" I suppose I am talking to Captain Newcomb?"

" Jes' so ; an' yeou air " —

" Wentworth is my name."

" Oh, yis. I heerd somebody tell 'baout haow yeou gin it tu the minister t'other day."

" We had some talk about books and reading, — all in a friendly way."

" They say yeou gin it to him, all the same."

" And are you not the man who objected to giving so much to the missionaries abroad, while there was money needed for schools at home?"

" I s'pose I be. I ain't ashamed on't. But I hear the minister says yeou air a Unitarian."

" He is welcome to say it. I have never talked about doctrines, and I don't belong to any church."

" Air yeou f'm Harvard College, daown ther' nex' tu Boston?"

" No ; but I should like to be able to graduate there."

" What sh'd make the minister say yeou was a Unitarian?"

" Unitarians are liberal, and he probably thought I was not strict enough in regard to the books that should be read."

" Weren't ther' nothin' said 'baout the Trinity ner futur' punishment?"

" Nothing."

" I'm kinder sorry. I was in hopes ter hear 'baout it. I don't take no stock in the lake o' fire an brimstun myself."

" I don't think such discussions do any good. I don't believe in any punishment that is endless, for that seems to me against the justice of God; but I never argue upon the subject. My notion is to make the best use of life, to get all the knowledge possible, to love God, be cheerful, and do all the good I can."

"A man who doos that, he's in heaven a'ready."

"So I think."

"Air yeou a-goin' ter preach?"

"Not that I know of. I haven't decided what I shall do."

"'Pears like yeou orter. Yeour talk is saound sense. Folks is tired o' doctrine, like bein' tired o' smoked an' pickled meat, an' want sunthin' fresh, like dewty an' sunshine. We've hed an awfle lot o' doctrine fust an' last; an' sometimes the more doctrine the more deviltry. What I mean is, the more doctrine was preached, the more the wicked pulled t'other way, like contr'y steers. I've often thought them critters might a' ben got hold on by the right man, — the man tnet'd take 'em right."

"You never have any but orthodox preaching here I understand."

"No, 'less it's Methodist; an' thet don't 'maount ter much. Ther' ain't but 'baout a dozen on 'em; an' jes' as soon's they git a leetle 'quainted 'ith their minister, off he goes. I dunno ez ary Unitarian or Universaller ever preached in Quabbin. We hear on 'em raound abaout, like fer-off thunder in a summer arternoon, but they never come a-nigh."

"I think, as time goes on, preaching will be more practical. Religion is a matter of life and character. Christ never talked theology, and if you could have asked his disciples, it isn't likely that any two of them would have agreed upon a *system*, for they probably had none ; but they all knew what Christ wanted them to do and be."

" Wal, young man, yeou're the man ter du it. Yeou sh'd take up preachin'. Folks is tired o' 'lection an' all thet ; many hain't the head to un'erstan' it. But ef they kin see thet they're in etarnity right *naow*, an' that *naow's* the time ter du good an' be good, they won't wanter go a-mournin' all their days, so's to make ready for the joyful hereafter."

" But in spite of doctrinal preaching, or, perhaps, on account of it, you think the place has been improving ? "

" Land sakes, yis. Ye hain't no idee what a state o' things ther' was when I was a boy. Ther' was some stiddy men an' good men, but ther' was an awfle lot o' drunken, fightin', swearin' fellers, thet made the village hot a'most every time they come into 't. They was allus raisin' Cain, cuttin' off hoss's tails, an' pizenin' honest dogs. Oh, things is quieted daown. Ther's less h'ash talk, more schoolin', comf'tabler haousen, an' nicer-lookin' women an' childern. Folks go an' come, sence the railroad, an' they bring new idees. Quabbin's a leetle taown, an' allus will be ; but ther' ain't no place so lonely's in the ol' times."

The conversation went on with increased animation, and the two men, strangers until that day, were becoming friends. Wentworth was always pleased to talk with a straightforward and natural man. They were leaning against the fence, and the farmer was showing him how he calculated the contents of a log.

There was a sound of wheels in the sandy road, and Wentworth, looking up, saw a light wagon coming, in which were Miss Wicks and the Grant sisters. They were evidently taking a drive around the hill. He raised his hat and bowed, and was civilly greeted in return. When they had passed, Captain Newcomb said, —

"A gal o' good sense, thet Miss Wicks is. She ain't no gre't beauty, but she looks *good* 'nough tu eat. She won't hev no gre't fortin', sech ez the Grant gals 'll git some day, but it's my 'pinion she hain't her ekal in taown."

"You think well of the Misses Grant also, do you not?"

"Oh, yis; they're smart an' well-eddicated, an' though folks say they air high-flyers, I don't think ther's anythin' *bad* abaout 'em. They've got larnin' an' hev seen life, an' air goin' to hev money 'nough ter du what they wanter; so I don't wonder they caper over Quabbin ez though 'twa'n't o' much 'caount. The youngest hed a love-scrape a year or two ago 'ith a schoolmaster; but I guess she's got over it, an' none the wuss. But the Wicks gal's the one for *my* money."

"Miss Wicks appears to be all you say."

"Yis; but her father's curus. He jest turns raound the minister like the moon raound the airth. Ef the minister says, 'It's fair weather,' why, 'tis fair; ef he says, 'Go back an' git an umberell,' why, he goes back. Ez long's the minister stays here, an' Mr. Wicks lives, no feller need think he kin git that girl 'thout hevin' the minister on his side."

"From the number of ancient spinsters, there does not seem to be much marrying here."

"No; we've lost aour young people, an' keep a-losin' 'em. This region hez gin' its life-blood ter the Western country; fust ter York State, then ter 'Hio, Indianny, Michigan, an' so on. 'Stonishin', when I think on't, haow they've gone. Eenamost every haouse hez lost its sons or darters, or both. No, ther's leetle merryin' naow, 'cep' naow an' then when some ol' gran'ther merries a widder in caps an' false hair. But thet ain't *merryin'*! It's on'y a trick to save usin' a brass warmin'-pan. Sech weddin's ez them on'y make me feel lonesome. I couldn't go to one on 'em; 'twould grip me by the throat. I'd ruther go tu a fun'rul, an' done 'ith it, ef so I could nomernate the corpse."

Two chance seeds had been planted in Wentworth's mind, whose development might determine his future; one, that it was, perhaps, his duty to preach the gospel; the other, that Miss Wicks was worth consideration.

"Du yeou ever go a-fishin'?" asked the farmer.

"Seldom," said Wentworth. "I walk about the country whenever I can: it refreshes me, soul and body; but fishing seems to me a rather indolent amusement; and then, I never have any luck, which is the same as to say I have no skill."

"I don't fish much, nuther, but I like sometimes to go to a quiet, shady place 'long with some sensible feller. While yeou 're flingin' a line yeou don't talk much; only a word naow an' then, — jest the notion of the minnit, — sunthin' like a float that bobs on the water when an idee comes along; an' the pond, an' the trees, an' bushes say the rest on't. Naow ther's a pond not more'n a mile f'm here, an' not fer f'm the road; an' when yeou 're on the bank yeou can't see a haouse nor a sign of a livin' creetur'. Yeou'd think yeou was ten miles in the woods; jest trees an' sky, an' a poorty leetle pond, raound ez a bowl, so still, an' a'most mournful-like, ef it wa'n't fer the water-lilies."

"You make me wish to see the pond," said the

schoolmaster; "and I like your notion of nature's filling in the gaps in a conversation. Yes, I should like to go with you some good day."

"Take the fust lowery day, when it ain't actilly rainin.' I've poles an' lines, an' yeou might bring 'long a couple of new hooks. Some leetle shaver in the village will git us the shiners" (minnows). "We mayn't ketch pickerel, but we'll hev the fun of tryin'."

"The good people of Quabbin will think us a couple of boys."

"I allus expect to be a boy myself. An' ther's no man that *is* a man, who can't be a boy sometimes."

CHAPTER XXX

AN ARRIVAL

THE morning stage-coach from the " Deepo " (the nearest railroad station), one day brought to the village hotel (styled "tavern" no longer) a passenger, whose appearance and "kit" excited some curiosity. There were straggling groups of people near the hotel veranda and about the post-office, who, besides diligently chewing tobacco, had the responsible duty of inspecting the daily arrivals, and, in consequence, felt themselves relieved from other work.

The stranger was of medium height, and wore a soft, gray, broad-brimmed hat, a brown velvet "cut-away" coat, conspicuous white wristbands, a wide linen collar turned down over a poppy-colored silk necktie, and a full, dark, wavy beard, showing gleams of red in the sun. He had been seated beside the driver, and stepped down lightly, as one to whom an alert movement was habitual. His features were pleasing, and the expression of good-humor in his brilliant gray eyes, together with the smile that at times lifted his ruddy mustaches and disclosed his white teeth, arrested general attention. This person was a problem for the inspectors on duty, both at the post-office and the hotel.

"Tell ye what, Hi," said a lank fellow in a palm-leaf hat, whose dress consisted mainly of a shady woollen shirt, and a pair of loose trousers, hoisted almost to his armpits by leather "galluses," the ends being tucked into the faded red tops of a pair of mouldy looking boots, "tell ye what, thet's a curus chap. Jes' look at thet baird!"

"Je-whillikins!" exclaimed the second inspector, thus appealed to, — a sturdy fellow all in russet from his hair to his boots. "'Tis a baird, an' no mistake. *Ain't* it nasty? I sh'd think I was some sort o' critter or other, ef I let hair grow all over my face an' mouth like thet air. I hain't seen nothin' like it, 'ceptin' ol' Lamson's, an' hisn was white. An', I say, Obed, jes' look at thet velvet jacket!"

"Yis," said Obed; "an' thet red neckhan'kercher. A pooty lively chap he must be."

"What d'ye think he is?" said Hiram. "A circus-rider?"

"Wal, no; I sh'd think he's more likely ter be a trillerkist" (ventriloquist), "or sleight-o'-hand feller, or one o' them thet crawls inter a hot oven, and drors in arter him a piece o' beef to roast."

"Anyhow, he's some sort o' showman. An', see ther'! What's the driver handin' daown? Some sort o' wooden frame. Some o' his kit."

"An' look," said Obed, "for the land's sakes! at thet air white umbereller! Big 'nough fer a Sunday-skule picnic on a rainy day."

"An' jes' see," continued Hiram, "thet all-fired long handle tu it, 'ith an iron spike on the eend! Wal, I vum, thet's the beatenest!"

"An' ther's his trunk, an' a carpet-bag, an' a m'hog-any box 'ith brass handles. Oh, he's some kind o' showman, fer sartin!"

The object of this attention disappeared within the hotel, and a few of the inspectors gathered to examine his " kit." The wooden frame was " a stumper" for them ; they could not make out the use of it. On the trunk were the initials L. A. S., and on the brass plate of the mahogany box was the name L. A. Stewart. The name was unfamiliar to the inspectors ; it belonged to no " trillerkist" or other showman they had heard of.

Soon from an upper window of the hotel was heard a voice calling in a marked New York accent, " Waiter ! waiter ! won't some one answer the bell ? I want a pitcher of water, and to have my boots brushed."

The last was an unheard-of request, and caused much unfavorable comment upon the veranda below : "Couldn't he bresh his own boots ? " — " Wonder who was his nigger ter hum ? " and other less complimentary remarks. Then the opinion began to take form that this " 'ristercrat who wanted so much waitin' on " was, maybe, " a lord, or some other kind o' furriner," and there was intense curiosity to know what had brought him to Quabbin.

The excitement was somewhat calmed when the schoolmaster was seen approaching the hotel. David Wentworth, who had been sent for, came to call on his old friend and sometime classmate, Louis Stewart, and there was a joyous meeting. Stewart was a landscape painter, and had brought his easel and a box of colors, to do some sketching. His sister had been a friend of Miss Wicks, and of Eliza and Lois Grant at school, and had recently been visiting them. The two friends made a brief call at both houses, and were warmly received. All the young ladies were impressed by the painter's manners and presence. He had the air which should belong to the best society, and his conversation though lively was unobtrusive. He quite outshone Wentworth on account of his knowledge of the world, and familiarity with men of distinction ; although, perhaps, in intellect and training, as well as in certain ideal traits of character, the schoolmaster was the superior. But Stewart's joyous nature, frank smile, and unfailing tact, were irresistible. Wentworth had the manners of a student, and his habitual life was more interior, so that he was often silent when a man of the world would have seen and improved opportunities.

If Stewart felt an inclination toward any of the ladies, it was not shown ; but Wentworth was transparent as a sunbeam, and his devotion to Miss Wicks was always evident. It was clear that it was thought much to the credit of the schoolmaster that he had such a brilliant friend. There was much talk of scenery, and plans were formed to take the artist to favorite spots. Promising to return in the evening, the young men took leave.

After the customary early dinner at the hotel, the two friends went up Great Quabbin, the schoolmaster being the guide. On the way, as they paused to look back, the painter's practised eye took in the calm impression of the valley with the village and river, the graceful curves of the cove, and the outlines of the so-called mountains. The autumn colors were just beginning to glow, and the landscape was as warm as a picture by Cuyp. At the top they roamed over the broad convexity, among the surprised cattle that ran and capered, and then stopped and snorted. Now they were looking at the blue cloud which was Monadnock, — now at the black and strongly marked Holyoke range, and toward the dim cone of Sugar Loaf, and now to the sharp outline of a distant hill in Connecticut.

"A delightful spot," said Stewart. "I could enjoy this air and this prospect for hours."

"I have always felt here a singular repose," said Wentworth, "a repose that is in effect a quiet exalta- tion, a pleasing loneliness, away from earthly affairs, and from black care."

"If it were new to you, it would not seem reposeful. The breadth of view, — over a hundred miles, I judge, — is glorious, uplifting. It is not the height of this hill, for it cannot be more than eight hundred feet, but its fortunate position which makes the grand outlook. Our eyes sweep over what seems like a vast plain on which young mountains have sprouted, and are just heaving up their round heads. No, this is not a place for repose. My thoughts rise from this plateau, hover over all those billowy ranges and deep-sunk valleys, and bathe in that mist of gold in the west. I could do anything here but paint. This scene could be repre- sented only in a panorama."

They walked down the hill toward Crombie's bridge, and then sauntered along the river.

"Now, here I could paint," said Stewart; "here are several points of view, — that quaint old timber bridge, the glossy black water, which looks evil enough to have drowned many a thoughtless swimmer, the frayed cur- tain of willows and alders; and then, looking the other way, that dense heap of tree-tops, and the white spire over them; yes, I could make some pictures here."

"A little farther down stream," said Wentworth,

"there is a place where the river has left its old bed and cut a new channel; and there is a series of curving embankments, one stretching out beyond the other, and always returning. Seen from below, they are like grass-grown fortifications; from above they are simply rings of excavations. Nature is smoothing them over, but will not soon obliterate them. There are some rather fine trees too. We will see them some day."

"The factories are ugly," said Stewart, looking toward the village, "but the little river is pretty; and the 'lay of the land' is charming. In early times, when the region was wilder, it must have been beautiful."

"I wish you would set up your easel somewhere in this meadow."

"I will; but first I want to look the ground over. Has any one sketched here?"

"Not that I know of. It is an out-of-the-way place. And besides, artists generally look for more contrasts or strong effects."

"I know that is the tendency; but an artist ought to find use for all his power and skill in painting even the simplest scene. There isn't a spot I walk over when I am in the country, not a tree or bush, not a living creature, in which there is not something that appeals to me."

"I am not an artist; but an untaught man, perhaps, may have a similar feeling. I see men with heavy boots trampling upon bunches of green and gold moss, or on leaves whose veins and colors are beyond art, and with no more thought of the delicate things they are crushing than an ox. Leaves must be trodden on, but, apart from that, there is seldom any sense of the sacredness of God's work."

"People suppose that beauty is to be sought for in some far-away region, and under exceptional conditions ; when it is at their own doors, and wherever they go. If they really loved nature, this would not be so."

"Love of nature does not seem to be common in the country, — not hereabouts. As for city people, I believe it is mostly the novelty that appeals to them ; while the feeling is fresh they are exalted, but unless it has some root in the heart it soon withers."

"The chatter of fashionable people about the loveliness of rural scenes never touches me," said the painter. "I prefer the frank brutality of a countryman, who, if he feels nothing, pretends nothing."

"'Frank brutality' exactly expresses the state of things here," said Wentworth, "both as to nature and art. I have seen only one picture in Quabbin that could be called artistic ; and that is the portrait of a retired China merchant, a man of evident distinction. It is well painted, and mellow as an autumn sunset. There isn't another picture in town, except one of an old doctor, that you would look at ten seconds. There are a few engravings, commonly heads of famous preachers or other public men. One that is often seen is a grim portrait of Caleb Strong, of Northampton, a former governor. Most frequently you will see in the parlor, among wrought 'samplers' and funereal urns, various-colored lithographs. Consider, if you can, what that means, — a coarse, ill-drawn picture of a general on a prancing horse, or of a girl with a kitten or puppy, or a mother with a child, or the like ; and then the color ! — crude red and blue, put on thick, as children daub picture-books. You will see such atrocities in the houses of worthy people who ought to know better.

But there is a lower deep. Image venders have found their way to this Arcadia, or Bœotia, and have brought, not the pretty figurines, the little Bacchuses, Venuses, and Mercuries, — those would be improper, and perhaps idolatrous, — but plaster vases of plaster fruits, rudely colored ; a vivid green apple, a yellow and red peach, and a bunch of purple grapes, stuck in a heap upon the ghastly white plaster. It makes one feel ill to think of it."

" And yet," said the painter, " while I sympathize in your distress, all this shows the existence of a longing for beauty, — in color, at least, — and a groping toward the light ; just as the flower-pot at the sewing-girl's window, and the poppies and pinks by the laborer's door, show a yearning for something beyond the satisfaction of primary wants. There is a foothold for art everywhere."

" Since people of taste generally agree about forms and colors," said Wentworth meditatively, " I wonder if the arrangements and harmonies of nature are absolutely beautiful in themselves, or if they seem beautiful because we have become accustomed to them, and educated by them ? The richness of color in those maples, with the ground of green grass, and with the blue sky and white clouds, seem to our eyes a perfect whole ; but should we have thought the arrangement ugly or incomplete, if it had been otherwise predestined ? "

" I will answer you with a parable that I have long had in mind," said Stewart. "There was a race of beings that lived habitually in a dim light, and found themselves well nurtured and content. The surface of their world was smooth, and of a uniform dark red.

Slight vegetation was apparent, except in tracts where grew tall, silky bushes, very frail and easily swayed. Some of these bushes appeared as tall as trees, but all had the same slender stalks, as if they were mere filaments leaning on each other. The colors of this vegetation ranged from silver gray to turquoise and beryl. The combination of the universal red ground with the gray, green, and blue shrubbery, whether in the forests and jungles, or in the more open spaces, was very striking. The inhabitants thought it perfect and predestined, and their philosophers taught that the existence of a Creator was proved by the fact of this harmonious correspondence, which could not have come about by chance, and which, they said, was absolute, and founded in the nature of things. They could not conceive of any other colors. Their artists also praised the frail, swaying, silky shrubbery, and found in it a new proof of wise design.

"Their world was pervaded by a peculiar odor, not wholly unpleasant; it was in themselves, the soil, productions, and atmosphere. They professed they could not imagine a world without this odor; and this was another proof of goodness and wisdom.

"Their world was of some extent, and few had travelled over it; where they were born, there within narrow limits they lived and died. But the most adventurous had never found rocks or caverns, or streams of water. It was wonderfully uniform, and was made to be the home of millions, — the best of possible worlds for material uses, and for the divine sense of beauty.

"Their happiness long continued under their dim light, with their fore-ordained harmonies of color, and with the odor which was a part of the system of things.

"But one day there came a flash that lightened the whole globe, then an earthquake shock, and a cataclysm. Trees and shrubs and clinging thousands were swept away in universal ruin.

"The grocer's boy had opened a wire gauze safe, and scraped a cheese."

"I see your drift," said Wentworth. "You think we have no faculty of independent judgment?"

"As much as a nursing child has to pronounce upon the flavor and bouquet of its mother's milk."

"Your parable is hard upon Paley."

"That is merely incidental. I was thinking of the contrast between our assumption of absolute judgment and our real helplessness. We are a part of the arrangement, and cannot get away, any more than we can jump from the globe into space. We talk of 'creation,' and have never drawn an original line. The genius is the fortunate fellow who comes upon things, — finds them. Forests and caverns taught us architecture; frost-work, flowers, fruit, shells, and other natural objects, have suggested ornament; and the earth and sky furnish our palette of colors. We combine pre-existing elements, and never conceive anything new. These thoughts, in some pedant's phrase, are *obviosities;* and I bring them up only to show that our appreciation of form and color is something inevitable. Therefore anything which repels the eye of a sane, cultivated, observing man is certain to be wrong. If, by and by, chemistry should produce new tones of colors that sting the eye, — some trenchant red, or piercing blue, or remorseless green, — the vulgar might be attracted, but the wise would shun them. The color you do not find in nature is false in art."

"Your statement," said Wentworth, "may be considered an artist's confession of faith, and it has suggested, perhaps vaguely, several analogies. In medicine, leading men are giving up the coarse and violent remedies called 'heroics,' and are relying more upon the curative power of nature. As air and water make climate, it is seen that slight and impalpable things are all powerful to build up or to undermine bodily health. In steering a boat the merest touch upon the tiller alters the course. In following nature man imitates the Eternal Wisdom, which never expends the least surplus of energy. And in theology there is a deep movement, a disposition to return to nature, a new faith in human possibilities. There is a growing distrust of metaphysical subtilties, and of religious systems laid out for demonstration, like theorems in geometry; of attempts at the analysis of the first cause, and of the geography of the moral universe, or at settling the future of all human souls. As we have what we think are natural sentiments of justice, we ought not to accept as true a scheme of the moral government of the world which outrages those sentiments. This sentiment of justice is the witness of God in our hearts, and it cannot be wrong or rash to trust it; for nature must be one with God."

Stewart looked at his friend with some curiosity, and saw by his earnest manner that there was something serious going on within.

They had passed the village, and were on the curves near the cove. The western sun was touching the spire, making its vane a gleam, and kindling all the maples to a blaze. The sheet of water above the dam showed fair reflections, and the hills were bright against the sky.

"We had better return," said Wentworth. "Late in the day it becomes chilly here."

"Well," said Stewart, "you can call for me after supper, and we will go to see the girls."

CHAPTER XXXI

AN EXCURSION

THE prospect from the Wilson place, on the western side of the Great Hill, was reputed to be the finest in the region. It was distant, and the road was hilly and rough, but all who visited it came back in raptures. David Wentworth had finished his school, and was on the point of returning to college; but he gladly stayed on a few days to be with his friend Stewart. A party was made up for an excursion to the famous spot, consisting of Miss Wicks, the Grant sisters, the painter, and the schoolmaster, and a newly arrived theological student, James Stowe, who was Mr. Grant's guest. A light stage-coach with a pair of horses was procured, and a stable boy was engaged as driver. The vehicle was not luxurious, but was comfortable, and the leathern curtains were rolled up, to allow a view in all directions.

It was a fine day in September, and though the sun was warm the air was cool and bracing. The forests were still mostly green, though showing here and there some brilliant spot of red or yellow. The maples along the roadside were in their glory of mingled colors; golden-rod flamed in the pastures, and deep red spikes of sumach were seen in the fence corners. Cattle were cropping the late grass in the meadows, while red pumpkins lay basking between the rows of Indian corn, whose stiffening leaves gave a papery rustle as the light airs lifted them. Crows gathered in the oaks in search of acorns, and now and then swept down with harsh cries upon the cornfields. Blue jays were screaming in hazel bushes, and blackbirds were merry and busy.

After passing the West Branch the ascent was steady for several miles, and the progress was slow. Farm succeeded farm, where men or boys were digging potatoes, or cutting corn-stalks for fodder, and stopped to see the gay-looking party go by. Houses looked poorer, and yards less tidy, as they ascended. At the doors were rows of milk-pans in the sun, and under the windows were strings of sliced apples or of red peppers. There were no signs of squalor or suffering, but life was evidently between narrow lines, and little enlivened by gayety.

When the back-bone of the hill was crossed, the coach stopped where the road began to descend, and the party got out to walk. The farm they were to visit was off the highway at the left, and the road leading to it was not considered safe. However, the coach followed slowly and joltingly, and reached the spot without an overturn.

While walking toward the pasture, Stewart said to Wentworth apart, "What sort of a fellow is this Stowe? He looks bilious and sullen. Divinity, I think you said. Is it a domestic parson, or a missionary for export?"

"I know scarcely anything of him," replied Wentworth. "I believe he is in the last year of his course, and is already licensed to preach. He seems to follow our friend Lois with his eyes."

"We will see to that," said Stewart in his gay and

triumphant way. "I don't want to lose a prize, — if it should be a prize; and I think a man might easily get the better of that gloomy fellow."

Wentworth fell back to talk with Miss Wicks; Stewart succeeded in detaching Lois, — not without some skilful tactics, — and the discomfited divinity student followed with Eliza. When they reached the spot, all sat down to enjoy the prospect. The driver had hitched the horses to a fence, and followed on with the luncheon-basket, volunteering to point out the places in sight.

"Thet nighest taown ther' is Ahmust (Amherst). Yeou kin see the colleges on the rise o' land, jest a leetle Saouth. Daown yander is Maount Holyoke; yeou kin see the haouse on top on't. Jest across f'm ther' is Ol' Hadley, wher' the river makes an ox-bow. In among them woods is Northampton. Yeou kin see tew steeples. Furder on is the Berksher Hills. It's all kinder mixt thet way, part woodsy an' part misty. Thet air hill up yander, all blue an' pupple, is Sugar Loaf. Ef 'twa'n't fer the mist you'd see a lot more taowns. It's fust-rate land all the way f'm Sunderland daown ter the p'int of Holyoke. Jest ez pooty's ever yeou see. Raise lots o' broomcorn. But to see it all ther's a better place by yander rock."

Here the volunteer cicerone was thanked, and allowed to retire.

"When we look across this beautiful basin," said Wentworth, "and consider the wide space that has been affected by the river in past ages, we try to think what a mighty flood it must have been, and what a time must have been required to cut its way between Tom and Holyoke, and spread out the alluvial soil."

"The aspect of to-day is what interests me," said Stewart. "For a painter, the earth is like a belle, — its beauty is only skin-deep. And then, Wentworth, some of us may be tender-footed on the antiquity of the earth." And he smiled at Mr. Stowe.

"Oh, no," said Stowe with solemnity; "religion accepts the facts of geology, but without admitting the necessity of such enormous periods of formation. God could have created the world in one condition or in another. He could have called it into being with all its strata just as they are."

"God could have done many things he has not chosen to do," said Wentworth. "Geology shows what he has done. And as to creation, let me ask you if in the Hebrew there is any notion of God's calling the world out of nothing? I don't know Hebrew; but I have been told that in the passage, 'In the beginning,' etc., the word 'created' signifies 'formed,' and that creation, as understood in theology, is the conception of a later age."

"Don't answer him," said Stewart, laughing. "This picnic isn't going to be turned into a Scripture debating-society." Then calling the driver, he sent him to the house for a teakettle of boiling water. "And now, Wentworth," he continued, "you and Mr. Stowe can spread out the luncheon; say, some stratifications of bread, with interstices of butter, and some bowlders in the shape of eggs. Divide that pie into six isosceles triangles with curved bases, and cut down that fruit-cake so as to exhibit the conglomerate elements, allowing sixty degrees of the circumference in each segment."

Wentworth smiled at the timely rebuke. The basket was opened, a cloth was spread on the grass, and,

by the help of the young ladies, the luncheon was tastefully laid out. The youth soon returned with the hot
water, Miss Wicks infused some of her fragrant tea, and
the party sat down to enjoy the repast.

Then Stewart produced a small canvas and arranged
for it a support with sticks, in order to make a rough
sketch of the central part of the landscape.

Mr. Stowe, who had been lingering near, endeavoring
to engage Lois Grant in conversation, suggested that
there would probably be a better view from the projecting point on the hillside mentioned by the driver,
which was a little distance farther; but when she
caught an expressive look from the painter, she sat
down by his side, saying, "We can come here again for
this view, but there will not be an artist with us, and I
am curious to see how a sketch is made."

The easy way in which she shook off the attentions
of the divinity student, and devoted herself to the
painter, was amusing to all but one person. If Stowe's
self-love was touched by the repulse, he had too much
pride to show it, and he began talking with Eliza as if
nothing had happened.

Said Wentworth to Miss Wicks, "The young preacher
would have preferred Rachel, but, if he cannot get her,
he will take up with Leah. After all, they should be
equally attractive; they are both beautiful, and they
will inherit alike."

"Do you think he has mercenary motives?"

"Clergymen, as well as other people, marry rich
wives when they can, and that he has come here with
matrimonial intentions is clear enough."

"I suppose every minister needs a wife to help him
in his work," said Miss Wicks.

"And he would not find a rich father-in-law an obstacle," said Wentworth.

"Does a painter like Mr. Stewart have a good position in society?" asked Miss Wicks with some hesitation. "I mean a painter who lives by his work."

"Yes, the best, — among liberal-minded people. If a painter is successful, and a man of good character, there is nothing equivocal about his position, either in regard to income or social consideration."

"Isn't his dress just a little peculiar?"

"Perhaps so; but artists are allowed to dress as they please; while a financier or a lawyer who should permit himself to wear a velvet coat or red necktie would infallibly lose credit. I know a man of character and solid means, who was lately refused a discount at a Boston bank because he wore mustaches. The cashier bluntly told him the reason. In the world of business there is no tolerance for eccentricity; while an artist is a 'chartered libertine,' — not in the evil sense, you know."

After a little time Miss Wicks seated herself by Lois, near Stewart, and looked on at his rapid work. Mr. Stowe and Eliza Grant had gone on to the place for the vaunted prospect, and for Wentworth there was nothing to do but join the girls who were watching Stewart's progress. He was not consciously jealous; but he felt his friend's social superiority, and he was looking intently upon Miss Wicks's face to catch any indication of her feeling. He saw that Stewart's fascinating manner had made an impression upon all, and that he might be, if he chose, a strong competitor, even with the gracious, sedate, or saintly Miss Wicks. The three adjectives floated over her image in his mind, and he was not sure which of them belonged to her. But what likelihood was there that Stewart, who was in the height of favor in New York society, would think seriously of any country girl? And if he did, would it not be the pretty and vivacious Lois? But, probably, he was intent only upon the pleasure of the moment. And then Wentworth judged himself a jealous fool to have been seeking to intercept glances of intelligence, and to have made himself miserable upon supposition. Jealousy, as he reflected, was an irrational self-torture at best. And what right had he to be jealous? Though he adored Miss Wicks, she had not manifested anything beyond courtesy and good-will. And then the insurmountable obstacles, — his unfinished studies, his lack of position and fortune, his liberal opinions. "Fool, fool!" he said to himself, "better cram your impulses back into your heart, get through this day, keep out of temptation in future, and leave Quabbin!" This wisdom, however, had only a short reign.

Meanwhile, the sketch was becoming a vivid impression, and the young ladies were full of admiration. Soon Mr. Stowe and Eliza Grant returned with a glowing account of the view from the rock. Stewart cast a rapid glance at them, and mentally observed that there was something in their faces besides scenery. But Wentworth's regards were only for Miss Wicks; and he said, "Since we have come so far, perhaps we ought to go there, and get the best view. Suppose we all go?"

"Thank you, no," said Stewart. "I must not waste a moment; and I don't wish to confuse the impressions of views from different points. The rest of you can go."

Wentworth looked an earnest interrogation to Miss Wicks, who, after a little hesitation, said, "Yes, I will go. Will you come too, Lois?" Lois was evidently reluctant, and answered, —

"Perhaps I may follow you later. I am much interested in *our* sketch."

The pair started off, while Mr. Stowe and Eliza strolled about arm-in-arm, leaving the painter and Lois by themselves.

If this young lady's thoughts could have been successively photographed, the train would have appeared something like this : —

"A charming man ; original, and a little brusque, yet delicate and not egotistic. I don't read him clearly. His heart is not worn on his sleeve. Can he be engaged already? All engaged men ought to be labelled, just as other mortgages are recorded. How he works! And he has not said one word that all the world might not hear. Yet his eyes asked me to sit down beside him. Perhaps he thinks he can throw his handkerchief, like a sultan. Or perhaps he isn't a marrying man ; artists are said to be queer ; and he talks about loving his art. To love a woman is more to the purpose. Now that Alma Wicks is away he might take the time to say something nice. Anyhow *she* can't have him alone. Eliza can have that dark-looking minister *for all me*. I wonder if the schoolmaster will propose to Alma? I believe he is dying to ; but she won't have him : her father wouldn't let her. I should be afraid to trust him ; he is too much like Herman Field ; too frank by half. I like this shrewd painter better. All the same, I wish Wentworth would sometime propose to me. I might play with him, — just a little, —

and then I should refuse him ; and my account with
schoolmasters would be square.   I wonder if Stewart
is like some artists, — the least bit of a *mauvais sujet*,
— what they call Bohemian ?   He is on the surface
free and off-hand, but perhaps —   However, as he
doesn't paint nude figures, he has no need or excuse
for a model.   Couldn't allow *that* on any account.
Wentworth and Alma Wicks will be coming back soon,
and that Stowe and Eliza may stumble in upon us at
any moment.   Really, isn't he going to take advantage
of the interim, and say something pretty ?   No, HE
WON'T.   I have a great mind to leave him, and follow
Wentworth and Alma.   But that would be mean.   Let
the schoolmaster have his chance, and be put out of
his misery.   How that brush goes, and how the distant hills start up on the canvas !   He doesn't dream
what I am thinking of.   Perhaps he doesn't care.   How
do the lines go ?

> " 'Alas, to seize the moment
>   When heart inclines to heart,
> And press a suit with passion
>   Is not a woman's part.
>
> If the man comes not to gather
>   The roses where they stand,
> They fade among their foliage,
>   They cannot seek his hand.'

"'Tis true, and pity 'tis, 'tis true.   I wish I had been
born a man !   No, for then — .No, 'tis better as it is.
I will queen it to the last.   But it is sometimes hard to
be passive when the active *rôle* might serve so well."

And while she mused and raged, Stewart was brush-
ing away, bringing out misty hilltops, clustered trees,
points of spires, and gleaming streaks of river, but

without a tender word to the maid beside him. Did he think of her? Yes, vaguely ; but it was as of "something that would keep." The thought was not importunate.

"Your friend is an accomplished man," said Miss Wicks to Wentworth, as they walked away.

"Yes ; and he was greatly admired in college. He has a good mind aside from his artistic faculty, and would have shone in any profession ; but he was born a painter, and after a time he determined to give up everything for art."

"There seems to be a distinct type of men in New York," said Miss Wicks. "They are easier and more agreeable in manner than most Bostonians. I have found Bostonians either meditative, or stiff, or self-conscious."

"Something of the Puritan manner survives in them," said Wentworth. "They are proud of family and wealth, though not more so than New Yorkers, and they add something of British 'grandeur' and implacability. The New Yorker calmly rests on his superiority ; the Bostonian doesn't intend that anybody shall forget it."

"I presume you may be right, but I have seen few young men from either city. You are not a Bostonian, I believe ? "

"No ; I am from a town near Boston."

"And you are about leaving Quabbin, I hear."

"Yes ; my school term has ended, and I must go back to college. I am sorry my time here has been so short. A schoolmaster makes but a little ripple in society ; but among my forty pupils I hope there may be some who will remember me."

"You are sure to be remembered. A teacher may influence his pupils' whole life ; and, in any event, if he is a man of ideas, he cannot fail to make a lasting impression upon young minds."

"But there is a deeper reason for my regret in leaving," said Wentworth. "I think you must have guessed it. I have no art to conceal my feelings, and you must have seen how much I admire you."

"You are very kind to say so, but I ought not to let you go on."

"And why not ? I know I must complete my studies, and that Time will not stand still for me ; but while I am with you I am not my own master. You are more to me than ambition or any earthly good."

"And if I cannot reciprocate, it would be wrong not to tell you, would it not ? "

"I know the obstacles," he continued, as if he had not heard her. "I know that in my present state of uncertainty I ought not to speak, — that silence would better become me ; but I cannot put down the wish ; I cannot forego the hope. I could not go away without telling you."

"It may be a relief to you, but you should know it is painful to me."

"Is the knowledge that an honorable man loves you painful ? "

"Yes, when I know that his love cannot be returned."

"Dear Miss Wicks, I do not ask for a return now. I know that I have to toil some years before that can be ; but, when Providence opens the way, if you should then be free, I shall come to offer you my love and my life."

" I am afraid that time is not likely to bring us any nearer together."

" May I ask if you feel aversion or indifference toward me ? "

" Not at all, Mr. Wentworth. You are very far from disagreeable. I esteem you highly ; but as to marriage, I could not think of it ; and I see I must be plain with you."

" If it is not in my person, nor in what you know of my character, I am at a loss."

" It would be enough to remind you of the time that must pass. An engagement with a young man who is still in college " —

" But is there not something more ? "

" I need not give any other reason."

" But is there not another — something quite different ? "

" I will be frank with you. My friends (and I mean chiefly my father) believe that you are unsettled in your religious belief."

" Your friends think I am not quite orthodox. But do you know that among the most conscientious men there are those who cannot fit their conceptions into the lines of any written creed ? I have never renounced the doctrines of the orthodox church in which I was brought up, but I confess I have some misgivings."

" When one begins to doubt, I have heard say, there is no knowing where he may end."

" He will not end badly if he determines to follow where truth leads."

" Our minister says the worst enemies of religion are the unstable, who make conscience an excuse for doubt.

Who can say where you will be found a few years hence ? "

" I trust I shall always follow Christ; and what Christian can do more ? But that is not enough, I know, for those who think there is no fruitful piety unless it is nailed upon a theologic frame. And, as I have declined assistance from the Education Society, because I would not pledge myself to preach, I fear I am regarded as little better than one of the wicked. But, I beg your pardon, Miss Wicks. It is not right or courteous to argue in this way. I respect your right to your opinions, and I hope we may never be wider apart than we are now. Let me repeat that, whatever you may say, I shall live in hope of becoming some day worthy of you, at least in a measure."

Miss Wicks gently shook her head, while a melancholy smile — if a look in which warm regard and hopeless pity were blended could be so called — played over her expressive features. She gave him her hand, which he kissed, and then they took their way back. Stewart looked a moment at them as they came near, and said to himself, " There seems to be something discomposing about that boasted view. When Stowe and Miss Grant returned there was a look in their faces that could not have been due to scenery, and now you two come back completely upset, both of you." Then turning to his companion, " It is well we didn't go, Miss Lois, isn't it ? There should be *one* sane and cheerful couple."

" I don't know," said Lois ; " I fear I belong to the flighty, rather than to those you call sane people."

" And *you* desert me ? " said Stewart, "then I am indeed unhappy. Well, wisdom will be justified of her one faithful child."

He had done all he proposed to his sketch ; and so, taking up the canvas, he started with it toward the coach, while Wentworth and Stowe gathered the dishes and napkins into the basket.

" I will sit beside the driver," said Stewart, " otherwise it would be difficult to save the ladies' dresses from being soiled by this fresh paint. Pity I haven't learned to use water-colors."

Miss Wicks and Lois sat at the back ; Eliza and Mr. Stowe took the middle seat, and Wentworth occupied the front. It was a preoccupied and silent party inside. The pair on the middle seat appeared thoughtful, yet not unhappy ; Lois was still wroth on account of the persistent silence of her companion during the day ; Wentworth felt bitterly that his impetuosity had led him into an *impasse ;* and Alma Wicks was wishing that he had remained silent. Stewart, meanwhile, was in excellent humor, holding his canvas on his knees edgewise, and, when not too heavily jolted, whistling, or humming, or singing in deep bass tones airs from the " Magic Flute."

After supper at the hotel, Wentworth and Stewart strolled down toward the Crombie bridge.

" Your departure seems sudden ; day after to-morrow, you say ? " said Wentworth.

" Yes ; I must be in my studio early in October, and I want to visit Lake George on the way."

" I shall go when you go. Of course your sister had told you, or written you, of these Quabbin girls, had she not ? "

" Yes ; and I confess I came here mainly to see them."

" And which one do you admire ? "

"Miss Wicks" — Wentworth's countenance fell. "Miss Wicks, I was going on to say," said Stewart gravely, "is an almost ideally perfect character" —

"Well?" said Wentworth, in a rising and imperative tone, indicative of extreme impatience.

"Ideally perfect in character for a wife" — and there was a coming smile.

"What pauses!" ejaculated Wentworth. "For Heaven's sake, do finish your sentence!"

"For the wife of a calm and philosophic person like yourself," with a merry twinkle in his eyes. "I am not worthy of her."

"Is any one?" demanded Wentworth excitedly.

"Probably no one. But I don't think it worth while to aspire. A less perfect woman would suit me better."

"Such as Lois Grant, for instance?"

"Well, she is pretty and bright, and would make a cheery wife for a melancholy man."

"You call yourself melancholy?"

"Whenever you see a fellow on stilts with good humor in public, you may be sure he is a desponding wretch when left to himself. I hope to go to Europe next year to see the galleries. It is an easy matter now; the New York clipper-ships cross in thirty days, and sometimes even in twenty. If I were to marry, that would be a glorious bridal trip. I shall try to be saving, if that is possible, and make preparations; and I may ask a young lady to go with me."

"Why don't you ask her now?"

"The proverb says, 'Never leap before you come to the stile.'"

"Proverbs are rubbish. They are always cynical,

and they are seldom fitted to actual circumstances. A word spoken now might prevent a sad misunderstanding hereafter."

" I'll think of it. By the way, you were eager just now to know what I was going to say of Miss Wicks."

" Naturally I was eager. I worship her ! "

" I rather thought that the prospect you went out with her to see was not that of the Connecticut Valley, but of the land of promise, like that from Pisgah."

" No promise in it for me, I assure you."

" The sad tone of your voice is catching. Let us cry."

Then Wentworth told his friend, what the reader already knows, of Miss Wicks's tea-party, and of the recent conversation on the hillside.

"The affair doesn't look promising," said Stewart. " According to Dr. Johnson, no one is ever reasoned out of a doctrine or position that he was not reasoned into. Prejudice is inveterate, especially when it has the sanction of religion ; there is no contending with it. There is little chance for you, unless the lady should go away from here, and come under different influences. And you have not shown much tact. Why must you blurt out your opinions ? As you haven't broken with her church, why need you have brought your pale doubts out of the cellar where they have sprouted ? And why should you have tried an assault instead of a carefully planned siege ? "

" I must follow my instincts," said Wentworth. " I *could not* restrain my impulses, though I see I was unwise ; and, as to my blurting out opinions, I cannot and would not conceal an honest thought, of whatever complexion, not for any advantage."

" Not for Miss Wicks ? "

"Not for any woman," said Wentworth doggedly.

"Well, we'll think about it. You know we are to take tea with the Grant family to-morrow. Curious way they have in this village. Tea, indeed! Why not a dinner?"

"Dinner-parties are seldom given; principally because everybody dines in the middle of the day. But a tea, with a re-enforcement of steaks, chickens, and oysters, is not a bad substitute for a dinner; and then a sociable evening follows."

"I suppose we shall meet the minister and his wife."

"Yes, and James Stowe, who appears to have got on well. You see, he didn't look at Miss Wicks, who, for a minister's wife, would be twice the woman that Eliza Grant is."

"Unreasonable and perverse man that you are," said Stewart, "to quarrel with a fellow because he did not try to cut you out!"

"If Mr. Wicks had been rich you would have seen; but Stowe knows that the Grant girls are going to inherit a pile of money, and he was bound to have *one* of them, if he could get her."

The long drive and the events of the day had brought fatigue, and the friends separated early.

CHAPTER XXXII

ANOTHER TEA—PARTY

THE tea-party given by the Misses Grant comprised the minister and his wife, Mr. and Miss Wicks, Mr. Stowe, Dr. Fletcher, Mr. Wentworth, and Mr. Stewart. Mr. Grant and his daughters received their guests with frank courtesy, and in the case of the minister it rose to an affectionate and reverent greeting. The " tea " was served in bountiful style, and Stewart afterward acknowledged that no (teetotal) dinner could have been more appetizing or substantial. After the repast was over, the gentlemen were shown into the "parlor," as the drawing-room was called, while the ladies lingered behind, according to custom.

The minister began to talk with the painter about the scenery of the neighborhood, and the places he had visited, and showed that he had some feeling for landscape, and some regard for art. Mr. Grant listened with interest; for though he knew that a painter might be famous after death, he was not quite sure he would be a man to be altogether respected while living. The feeling among country people in regard to artists was shown by the questions put to Wentworth by Miss Wicks the day before. It will be remembered there had never been an artist in Quabbin, and the idea that landscape painting could be really an honorable and lucrative profession had never occurred to such men as Mr. Grant and Mr. Wicks. The latter said to Mr. Stewart, " I wonder yeou don't paint portraits." — " Ah, no," said Stewart, "that is a distinct branch of the art. Many great artists have painted portraits, but they usually chose their subjects. In a portrait, character is the thing ; and an artist might have twenty orders before he would have a chance to do himself credit. What is he to do when he is asked to paint all sorts of people, — the dull, the mean, bigoted, avaricious, or cunning ? How will he make a brilliant picture out of an insipid or vulgar woman ? "

" But if he makes likenesses ? " said Mr. Grant.

" A mere map of the features is nothing without the soul," said Stewart. "If a portrait does not reveal character it is not art. The new and wonderful sun-pictures of Daguerre, taken on silver plates, ought to satisfy those who want mere likenesses ; although, as the sitter has to be motionless in glaring sunlight for some minutes, his eyes are apt to blink. I suppose you you have seen them, Mr. Grant ? "

" Yes ; I saw them in Boston at Plumb's. They are not taken in the country yet."

" You are from New York ? " said the minister to Stewart.

" I live there, though I was born at some distance from the city."

" By your name you must be of Scottish descent, like myself."

" Yes. My grandfather came from Scotland."

" We have great reason to rejoice in the Christian light and liberty of this land," said the minister. " It is in many things like Scotland."

" And yet there are differences," said Stewart. " For instance, liberty has a meaning here that is not known anywhere else."

" In speaking of liberty," said Wentworth, "you mean probably to include equality."

" Certainly," said Stewart. " Where there is not political equality, there is no true liberty."

"Where did the notion of political equality first appear ? " asked Wentworth of the minister. " Do you find it in the early laws or customs of the colony ? "

" It had not occurred to the Puritans, I think," replied the minister. " They were Britons, and apparently had never questioned law and usage as to established ranks and orders of men. They were little given to theorizing, and let things grow."

" The most remarkable of their institutions," said Wentworth, " was the town, and that, as you say, grew up. It is the most important feature in local government, the realization of democracy. As to equality, it must have come from France. It was never heard of, as I believe, before it was incorporated in the Declaration of Independence."

" Well," said Stewart, " there is another idea which appears to be embraced in your phrase 'Christian light and liberty,' and that is religious toleration. Where did that come from ? "

" Evidently not from the founders of Massachusetts," said Wentworth. " The history of the colony is full of painful proofs to the contrary."

" No," said the minister ; " it must be confessed the fathers of this State were not 'tolerant.' Unhappily they did not see that truth by its own nature and panoply is invulnerable, and needs no protection from the temporal power.   Roger Williams, whom they did not understand or appreciate, appears to have been the first in Christendom to perceive this just doctrine."

" I am glad to hear you say that," said Wentworth. "Many are so fearful of countenancing reproach upon the Puritan fathers, that they wander away from the point of ethics, and defend the early intolerance on the ground that the exclusion of heretics and malecontents was a political necessity."

" Was it *not* a political necessity ? " asked Mr. Stowe. " And, as the colonists were what we might call a private corporation, were they not right to keep out any intruders whom they judged dangerous to their little state ? "

" The political reason may have been urgent," said Wentworth ; " but that is not taking high ground.   It is defending a false position in morals by reasons of expediency."

" The fathers were wise in their generation," said the minister, " but I don't think they consciously took a low position in regard to Christian ethics.   They were taught by many trials, and generation by generation they rose into clearer light ; but from the beginning they had high and noble aims, and impressed their character upon the colony.   Few founders of churches, and few lawgivers, have higher claims upon the admiration of mankind."

" What you say of their character is true," said Wentworth.

" There is another criticism," said Stewart.   " A friend of mine, who is a student of constitutional law, finds fault with the early legislation, and especially with the administration of law, as showing ignorance of legal principles, as well as low and narrow views of the functions of government. He says that lawyers had been excluded, and not allowed to practise, and that they had no standing — in Massachusetts at least — until about the time of the Revolution; that for a hundred years persons were appointed magistrates who were notoriously incompetent; that the clergy did their best to set up the Mosaic code; that, in short, there was an almost total subversion of justice as it had been administered for centuries in English courts. You see, I reel off what my friend told me. I am not a lawyer."

"The influence of the clergy has been often the subject of unfriendly comment," said the minister, "and the government has been called a theocracy; but I believe that in early times the Puritan ministers had no undue influence, no more than was exercised by the Romish or the Episcopal clergy. The times are altered. In an age of faith the people willingly followed their spiritual leaders."

"That hardly meets the case," said Stewart. "If what my friend says is true, the Puritan clergy not only wanted the influence and leadership to which they were entitled, but determined there should be no other. They feared able lawyers, and preferred uneducated magistrates whom they could manage. No other leading church has suppressed lawyers."

"Are lawyers so very important?" asked Mr. Stowe. "Do they not, as a class, stir up strife, and despoil both plaintiff and defendant by the machinery of courts?"

"Can you have an intelligent school of medicine without physicians?" said Stewart, "or of theology without an educated clergy? And can there be a system of law without trained lawyers? It is not worth while to dwell upon the knavery of pettifoggers. It is better to look at law with the eyes of Hooker or Bacon. What basis has society, what protection is there for property, for liberty, or for life, but in a settled system of law?"

"I should think that many of the troubles of the colony," said Wentworth, "arose from the want of legal knowledge, and from disregarding the rules of judicial procedure. I am a Puritan to the last drop of my blood, but it appears to me that the course of the early rulers of Massachusetts in endeavoring to administer justice without regard to what we should now call constitutional principles and methods was the occasion of calamities and scandals."

"The Christian liberty and light of which you speak," said Stewart to the minister, "is complex, and seems to have largely come from without. The legacy which the Puritans left was personal liberty (as far as it was then possible), and with it an exalted character, full of faith and zeal. For political equality, which is the latest phase of democracy, we are indebted to Jefferson and Rousseau; while for toleration, which is the Christian corollary of equality, we are indebted, as you have said, to Roger Williams. These related doctrines are now so universally accepted, we easily forget that equality and toleration are so modern, and were once so foreign to the thought of the fathers."

"I haven't anythin' to say agin toleration," said Mr. Wicks, "though what them Methodists (not more'n two'r three dozen on 'em), git by goin' tu their meetin' which they couldn't git by goin' to aourn, I dunno; but I shouldn't like to see the time come when the ministers won't hev any word ter say abaout makin' the laws. I was allers sorry when people was let out from payin' the minister-tax. The whole people oughter contribute ter the s'port of the gospel, ez the whole people gits the benefit on't."

Mr. Wicks was a man of fair practical sense, but his mind moved in unexpected curves, rather than in right lines.

"True," said Mr. Grant. "What would liberty and law be worth without Christian principle?"

"The preachin' of the gospel, an' the influence of the church," continued Mr. Wicks, "is what holds things together. Religion's better'n sheriffs an' constables. Who makes th' expense of courts but the unbelievers? Who fills the jails an' poor-haouses but th' unbelievers? The taxes for sech things fall on sober an' God-fearin' men, who ain't responsible for the bad behavior. So I say the unbelievers oughter pay their sheer fer preachin'."

"I am afraid your arguments," said Dr. Fletcher, "are like tools carried loose in a basket, — they cut one another. If we admit that the church restrains crime, and so lessens the expense for criminals, then the minister tax is for your advantage. But do you think the unbelievers would behave better if they were compelled to support worship which they wouldn't attend?"

"I can't say," said Mr. Wicks. "On'y I feel 't they oughter be made ter du it."

"I lately had a talk with one of your elderly people," said Wentworth, "and he told me that in the old times when all paid the minister tax, the conduct of the intemperate and depraved was far worse than now. They were often drunk, or indecent, or malicious, from sheer perversity or defiance."

"It is pretty certain," said Dr. Fletcher, "that men are not reformed from drinking-habits, nor made moral or religious by law."

"Certainly not," said Mr. Stewart, "as long as they think they are wronged as well as coerced."

"True religion," said Mr. Stowe, "comes from divine grace, and is an inward life, while law can only control the outward action."

"I have been reflecting upon the analysis you made of liberty," said the minister to Mr. Stewart, "and I would suggest that, although neither political equality nor religious toleration originated with the Puritans, yet their character counted for so much, — I mean their sublime faith and truth, their conscientiousness, courage, and self-devotion, — that the State and society they founded was in many respects unexampled. We admit that Rousseau developed the doctrine of political equality; but what a wretched use his disciples made of it! Roger Williams was the apostle of toleration, — all honor to him! — but is Rhode Island to-day in any way more advanced than Massachusetts? A people actuated by high and holy motives goes on developing its powers, and receives new light from whatever quarter. But the most perfect system of political and moral philosophy would not have built up our State, if the character of its founders had been other than it was."

"I cannot abide the spirit that is forever seeking to disparage the Puritans and Pilgrims," said Mr. Stowe with warmth. "It isn't honorable or decent to belittle our ancestors; nor is it just to try them by modern

standards. In actual worth they were heroes compared with the puny time-servers of to-day."

"The Puritans were not my ancestors," said Stewart
calmly. "They are entitled to veneration for what
they were and did ; but their principles and policy may
be properly judged in the light of history, as we judge
of the ideas and conduct of the Covenanters, and of the
Long-Parliament men. It does not appear to me dis-
honorable or indecent to point out their errors or fail-
ings ; because such lessons are proper for the instruction
of mankind."

The entrance of the ladies put an end to the discussion ; and after a little time the piano was opened, and
there were songs, duets, and instrumental pieces. The
minister had a refined taste in music, within certain
limits, and was an attentive listener ; his wife was a
woman of vigorous mind, with few feminine elegances,
and wholly absorbed in her husband and his work ; but
she smiled upon the singers in a way that was meant
to be gracious. Dr. Fletcher, who was a frequent guest,
stood by the piano, and turned over the leaves, while
his head kept airy time with the music, turning now
and then with a triumphant look at the company, as if
to emphasize some striking passage. He had been an
admirer of Lois Grant, and had worn for her his finest
costumes ; but, as he had made little headway, he was
now thinking of cultivating an intimacy with Eliza ;
and his attentions to her were so marked that the
divinity student's dark face soon became a dingy green.
Wentworth was near Miss Wicks, and was very quiet.
He felt that if he should ever win it would be in a
waiting race.

The painter was in excellent humor, in spite of the

little breeze in the discussion, and he adapted himself
with easy grace to the gayety of Lois, the gravity of
her father, and the sombre dignity of the minister, in
turn. The minister often smiled, but it was like the
play of wintry sunlight on marble. He could not make
out Stewart. The painter was a man of the world, and
that was not the sign of a godly man. Evidently, also,
he was a man of ideas, well read, and well trained ; and
that of itself was a problem ; for half a century ago
there were few cultivated men outside of the learned
professions. The minister continued to look askance
at Wentworth, and was uneasy at the thought that the
teacher and his friend Stewart had become intimate
with favorite members of his flock.

The party was soon divided into groups. The minister had a quiet conversation with Mr. Stowe, and
learned that he proposed to enter the service of the
"American Board" as a missionary to the Nestorians,
and that he desired to take with him Eliza Grant as
help-meet. The minister seemed pleased, and promised
to support him with Mr. Grant, if it should be necessary.

Meanwhile, Mr. Stewart had approached Lois, and
in a few low-toned sentences let her know that he was
to leave Quabbin the next day, and on one account
(not named) deeply regretted going ; that he should return the next spring, and in the latter part of summer
intended to sail to Europe for a long visit. Lois listened eagerly, but, except in the play of her expressive
features, made no reply.

Turning to the minister Stewart said with a frank
smile, "There was one matter I did not mention when
we were talking of the Puritans, — a matter that concerns me personally. It is, that in those old times

I might have been arrested and put in the stocks, or banished along with fiddlers, beggars, and other vagabonds."

"Hardly possible," said the minister.

"I am quite sure of it. To begin with, no one would have bought my pictures, and so I should have been 'without visible means of support.' My vagrant life while sketching would have been a scandal. My fancy for neckties would have made me a suspect, and my velvet coat might have brought me within the sumptuary laws. Well, perhaps not an arrest, but an intimation. I should have been made to understand that there was no room nor welcome."

"I see you are jesting," said the minister.

"No, indeed, replied Stewart; "and the ground you take shows how public sentiment has changed. Half a century ago the clergy and magistrates would not have looked upon me with your friendly eyes."

Seeing that Mr. Wicks was listening, and believing that his daughter was taking note also, the painter continued, —

"Then as to toleration, that beautiful trait of Christian charity, permit me to say, with all respect, that I fear the descendants of the Puritans have not quite got hold of it. It is hard for them to admit the possibility of being in the wrong; and their behavior to those who are unsound in the faith is, to say the least, seldom quite brotherly. I believe my friend there," pointing to Wentworth, "has been made to feel it; and he is the most conscientious man I ever knew. If there was ever a sincere and devout seeker after truth, he is the man. He is of the stuff of which martyrs and heroes are made ; and yet his life is overcast, and his future is uncertain, on account of a *perhaps*."

Stewart did not raise his voice, but it had a vibrant and carrying quality, and he felt sure that every word told upon those around him.

"Your warmth does you credit," said the minister; "but, as we are both speaking plainly, you will pardon me for suggesting that the value of your opinion, for us, depends upon your own conceptions of divine truth, and your relations with evangelical believers."

"I think I can testify to what I have seen, no matter what may be my opinions; and I know the working of my friend's mind, as a watchmaker knows the movement of a watch."

"That is more than I should undertake to say of any friend, however intimate," said the minister. "God only knows the heart. Let me ask if you are a member of a church?"

"I have been, but I fear my membership has lapsed."

"I thought that might be the case. How can you expect that we should accept your judgment, when you confess that you are not qualified by any relation with the church of Christ? A worldly minded man may lead a moral and respectable life; but his views upon the religious character of a friend who, I may say, is noted for a tendency to doubt, cannot carry much weight."

"What you say," said Stewart, "shows that there is a wide difference between modern Christianity and that of the New Testament. Christ never talked theology; his creed had but one article, and he gave but two precepts. But I had not reflected. People do not easily get out of the subtilties in which they have been trained. I fear I have done my friend hurt instead of good. We are both to leave this place to-morrow, and I hoped to

say something that might make him regretted, and
welcomed if he should ever come again."

Mr. Stowe by movements, gestures, and frowns succeeded in driving away Dr. Fletcher, and then took his
place by the side of Eliza Grant. Once there, his serious features wore a look of gloomy content. He did
not seem an ardent lover, but a lawful and godly possessor. What fascination he exerted upon his partner
could not be divined. Women when they marry generally prefer looking up to a master, rather than down
upon a suppliant or servant. She was going to leave
her home, her father and sister, for a husband whose
love was more allied to duty than tenderness, and go
into a distant land to encounter hardship and danger,
and would not return for many years. It was the old
Puritan courage, devotion, sacrifice, such as has been
shown in every generation.

Miss Wicks was talking absently with Dr. Fletcher.
Her father and Mr. Grant were listening to the minister, who counselled standing fast in the old ways ; and
the minister's stately wife, who had seen everything,
was talking earnestly with Lois. At this point Wentworth and Stewart took leave of the company with a
word of farewell and a shake of the hand of each.
Their absence produced a void.

"I tell you," said Stewart, in walking home with
Wentworth, "it is not religion itself which is antagonistic to human progress ; but it is the design of men
like yonder minister to make it so. You told me how
he talked to you about Scott and Shakespeare; how
jealous he was of literature ; and it is the same with
everything. Give him, and people like hi.n, full swing,
and there would not be a poet, novelist, painter, or com-

poser. The clergy have yielded somewhat, but grudgingly, and because they have been obliged to. They would like to have the old darkness return. They would have music 'experience religion ;' they would frighten gayety into tears, put scientists in leading-strings, smash the classic statues, and turn the splendors of Titian and Leonardo to the wall. What a world they would make of it ! And let the best and purest man say a word in favor of light, life. and beauty, he is the target of arrowy texts."

" You are 'riding the high horse,' " said Wentworth, "and you are not wholly just. The orthodox clergy show some traces of the old intolerance ; it is born in them ; but they are generally just and considerate, especially in populous communities, and they do not wish to deprive their people of innocent pleasure. In this town there is a provincial, or rather a parochial narrowness ; things move slowly, the old shadow overhangs."

" There is no need of my repeating things which you know perfectly well," said Stewart ; " but let me say, the things which make for humanity must move on together. A broad system of education, including religion for the soul and athletics for the body, holds the centre ; but law, natural science, industrial training, medicine, literature, music, the fine arts, and organized philanthropy, all have their separate claims, and not one of them can be slighted. Why should religion limit literature or crowd out art, any more than these should restrict religion ? I think there are *many* things 'needful ;' and it is a wrong and shame to arouse or play upon a morbid fear of death, in order to secure for worship or piety, or whatever you please to call it, an undue share of men's time and thought. We have so many useful and agreeable things to do, that we ought to spend our hours as a miser pays out gold, giving none without value received. And to think that minister was not willing to allow those bright young women to read Shakespeare, the one transcendent genius! It is shameful! I have a mind to found a new religion, without a creed. Life shall be fully employed. Labor, study, country walks, poetry, music, and art, WITH love to God and man, all together will make life worth living."

" It is not so much a new religion that is wanted," said Wentworth, " as common-sense, broad culture, and liberality."

The subsequent history of the young people who have engaged our attention does not concern the progress of Quabbin, and may be briefly dismissed.

In the course of the year the Rev. James Stowe was married to Miss Eliza Grant, and the pair set out upon their long journey to Asia.

Mr. Stewart returned, as he promised, the following spring, and made numerous sketches, besides one lovely portrait of a young lady. He was courteously received by Mr. Grant, who had taken pains to make inquiries in New York as to the painter's character and social standing. In the course of the summer Lois became Mrs. Stewart, but not until she had told her lover of her being brought down the mountain, and of her dramatic parting from Herman Field.

Miss Alma Wicks, after remaining single for a number of years, married a man somewhat older than herself, in a neighboring town. She was a pattern of motherhood, adored by her husband and children, held in honor in the church, and the friend of all who needed help and sympathy.

David Wentworth finished his studies with honor, and having grown more and more reluctant to bind himself to a creed, renounced theology, fitted himself as an instructor in English literature, and became a professor in a Western university. At forty he was still unmarried.

It is not to be supposed that Quabbin had reached its possibilities in the time of the good Robert; it had been merely set on a moral and intellectual foundation, and was in a condition to receive the benefit of the improvements which time was to bring. Its institutions, like its shade-trees, were undeveloped. The subsequent years, which have covered its dwellings with foliage, so that from the hill the village seems to be sunk in a billowy sea of green, have also brought new and unexpected advantages to the people. Town and country are in substantial accord. The public schools have been reorganized and graded; and now, with able and permanent teachers, efficient supervision, and pleasant surroundings, are probably as good as they can be made for the present population. The school of the highest grade receives pupils from all parts of the town, and the most distant of them are brought in wagons at the public expense. The roads have been greatly improved; the common and most of the private yards are neatly kept, and sidewalks are extending from the centre in various directions. The meeting-house has a large and fine-toned organ. A substantial town hall has been built, and in it is maintained a free public library of varied and solid excellence.

The chief feature in the modern church is the increased share of labor undertaken by the laity. In the old times the brethren assisted in the Sunday-school and in the prayer-meetings, but now they are organized in disciplined bands, Orthodox and Methodists together, and go out on missionary tours in the outlying districts, and in adjoining towns. An amusing story is told, that one of these Quabbin bands, on its way for the first time to a meeting to be held on a Sunday afternoon in a hill town, came upon a farmer who was killing and dressing hogs, and another who with his men was making cider. Seeing the unlooked-for invasion of the church militant, the Sabbath-breakers took to their heels, and remained hid until daylight was past. Generally the people so visited receive the Christian workers kindly, and often return the compliment.

How strange all this would have appeared in the time of Joshua I.! Equally strange to him and his people would have appeared the antiphonal reading of the psalm in the morning service, and the profuse floral decoration of the pulpit and communion-table. The disciples and contemporaries of Cotton Mather, or of Jonathan Edwards, would find little to please them in the worship or sermons at Quabbin or elsewhere in Massachusetts.

Quabbin has some right to self-gratulation. Few towns of its size — about one thousand souls — have done so much; but it remains quiet and modest: the only pæans heard are from the song-birds which have repeopled the orchards and copses, and fill the air with delight all day. With morning newspapers, the telegraph, and three daily mails, Quabbin belongs to the great world; but it breakfasts before seven o'clock, dines without ceremony at one, and goes to bed after an early supper. Comfort and content lodge in every house, for there is not a pauper in the region. The sunlight nowhere lies fairer than on its three hills, and the heat of a midsummer's day is followed by the cool south-west wind that sweeps up the valley in the evening.

Then let the elderly people say "Haow," if they prefer that locution ; and let their thoughts be bounded by their daily vision; for as good English is heard in the pulpit and in the schools, and as a well-chosen and growing library is to furnish the coming generation with knowledge and broad ideas, the future of Quabbin is assured.

CHAPTER XXXIII

LITERATURE

THERE are familiar facts which at times strike us with a sudden sense of novelty or strangeness.

The name of New England suggests a modern origin; and it is sometimes with surprise, as if history or arithmetic must be at fault, that we find the date of its settlement to have been as long ago as the early part of the reign of Charles I. Then, when we look back along the mighty course of literature, and think of the great names in the Victorian era, in that of the Georges, of Queen Anne, of William and Mary, and of the Stuarts, we see that the largest part of English poetry, history, fiction, and essays, has been produced since the Pilgrims sailed from Southampton. So, during the two centuries while the Puritans were vanquishing Antinomians, Baptists, and Quakers, or recording the miraculous providences of God in favor of his exiled servants, or reiterating and fortifying the scheme of salvation according to Calvin, or combatting demons by the exposure of witchcraft, there appeared in the British Isles the poets from Milton to Tennyson, historians from Clarendon to Carlyle, novelists from Fielding to Thackeray, essayists from Addison to Macaulay, as well as other men of genius unclassified.

In the New World there was no literature of general

interest, aside from the discussion of American independençe, until Bryant's "Thanatopsis" and Irving's "Sketch Book" appeared. In spite of the many obvious reasons that have been given for this protracted barrenness, the fact remains a matter of wonder; for many of the colonists were able and liberally educated men.

Genius is seldom equally distributed as to time or place by any system of averages, else there should have been some few striking works in Boston or in New England in the course of two centuries. But no; their poetry ranges between the platitudes of the Bay Psalm Book and the painful seventeenth century verse of Anne Bradstreet; their annals are without literary art, and their discourses void of almost everything but energy and piety. Excepting the lively and pedantic Cotton Mather, their writers seem to have benumbed whatever they touched.

Water in a flowing current retains its life and freshness, but left in a hollow or slough, away from movement, it becomes stagnant. The colony of the Bay was like a solitary pool which no angel came to trouble.

Whether genius be the rare flower of intellect and feeling, or, as some say, only "a splendid disease," its manifestations are capricious and inscrutable. The speed of a well-descended colt can be predicted from the time it is foaled; but who will venture to say of a babe, no matter of what parentage, "This child is to become a poet"? A fond father, who had allowed his son to study music instead of going into business, said apologetically, "Why isn't it a good thing to have a Mozart or a Be-tho-ven in the family?" If the singer's wish could make the song, the top of Parnassus, as Lowell observes, might be the most thickly settled part of the country.

The soil and atmosphere of Quabbin, at least up to the time of our narration, must have been unsuitable for rearing a poet or artist. There was in progress some mental cultivation and taste for the beautiful, but no freedom or expansion ; mind was constrained to act in grooves and upon practical themes. But it is interesting to know that in a similar small town, some forty miles west, and under almost the same conditions, Bryant had already written poems, which his father, a country doctor, carried in his odorous saddle-bags, and read with tears of honest pride in the houses of his patients. The youth had been named William Cullen, after an eminent Scottish medical writer, and perhaps with a paternal intention ; but the wish, if it existed, was not fulfilled ; it was a poet, and not a doctor, who had come into the world.

About the same time Emerson was occupied with philosophic thoughts tinged with poetry. He had already (1837) delivered his address upon the American Scholar, in which was a definite renunciation of dependence upon Old World thought and models. Quabbin had never heard of him, and did not hear of him until long afterward ; but no literary contemporary, whether friend or foe, escaped his influence. All weather-vanes high enough to be touched by celestial airs pointed to Concord. The ideas and even the language of the time bore witness of the genius that stamped its fresh phrases upon the memories of men. His direct influence never affected Calvinists, and it is not at all probable that the good Robert IV. ever read a line of his essays or poems; but he was an abiding force, and affected, directly or indirectly, a generation of writers, so that people of even moderate attainments, and in obscure places, were unconsciously his disciples.

Hawthorne was just beginning his career with the simple yet exquisite tales which were the precursors of his romances. They were written for magazines, and attracted very little attention. Unaffected simplicity is not often understood at first, because most people think that genius is shown by glitter and point. Time and the study of classic models are necessary for the due appreciation of such perfect work. If Hawthorne had any readers in Quabbin before the publication of the "Scarlet Letter," which is doubtful, he would have been considered as quite inferior to N. P. Willis, the idol of romantic readers of that day. In *his* stories there was vigor and dash; his heroines were brilliant and impossible, like their pictures in the annuals and ladies' magazines; nature sat to him in full dress, and his triumphant heroes recoiled before no obstacles. In his verse was thought to be blended the passion of Byron, the sweetness of Moore, and the magic of Scott. And his sacred poems, easy amplifications of biblical narratives, how they were copied, quoted, and declaimed, even in little places like Quabbin! For some years his popularity was almost universal. In this early period he was the writer who was always named first; some few critics rated him more justly, but meanwhile, his supremacy was seldom questioned. Had a youth written verses, it was to Willis they were sent for an encouraging word. It was to Willis that most literary novices applied for advice, and seldom in vain; for never was a reigning favorite more amiable and helpful.

Longfellow, too, was being heard of. When the "Voices of the Night" appeared (1839), the impression upon cultivated readers was solemn and thrilling, as well as tender and delightful. It was the first time in America that such sustained melody, such delicate and spiritual thought, and such touching lessons, had been united in verse. It was an uplifting sensation to feel that after so long a time a poet had arisen who might become the Voice of the New World. "The human heart," says Landor, "is the world of poetry; the imagination is only its atmosphere." In "The Psalm of Life," "The Footsteps of Angels," and "The Beleaguered City," there seemed to be embodied what men love, — the poetry of their own lives. Probably no poet ever had more immediate and loyal recognition. In our later times, when the heart has yielded to the brain, the notion of poetry is something in which Kant, Pascal, and Omar Khayyam have an equal share. Simple lays of human feeling are banished to the nursery, whither their old-fashioned lovers must go.

Whittier, also, had begun to write, though not in the free and large-hearted style which he afterward attained. But some of his Indian legends, his Quaker ballads, and his burning appeals for the slave, had already impressed men of liberal minds and generous sympathies. At that time, as has been stated, Quabbin had but one zealous anti-slavery man, and he read the poems of Whittier, as they appeared in the *Liberator* and the *Emancipator*, with ever-increasing admiration.

Fitz Greene Halleck was already known by his beautiful poem on Burns, and by his tribute to his friend J. R. Drake; and Drake was known by his "Culprit Fay," a piece of fancy which greatly pleased youthful minds. J. G. Percival was remembered as the author of the " Coral Grove " and other poems copied into the school-books.

In all these instances an acquaintance with the new authors came primarily to school-boys through their reading-lessons. The " American First-Class Book," compiled by the Rev. John Pierpont, himself a poet, was the first and most effective instructor in modern literature ; and, as his compilation was in the hands of all the youth, he did more to cultivate the literary taste of New England than all the magazines, and all other agencies together.

Cooper and other early novelists were only names in Quabbin, for obvious reasons.

The brilliant and polished Everett, who was for four years Governor of the State, during the second min- ister's reign, appeared, from the standpoint of Quabbin, as one might imagine an ancient orator in classic robes, who had been turned to marble and pedestalled for the admiration of posterity. But Quabbin knew only his utterances in public life ; it did not know his literary essays, nor the animated part he had played in the awakening of Harvard College.

George Bancroft, who had been a teacher in a town not very far from Quabbin, had, at the time of our nar- ration, begun his life-long studies in American history, and had published his first three volumes. The time had not come when a Democrat could make any deep or favorable impression upon the people of Western Massachusetts, nor when a history based upon the ideas of Jefferson would be received as authentic among the sons of Federalists. It is unlikely that he had either admirers or readers in Quabbin. It was early for the appreciation of a philosophic history of America ; in fact, the time has hardly come even now.

It would be expecting much to look for any acquaintance with Prescott's " Ferdinand and Isabella " (published in 1837), in a small town so far away from the literary centre. It was an event of some importance for the capital, as it was the first historical work of a high order produced in America ;[1] and its thoroughness, no less than its form and finish, were acknowledged by competent judges everywhere. It was a most encouraging sign of the times, and added to the light that was beginning to illuminate the State and nation.

Lydia Maria Child had published two novels, and some works upon education and domestic economy. In one of the novels were supposed addresses by James Otis and the celebrated Whitefield, which were everywhere copied, and often believed to be genuine. The patriotic speech attributed to Otis was often declaimed in schools.

Much inspiration came to the youth of New England from the orations of Daniel Webster. Their most striking passages were in the school-books, and were admired more than any other specimens of rhetoric. The oration at Plymouth in 1820, upon the two hundredth anniversary of the landing of the Pilgrims ; those at Bunker's Hill upon laying the corner-stone, and upon completing the monument; and the celebrated reply to Hayne of South Carolina in the U. S. Senate, furnished the most brilliant and admired selections. Webster had formed his style by reading the Bible and Bunyan ; seldom was purer or more idio-

[1] Bancroft's work, dealing largely with British treatment of the colonies, though " of a high order," is controversial for English critics.

matic English spoken than his; but he had a glowing
imagination, and great depth of feeling, and, as he
went on speaking, his simple phrases became ample
and majestic; his figures, in which he was a consummate artist, were more dazzling; and before he finished
he always raised his auditors to his own high level.

It is said that such orations are out of date, but it is
equally true that no such orator has since been heard.
Whoever will read any of the familiar and well-worn
passages understandingly and with due emphasis, and
will endeavor to keep in mind the impressive scene in
which the oration was originally delivered, will find
the spirit of the author gaining hold of him, and when
he comes to the end will confess to having a lump in
his throat.

The literary periodicals of this time (about 1840)
were generally feeble and superficial. Some of them
were largely made up of articles "borrowed" from
British magazines; and their original contributors
were poorly paid, when paid at all. Five dollars was
not considered a contemptible sum to offer a writer;
some of Hawthorne's early tales brought him no more.
In looking over these magazines we get an impression
that is both painful and comic. Among the inapti-
tudes and the crude attempts at fine writing, there are
occasional gems from poets who were just becoming
known; but it is evident the number of cultivated
readers was small, and the managers strove to attract
the public by means of fashion-plates, meretricious
engravings, and other devices.

The progress of American literature, and of literary
taste among readers, was exceedingly slow, — almost
imperceptible. Excepting the eminent preachers and

the public orators, few literary men had any following, or any serious consideration. British authors held the field, and it was not supposed they would ever have successful American rivals. The history of this development would take us far beyond the limits of time and space proper for the story of Quabbin ; but even fifty years ago the change was in progress, and the faint streaks of dawn have since brightened into a still advancing day.

Of the difficulties which sixty years ago stood in the way of acquiring a fair knowledge of literature, enough has been said in former chapters. For the elder people of Quabbin the great authors were only luminous names, — mere points of light, distant and unknown, like stars. By stated reading-lessons, and by the efforts of a few enlightened schoolmasters, the younger generation got some notion of the power of thought and imagination, and the distinction of style of the masters of English. But a general acquaintance with literature is not to be expected until after education has been universal, and society has acquired a literary tone ; nor, indeed, until ample public or private libraries have been established and used.

The qualities of literary works can only be estimated after repeated comparisons, and after free interchange of opinions with other readers. When men come to see that literature and art are the only enduring titles to renown, and that merely commercial nations have no place in history, then the great poets, thinkers, and artists loom up like mountains. People who have taken up reading systematically, or who read much, even cursorily, soon recognize the fact that there is no pleasure like it, and that it is almost the only distinction between the wise and fools.

After the earning of one's livelihood, the care for religion, public order, and common schools, there is nothing so important as the general circulation of well-chosen books. This truth gradually dawned upon Quabbin, and in recent years, as has been stated, a public library has been set up in its town hall.

It was not the fortune of such a small town to have any part in the literary awakening referred to in this chapter; it was much if some of its people could appreciate the new and reviving spirit which was abroad.

The beginning of a native literature was in one aspect an offshoot from the parent stock; and, in another, a new and distinct growth. American literature, which is a fact, and not simply a future possibility, is connected with its venerable parent by indissoluble ties. Physical barriers, such as the ocean, do not interfere with the intimate union of a dual literature any more than they separate spiritual existences. In its origin and traditions American literature is necessarily English to the core; but in time its material characteristics, springing from soil, climate, and vegetation, together with the virile spirit of democratic institutions, and new tendencies coming from the mixture of races, gave it such distinctive qualities that the *alma mater* might hesitate about recognizing her offspring.

Few of these considerations had occurred to the people of Quabbin, or of Massachusetts, sixty years ago. Bobolinks and catbirds were singing merrily in meadows and bushes, and golden orioles hung their " hammock nests " at the tips of elm-tree boughs; but in the accepted poetry one read only of British larks, thrushes, and robins. The hillsides were rosy with acres of laurel; azaleas brightened and perfumed the river-banks ; the cardinal flower flamed in swampy nooks ; in the spring woods the mayflower crept out with its pink-and-white blooms from under the melting snow ; but all these indigenous beauties were unsung. Country life, seen too near, was coarse and vulgar, because no poet had looked at it with the Claude Lorraine glass of genius.

Under equal laws, a well-descended and well-taught people were making progress in civilization, and in establishing a national character ; and there was no hint of it in literature, except in the tasteless declamation of popular orators. But all these things were to appear in good time, in romance, poem, and essay. Western grapes might spring from imported vines, but the racy flavor and perfume drawn from the soil of the New World was sure to be manifest in the ripened clusters.

CHAPTER XXXIV

THE RETURN OF THE NATIVE

WHEN a new ship glides on its ways into the water, the least imaginative of the spectators lets his mind run forward upon its course over oceans, up to the time when it shall sail no more. Will it go from haven to haven in safety? Or will it be buffeted by winds and waves until it founders and plunges into the depths? Will its ribs and keel lie bleaching on a coral island? or will it float, waterlogged, in the track of navigation? How small the chance that it will return to anchor in the river-mouth where it was launched!

A youth who sets out from his native town may have as many good wishes as follow a newly launched vessel, but no voyage is more perilous or problematical than the voyage of life. If the native should return crestfallen and despondent, he may perhaps be comforted by sympathy from the friends of his youth ; but if he holds his own while abroad, and needs nothing from those he left behind, he may get an indifferent welcome. This is not to say that townsfolk bear malice toward a native who has won a place in the world ; but the Scripture saying remains true, that a prophet is without honor among kindred and in his birthplace, at least until the generation that knew him

in boyhood is passing away. The townsfolk may remember too vividly the day of small things, — the boyish scrapes and peccadilloes, the grime of some menial
service, or the undignified early associations.

A native who contemplates returning to end his
days among his kindred, will do so, if he is wise, while
he is still in the vigor of manhood, and before failing
memory and other infirmities make him a dazed and
dumb creature, and before those who should know him,
and whom he should know, are ready to look upon him as
a stranger. The ties of old friendship may be broken,
or may be stretched and atrophied ; in either case the
genial current passes to and fro no more. A group of
silent, apathetic, indifferent townsfolk gives to a
native a strange chill ; he would be more at ease with
the ghosts of all their fathers and grandfathers.

If he could adapt himself again to the old life, and
step back with the fresh feelings of youth into the
society he left, that would be a delight ; but in most
cases he might as well attempt to fit his broad shoulders with the boy's coat which his fond mother had
saved as a souvenir.

While memory is active, and faces come to him as
they did when he played and fought with his school-
fellows, he has an unutterable pleasure in recalling the
beautiful days. The hills smile upon him as they lie in
sunshine ; the swift river is gurgling for him under
alders and vines ; for him the gilded vane is shining on
the steeple as it points to fair weather. If he could
only annihilate the interval of his absence, and forget
what he learned and unlearned in the world without !
But he comes back a changed man ; politics, finance,
professional studies, art, and literature, some of them

have been possessing him and overgrowing him, as a coiling parasite grapples and masters a tree. The free and simple-hearted youth has been merged in the absorbed and preoccupied man, and between him and his old life the way has been closed up. As he looks back, the pictures of memory are touched with an unreal splendor, and are as distant as fairyland. In the depths of his heart he loves the old town, and has nothing but kind feelings for the old people, even for those whom he knew least. How gladly he would renew old friendships and intimacies, if it were possible ; but circumstances are often stronger than inclination.

A popular writer once deplored the tendency among literary men to hold themselves aloof from the common people. Literary influence, he thought, like Christianity, ought to be diffused among all classes; and how could this be, he plaintively asked, if writers and thinkers should continue to isolate themselves ? Like many plausible suggestions made by impulsive men, this is wholly illusory and incapable of realization. Like consorts only with like, and without some community of thought, habit, taste, or purpose, no intimacy is possible. The training of a poet, critic, or man of science, necessarily isolates him, because he is occupied with ideas which the uneducated cannot be made to comprehend. The vocabulary alone is an effectual barrier. A beginner with Herbert Spencer or Huxley has first to master a new language, and then to become familiar with a world of new ideas.

Writers and thinkers in their hours of leisure must seek the society of those with whom they are in sympathy, and those from whom they will receive the stimulus which comes in the clash of mind with mind. The intellect is never so active, original and forgetive, as when it feels the shock from collision with another of kindred temper. The philosopher cannot translate his ideas into the English of the field and the workshop. In literature and science there are middlemen engaged in letting ladders down from the thought of Darwin, Emerson, Browning, Comte, and Hegel; and even after one descent other ladders are often necessary to land any lucid and comprehensible ideas upon the lower level of the unread.

A client was told in court by Rufus Choate that judgment was given in his favor "on demurrer." The client, who had expected to witness a display of oratory by the great advocate, was disappointed to see the case ended after a short and (to him) unintelligible colloquy with the presiding judge; and when going out of the chamber he exclaimed, "I don't understand about this demurrer." — "The Almighty never intended you should," said Choate.

When two men meet for the first time, the x, or unknown quantity, representing the studies, pursuits, tastes, and habits of each, is the subject of curious reciprocal inquiry; and there ensues a series of tentative equations made on the one side and the other, until approximations have been reached.

Here is a man, for instance, who makes mathematical calculations in molecular physics, — the architecture of the universe of atoms; or he estimates the solar energy, or computes the totality of force effectuated by winds and waves around the globe. These vast trains of thought and speculation occupy a large part of his interior mental space, if such an expression may be allowed; yet he may talk agreeably upon politics, poetry, or art, and a stranger might not suspect the existence of that interior laboratory whose bulk almost equals the sum of his being. Such a man might seldom speak upon the themes which occupy him, for the reason that few would comprehend him. His intercourse with mankind would therefore be upon superficial things; and in his case the x would be huge, and his totality, *minus* the x, a disappointing remainder.

Many a man carries about an x of more or less magnitude, — something for which he lives; and few, beside egotists and other bores, let the secret be known except to closest friends. Lower down in the scale of intellectuality, unless it is among criminals, the x becomes insignificant. When two uneducated farmers meet they readily unpack their respective wallets. The weather, the crops, prices, wages, and taxes, are all their intellectual counters, and an exchange is easily made. In like manner two gossips have no difficulty in overhauling each other's mail-bag.

Now, if a man who is almost wholly absorbed by some study meets another whose intellectual outfit is like a native African's wardrobe, on what terms can there be an intimacy, or more than a passing recognition? If there were to be a closer relation, it must be that of teacher and pupil, which is seldom agreeable.

So, if the native has remained long enough away to have become a changed man, whether for better or worse, there will be difficulties in the way of resuming old intimacies. The townsfolk are likely to misunderstand him, and to misinterpret his conduct, even in the most trivial particulars; for they do not know the nature and power of the x which dominates him.

Few of the inhabitants of any small village can have a very wide experience of life; and it is not impossible for them to mistake slang for wit, and to be impressed by demonstrative manners and dress, which, with a fuller knowledge of the world, they would at once recognize as vulgar. But though the young people may be dazzled by jewellery, and may admire clothes of eccentric pattern, yet it does not take long for the elders to "size up" an ill-bred fellow who assumes to be "the glass of fashion."

The reign of slang phrases, though brief in a city, may be interminably tedious in a remote place; when they have had their ignoble day at the capital, they are still fresh in villages like Quabbin, especially among overgrown boys. And for a while the slang, with an occasional razeed oath, gives a curious piquancy to the rustic dialect. The Yankee does not indulge in solid and obtrusive oaths, but allows himself modified oathlets, or colorable imitations. Sometimes two or three senseless collocations which have been "translated" (*à la* Bottom) from their natural meaning into nonsensical catch-words are bandied about during a whole season by "knowing" youths, until nervous people would wish them struck dumb. Probably this is a Yankee peculiarity; for the British call all the current slang, and all the ready-made or second-hand jokes, Americanisms.

The returned native may notice these and other things which are not agreeable subjects of meditation; such as flippancy, unknown in earlier times, a disposition to treat sacred themes with a familiar irreverence, a boastful defiance of parents, a derision of the maxims of the elders, a self-sufficiency wholly in contrast with the modesty or "humility" of the old time, and a chuckling approval of successful sharpness. As to the last, he will see that the tendency is not universal, though sometimes painfully conspicuous. It would appear that the career of the notorious Jim Fisk, chief wrecker of the Erie Railroad, who in his younger days was a well-known and successful pedler of dress fabrics, etc., in a large district which included Quabbin, had a demoralizing influence upon the country youth far and wide. It came to be the habit to say of a successful rogue or sharper that he was "smart." One story of Fisk was long current in Quabbin. His father, who was also a noted pedler, and, like his son, drove a handsome turnout, had sold a woman a dress pattern of calico which, though warranted fast in color, faded lamentably when washed. The woman complained to Jim when he called at her house on his round. " How much did yeou pay a yard fer the caliker?" he asked. "Ninepence" (twelve and a half cents), was the answer. " No," said Jim reflectively ; " no, the old man wouldn't du that ; he wouldn't 've told a lie fer ninepunce, — but he *might* ' ve told eight fer a dollar ! "

The unpleasant change in moral tone, as it appears to the returned native, may be only superficial. And he will recollect that there must have been a reaction after the slackening of the old and rigid rule. Those who live under mild laws keep an even mind when a change comes; it is only when laws have been grievous that their repeal is followed by excesses.

One of the inevitable experiences is to find all boyish recollections of size and distance ridiculously diminished. The returned native discovers that the

well known hills and fields are small, and that the river
is scarcely more than a dark and rushing brook ; that of
the distances to neighboring towns, so formidable in
boyhood, not one is too long for a comfortable morning's walk. The white steeple with its gilded vane,
once so much admired, now that he looks at it would
not be too large for one of the lesser pinnacles of a
cathedral. The mansions have dwindled to modest
houses, and ordinary dwellings appear small and poor.
There is not room to turn about in the heart of the
village ; and as for the narrow common, he wonders
how the boys ever played round-ball upon it. But his
exaggerated notions soon settle down, and he gradually adjusts himself to the old dimensions ; it was he
that was wrong ; the town remains unchanged.

In the country round about it seems that the crops
have decreased ; the great barns are no longer burst-
ing with hay, nor does the gold of Indian corn gleam
through the chinks of the lean-to ; all the people are
fed with Western beef and flour. Many farms, though
not abandoned, yield little return, except in shelter,
garden vegetables, pasturage for a few cows, and plenty
of fresh air.

The owners must pick up a living as best they can ;
the thin and stony soil can do no more for them. As
we have seen, their sons are away in the cities, or in
the far West, and their daughters are teachers, or are
married and settled, and not in Quabbin. The houses
of these people have a plaintive look, such as they
themselves wear when they go to meeting.

He remembers that the early settlers clung to the
soil, like a colony of sea-cucumbers to their rock. A
house seldom sheltered strangers ; long journeys were

uncommon, and letters from foreign countries and distant States rarely came to the post-office. A family's lines of intimacy, however numerous, were as local and limited as those of the clothes-yard; but the native now knows that there are few houses, especially in the village, from which there are not ties of interest and relationship extending to some of the large centres of business, or perhaps to the uttermost parts of the earth.

But whatever may have been the changes in the life of the town, the returned native finds himself everywhere on familiar ground, and memory connects each spot with some event or emotion. Filaments from the core of his heart strike into the natal soil. Each bodily faculty is alert to bring out something from its own record of past sensations. The ear remembers the songs of native birds, and preserves them distinct from the carollings heard in Scottish valleys, in English meadows, and German forests. It recalls the different voices of the men and women who once frequented the village. It hears anew, but faintly and far away, as in the telephone, the psalms and hymns of the long-silent choir, and the voice of the minister in warning, expostulation, and prayer.

So, in miraculous freshness, flavors and scents return, associated with images of color and form. On the bosom of the cove are spread anew the lily-pads, as in the old time, forming a green patchwork, whose rifts are studded with cups of dazzling white petals, enclosing tufts of gold. The coolness and fragrance of those lilies are as palpable to touch and olfactories as if they were that moment pressed to the lips.

On warm nights in spring there used to come up

from the cove the cries of thousands of frogs, — booming basses, croaking baritones, and keen-piping falsettos; and now, when the eye of the returned native catches the lilies, or when a thin mist draws attention to the still basin, the confused medley of those monotonous concerts seems to return.

On the shady, steep bank of the river, and on well-known hillsides, there were and still are checkerberry plants, sought by children in spring for the sweet pungency of the young shoots, and later for the delicate flavor of the dainty pink berries. This flavor and aroma, like that of the young bark of the fragrant black birch, belong to the New World. At the thought of the dark, glistening leaves and the sculptured, coral-tinted berries, the characteristic taste and scent are in the air, as if memory kept a store of nature's woodland essences. So it is with the more pronounced aromatic warmth of sassafras and sweet-flag, each *sui generis* and indescribable. The native well remembers the rocky ledge from whose crevices he dug the one, and the swamp where he pulled the other.

As he passes walls and fences overgrown with vines and clematis, how the odor of wild grapes and of dusty white blossoms comes back to him, even in winter! In bushy pastures the perfume of sweet-fern lingers like a breath of incense. On the arid plains is the wholesome and enduring scent of the silvery everlasting; the native perceives and snuffs it, though it lies untouched at his feet. Form, color, and sweetness are one in memory.

When he thinks of the old-fashioned gardens, what delights for every sense! The tinted bells of tall hollyhocks, the flat-topped bouquets of sweet-william, the convolutions of pinks and marigolds, the jaunty pin and-purple caps of sweet-pease, the deep crimson globes of peonies, the starry eyes of pansies, — all these are seen by the native in any spot " where once a garden smiled," even though it is neglected and grass-grown ; and along with their vanished beauty come the odors of lavender, sweet-brier, mint, sage, and southernwood.

Without going to the pond he sees in the still water near the shore the round beds scooped in the sand by the roach for the cradle and playground of its young. The " pumpkin-seed," as boys call this short and chunky fish, with shadings of pale-green and black, and with scarlet-tipped fins, continually playing in exquisite curves, — a motion which men clumsily imitate in feathering an oar, — is ceaselessly hovering around those tepid shallows ; and its wariness, its arrowy flights, and the gleams of scarlet fins, are reproduced in the mental picture.

Thus, while the native walks about amid the scenes of his childhood, he is reminded of the past by innumerable associations with every sense. He lives over again his school-days with former playmates ; and his toils, his sports, his trials, and his hopes, come back with glimpses of hill, field, and river ; with the bloom and scent of flowers, and with the colors, flight, and song of birds. Subtle lines connect whatever he has perceived by any of the senses, so that as he walks he constantly touches some electric knob, and all his nerves feel the thrill.

In all these scenes are beheld the human beings whose figures, lineaments, voices, and movements form for each a never-to-be-forgotten whole. Whatever was poor or mean has dropped away, and the men and women, at their best, and as they aspired to be, welcome the native with friendly glances. Venerable hands that blessed him in infancy, hard and honest hands that have clasped his own fervently, and dainty white hands that he has dallied with, are beckoning to him. Faces that are brown and sober, or round and rosy, or refined and delicate, look as if they must speak of the unreturning past. They are voiceless, but their eyes are eloquent.

He climbs the hills, and sees the faint plumes of smoke over distant dwellings, thinking of the patient labor he has witnessed on those farms, and of the love and content sheltered for generations by the gray roofs. Returning, he visits the graveyard, and tarries long by the mounds which cover his beloved ones. In the rustle of the trees he seems to hear a voice, "Wait a while! Soon shalt thou, too, have rest."

In the cool evening, by the margin of the wood, he hears the plaintive whippoorwill; and it seems that it must be the same bird which he listened to with strange pleasure when a boy.

With the waning light the sounds of day have sunk into silence. Night comes with the train of ancient stars which know no change. What unutterable thoughts come as he looks at the shining host! In the morning he is awakened by the sun peering over the eastern hill, and touching the vane of the steeple. There is a new day, and the world begins its toil. And so it will be when he does not rise at that call, and the grass is beginning to grow over him.

APPENDIX I

IT has been mentioned that within half a century the living theology and the methods of the church, in Quabbin and elsewhere, underwent a silent change in fact, without any material alteration of the time-honored covenant. The change is still in progress, and is likely to be far-reaching. For instance, there was a strong controversy a few years ago, in an ecclesiastical council held in Indian Orchard (Mass.), over the ordination of a young minister who, in his examination, declared he was not satisfied that the heathen would be forever damned. In spite of his denial of one of the cardinal doctrines of Calvinism, the majority of the council consented to his ordination.

The trials of Andover professors for heresy are familiar to all readers. If these trials appear to have been conducted in a superficial or half-hearted way, it may be because no living theologian is so grounded in the faith once held by the orthodox as to be an effective prosecutor. It would be instructive if some theologic Landor would write an imaginary conversation between a modern Andover man and Jonathan Edwards. With what indignation would that Boanerges disown and denounce the orthodoxy of to-day!

The controversy is enveloped in a cloud of words, but the most vital questions, are these: Will the future punishment of the impenitent be without end? and are the Scriptures wholly inspired, in words as well as ideas?

Discussion of doctrine is no part of the plan of this book; but it may be observed that the Calvinistic position on those questions has not been forced or turned, but rather silently abandoned. If the scheme of Calvin be regarded as a framed building, it has hopelessly *sagged*, so that there are no more levels, or perpendiculars. We are concerned with this fact (if it is a fact) solely on account of the attitude of the church toward what is generally called the progress of civilization.

Whenever any comment is made upon the rule of the early Puritan Church in Massachusetts, stereotyped replies, kept in handy pigeon-holes, are at once forthcoming. The case for the colonial magistrates and clergy was presented by Lowell in an able and brilliant article, " New England Two Centuries Ago." The essayist had every qualification for his task, excepting, perhaps, an active sympathy with the progress of religious ideas. Every student of history admits the main contention ; namely, that the exclusion of religious opponents, of " cranks " and impracticable theorists, was, at the beginning, a necessity for the existence of the colony. It could not have defended itself against the crown on one hand, and the Indians and French on the other, unless it had been a compact and homogeneous body, directed from the centre. In view of what the colony, or rather the people of Massachusetts, *were to become*, after being emancipated, enlightened, and liberalized, this " survival of the fittest " was providential ; but if the result had been only to perpetuate and enthrone unenlightened Mathers and " Simple Coblers," with all that would follow such a rule, the downfall of the theocratic fabric would not have greatly disturbed the moral balance of the universe. Massachusetts became great, not by adhering rigidly to tradition, but by interweaving it with new ideas. It is freely admitted that the most of the ministers acted according to their light; but they naturally supposed a seventeenth century Puritan the highest ideal of a man ; and that further development was impossible, or not to be looked for.

The intention of the leaders was to set up a theocracy, and to govern the people as nearly as possible by the Mosaic code. It is true there were Deputies and Assistants, who formed in a way an Upper and Lower House, and who, besides supervising the churches, exercised both legislative and judicial powers, unfettered by the common law, or by the statutes of the mother country, and often with little of Christian charity. Had there been lawyers of experience in the colony, many acts of injustice and cruelty might have been prevented, and the reputation of a Christian commonwealth might have been preserved from dark and indelible stains. But no lawyers were permitted in Massachusetts until the colony was merged in the province ; nor had they even then any proper standing in

such travesties of courts as existed, until a little before the outbreak of the Revolution. The reason is obvious. At the elbow of
every magistrate and deputy was a minister; the office-bearers
governed in the interest of the church, and the will of the ministers
was never thwarted. Had there been independent courts, and
learned, courageous lawyers, such outrages as the banishment of
Roger Williams, the scourging and hanging of Quakers, and the
sending of Anne Hutchinson to her death in the wilderness, could
not have happened. Under the provincial government, in the
trials for witchcraft, the rules of law and evidence, and the established usages of British tribunals, are said to have been substantially followed. If this is true, it proves the barbarity of our
race two centuries ago. Persons convicted of offences in the
early years of the colony were frequently punished not according
to statute, but according to the law of Moses, interpreted by the
clergy.

It is not necessary to elaborate these points, as the subject has
already been exhaustively treated.[1]

It is obvious that the fabric of society, with civilization and
religion itself, has its foundation and defence in law. Until the
domination exercised by the ministers was thrown off, there was no
hope of a stable government based on the will of an intelligent con-
stituency; of equal laws and orderly procedure; of free thought and
free speech; of literature or art; of the civilizing influences of commerce; of learning, science, or invention; of toleration or human
brotherhood. In a state of society such as prevailed down to the
time of the trials for witchcraft, any progress in enlightenment was
impossible. For that reason any shock which that theocracy met,
however rude or malevolent, was a blessing to after-times.

In the work just referred to, Mr. Adams seems to regard the
emancipation of Massachusetts as completed by the Revolution.
Potentially this was the case, but the era of full emancipation appears to be of much later date. The rule of the clergy did not end
until the divorce of church and State was accomplished, and the
ministers were left to depend wholly upon voluntary contributions
for their support.

The orthodox Congregationalists have an historic position as
lineal descendants of the Puritan Church; and probably some of

[1] " The Emancipation of Massachusetts," by Brooks Adams.

their leaders have deplored the changes which have deprived the body of its former prestige; but the changes have brought compensations. When that church lost its hold upon the government; its control of the schools and the college; its power to lay taxes in every town for the support of its ministers, — losses which were inevitable in the changed circumstances and ideas of the time, — it was gaining new vitality and making sure its future prominence in the State. A church and its ministers are never so strong as when, dispensing with statutes and privileges, they rely upon loyal hearts and willing hands.

Cotton Mather, after mentioning the niggardly support given by a certain town to its minister, averred that there immediately followed a wide-spread and fatal murrain among the milch cows in that region; and, as if he himself had let loose the pestilence, exclaimed exultingly that it would have been better for those people to have been more liberal with their minister. Nothing could illustrate more vividly the difference between the notions of his time and ours than this foolish story, in which priestly arrogance, ignorance of natural laws, and a mean and degrading conception of the Deity are equally conspicuous. What would be thought to-day of such a scare-crow appeal to tax-payers?

The Orthodox Church is now fairly in touch with the ideas and movements of the age. Its preachers are often men of commanding talents, and are generally literary by taste and habit. Its members in all enlightened places may be prominent in science, in historical research, and in authorship. How different the case was sixty years ago, except in regard to theology, is well known. Perhaps other and even more vital changes may be witnessed in the next generation. If Unitarianism be considered a protest or reaction against the extreme doctrines of Calvinism, it may in good time have fulfilled its mission; if it is based upon broad affirmations, sufficient for the intellect and with free scope for the religious sentiment, it will endure. Vital ideas are as indestructible as matter.

APPENDIX II

IT seems desirable to look at the idea of civil liberty as it was conceived by the founders of Massachusetts. It is probably impossible to say anything new in itself, but it may be possible to combine in one view something between indiscriminate eulogy and malevolent criticism. Nothing in this book is meant as disparagement of Pilgrim or Puritan. They acted their part according to the light given them; and they believed that principles and forms of government, as well as personal liberty, should be subordinated to the rule of Christ on earth, or, what was the same thing, to the interests of their church. The State they founded became eventually the noblest of free and Christian commonwealths; but though the original spirit came from them, it was modified and controlled by other influences, against which they and many of their descendants strove with their might.

If we think of what is contained or implied in the notion of a free State in this century, we shall find these to be the chief: 1. Personal liberty, subject to be restrained as a punishment for crime, or to prevent injury to others. 2. Political equality, absolute and universal, except for public malefactors. 3. Toleration, or the inalienable right of opinion upon religious and all other topics, but subject to restraint as to public utterance, when such utterance is subversive of law and order. Where these three notions are recognized there is freedom.

Pilgrims and Puritans steadfastly upheld the first. The second they did not know, as it had not come into being. To the third they opposed all the energy of their convictions.

There may have been previous attempts to set up political equality, but never by an enlightened, reasonable, law-abiding people, until it was made the ground-work of the Constitution of the United

States by the hand of Thomas Jefferson. And it is obvious that even he shrank from carrying the doctrine to its logical result in the general liberation of African slaves. He felt the incongruity, as his writings show, but it was left for later believers in the doctrine to complete his work.

The distinctions in social rank, as recognized in England at the time, were preserved in the colonies, and had the sanction of law. It is well known that few servants were named in the list of the Mayflower's passengers. Sumptuary laws were justified by a clause stating that it was monstrous for people of mean condition to imitate the garb of gentlemen by wearing wide ruffs, laces, or long boots. The " seating of the meeting " was a deference paid to superior rank. For an offence a man might be deprived of the title of " Mr.," and condemned to be called thereafter " Goodman " so-and-so. And no man could be a " freeman," that is, a citizen and voter, unless he were a church-member, and unless admitted by special vote of the General Court. A person who was not a freeman lived on sufferance, and had few rights which the rulers were bound to respect. These facts, which are tediously familiar, show that there was not the least notion of political equality. The vision of a free commonwealth resting upon universal suffrage is wholly modern, and had not dawned upon the settlers of Plymouth or Boston. There is no reason for reproaching them on that account, for they were Britons, with the education and inherited prejudices of a people to whom political equality was unknown. It is commonly said that the feudal system came to an end in Great Britain some centuries ago, but there was never a greater error.

Slavery lingered in Massachusetts until after the adoption of the Constitution in 1820. The system of indentured apprenticeship, and the binding out of friendless girls as house-servants, continued much longer.

Political equality is to be considered as a purely legal status, and not confounded with social equality, which has never existed anywhere except among obscure religious sects, such as the primitive church. The communism of the New Testament has never been taken seriously by any considerable body of Christians. In the United States a man has his right in court and at the polls, but no legal claim for social recognition, still less for brotherly love.

As to the third element in a free State, toleration, it would be superfluous to dwell upon the position of the founders of Massachusetts in regard to it. It was established after long struggles. It conquered by the suppression of Episcopalians, the scourging and hanging of Quakers, and by the banishment of Anne Hutchinson, and of Roger Williams.[1] The persecution, which at the time seemed to strengthen the government, had a reflex action little suspected. Every violent measure brought the triumph of peace and good-will nearer. Toleration became the rule in Massachusetts only when theological dogmas had been softened, and the church and State dissociated.

In this matter, as in regard to political equality, we are indebted to Jefferson,— the Constitution of the United States forbidding religious tests. This is a boon that will endure; there can never be even an attempt to fetter the free mind.

One anomaly still exists in Massachusetts, and perhaps in other States : that those who do not believe certain abstract doctrines are liable to be impeached in the witness-box. In its results this is an infringement of natural justice. If an atheist were assaulted and beaten, or injured in his property, he would be without redress,

[1] Bancroft thus summarizes the views of Roger Williams : "The civil magistrates should restrain crime, but never control opinion ; should punish guilt, but never violate inward freedom. The principle contained within itself an entire reformation of theological jurisprudence : it would blot from the statute-book the felony of non-conformity ; would quench the fires that persecution had so long kept burning ; would repeal every law compelling attendance on public worship ; would abolish tithes and all forced contributions to the maintenance of religion ; would give an equal protection to every form of religious faith.

"Almost half a century before William Penn became an American proprietary, and two years before Descartes founded modern philosophy on the method of free reflection, Roger Williams asserted the great doctrine of intellectual liberty. It became his glory to found a State upon that principle, and to stamp himself upon its rising institutions in characters so deep that the impress has remained to this day, and can never be erased without a total destruction of the work.

"He was the first person in modern Christendom to assert in its plenitude the doctrine of the liberty of conscience, the equality of opinions before the law ; and in its defence he was the harbinger of Milton, the precursor and the superior of Jeremy Taylor.

"We praise the man who first analyzed the air, or resolved water into its elements, or drew the lightning from the clouds. . . . A moral principle has a much wider and nearer influence on human happiness ; nor can any discovery of truth be of more direct benefit to society than that which establishes a perpetual religious peace."

if the case depended in any way upon his own testimony. " Atheism " has often been fastened upon foolish talkers, as well as upon conscientious persons who professed themselves unable to bring the tremendous and unthinkable attributes of the Former of the universe into the limits of a personal or anthropomorphic God. It has also been required by statute that witnesses should qualify by avowing their belief in " a state of future rewards and punishments." Many an honest man might find it difficult to do this, if the words were literally construed ; and the more conscientious he was the less would he be disposed to frame an answer that would comply with the law.

The natural remedy is to abolish oaths in courts of justice, and to substitute affirmations, annexing the penalties now provided for perjury. The taking of an oath is a relic of superstition, useless as a guarantee of truth, and, in fact, a prolific source of falsity.[1]

If we consider now all that is included in the idea of a free commonwealth, we shall be able to give such credit as is due to our Puritan ancestors. We are to remember that we owe to them exclusively free schools and local government by towns, — two agencies more important than any others in diffusing intellectual light, in making men worthy of freedom, and in fitting them to maintain it. Without these the doctrines of political equality and toleration would have had little practical influence ; with them, aided by the deep religious spirit, the truth, self-devotion, and ideality which marked the fathers, there has been set up a republic, strong in the hearts of men, firmly based also on law, and which recognizes the highest ethical principles ever embodied in a government.

Perhaps the delay in the development of freedom was not only inevitable, but in the end advantageous. Perhaps the rule and the methods of the Puritan clergy were best for the future prosperity of a small, remote, and isolated colony. They could be useful and successful only so long as the people were obedient as one man to spiritual rulers ; only so long as intercourse with the great world was cut off; only so long as the wretched roads made inter-

---

[1] After a trial in the Superior Court in Boston, in which the false swearing on both sides was evident and appalling, the chief justice, Charles Allen, pointing to an old and dirty volume on which the witnesses had been sworn, said, " Mr. Clerk, get a new Testament : that calf-skin is saturated with perjury ! "